An Illustrated Encyclopaedia

WONDERS
of
ANIMAL LIFE

also available by the same editor

An Illustrated World Gazetteer

Peoples of all Nations

Their Life Today and Story of Their Past

In 14 Volumes

Volume One
Abyssinia **to** Azerbaijan
Volume Two
Belgium **to** British Empire in America
Volume Three
British Empire in Asia **to** Canada
Volume Four
Ceylon **to** Dahomey
Volume Five
Danzig **to** England
Volume Six
Esthonia **to** France
Volume Seven
Georgia **to** Iceland
Volume Eight
India **to** Italy
Volume Nine
Japan **to** Mexico
Volume Ten
Monaco **to** Oman
Volume Eleven
Palestine **to** Rumania
Volume Twelve
Russia **to** Sin-kiang
Volume Thirteen
South Africa **to** The Ukraine
Volume Fourteen
The United States **to** Wales
with General Index

About the Editor

Sir John Alexander Hammerton (1871-1949) was an English statesman and author, best-known for his editorship of popular encyclopaedias published in the first half of the 20th century, such as the 10-volume New Book of Knowledge.

From 1914 to 1919, Hammerton was joint editor with HW Wilson of the periodical "The Great War: The Standard History of the All-Europe Conflict", published by the Amalgamated Press. It was lavishly illustrated with photographs and with realistic drawings which were sometimes hardly distinguishable from photographs.

He was also a contemporary and friend of Arthur Mee, about whom he wrote a biography.

An Illustrated Encyclopaedia

WONDERS *of* ANIMAL LIFE

by Famous Writers on Natural History

Volume Five

Edited by

J.A. Hammerton

Over Three Thousand Illustrations from Photographs and Thirty-three Colour Plates

LOGOS PRESS, NEW DELHI

ISBN -13: 978-81-7268-175-3 (Set)
ISBN -10: 81-7268-175-5 (Set)

ISBN -13: 978-81-7268-176-0 (Vol. I)
ISBN -13: 978-81-7268-177-7 (Vol. II)
ISBN -13: 978-81-7268-178-4 (Vol. III)
ISBN -13: 978-81-7268-179-1 (Vol. IV)
ISBN -13: 978-81-7268-180-7 (Vol. V)
ISBN -13: 978-81-7268-181-4 (Vol. VI)
ISBN -13: 978-81-7268-182-1 (Vol. VII)
ISBN -13: 978-81-7268-183-8 (Vol. VIII)

ISBN -10: 81-7268-176-3 (Vol. I)
ISBN -10: 81-7268-177-1 (Vol. II)
ISBN -10: 81-7268-178-X (Vol. III)
ISBN -10: 81-7268-179-8 (Vol. IV)
ISBN -10: 81-7268-180-1 (Vol. V)
ISBN -10: 81-7268-181-X (Vol. VI)
ISBN -10: 81-7268-182-8 (Vol. VII)
ISBN -10: 81-7268-183-6 (Vol. VIII)

Edition : 2008

Printed & Published by

LOGOS PRESS

Building No. 4788-90, Street No. 23, Ansari Road, Darya Ganj, New Delhi-110 002 (India)
Phone : 23272187

Foreword

Here is not a 'natural history' in the accepted meaning of that description. There exist many and excellent natural histories and more than fifteen years ago the present editor was associated with the publication of one which, in its authoritative letter-press and profuse illustration, had wide acceptance. But it is undeniable that the general reader finds large and exhaustive treatises on animal life, encumbered with Latin names, somewhat hard reading, however fine their illustrations, if they are arranged on the approved scientific divisions—order, family, genus, species—into which naturalists split up animated nature. A proper natural history, however, must follow this method of treatment if it is to form the basis of a scientific knowledge of the subject.

Does the ordinary reader desire such knowledge? Does he require it?

The answer to both questions is a negative: emphatic in the first and modified in the second case. No matter how slightly youth is drawn to the conventional study of zoology, not even the forbidding scientific approach to natural history can rob it of its inherent fascination.

A boundless curiosity about the infinite diversity of creatures that share the life of the globe with him is a deep and abiding and a most natural trait in man. The stories of a Adam naming the beasts, and of the animals, two by two, going into the ark are ancient evidence of man's interest in his fellow-creatures of the so-called lower orders. A study of the life-histories of many animals and birds, fishes and reptiles, or of the astounding social systems of certain insects, is calculated to limit man's pride in himself as the incarnation of the highest intelligence or the finest physical product of the animal world. Especially is it likely to extend his sympathy to all lowly things that are living out their little days with him upon this planet. It lies at the root of humanitarianism. Interest in animal life is never an idle curiosity, and it may prove more absorbing than any other interest that could be named.

Not, then, to add a new natural history to a list already adequate, but to meet this universal and most healthy interest in the astonishing realities and the mysterious ways of the animal kingdom is the purpose of WONDERS OF ANIMAL LIFE. Its title adequately suggests its scope: to enquire into and to illustrate all that is of uncommon interest in the life of the animal kingdom.

While the reader will find in our pages a constantly changing panorama of animal life, with no more apparent order than the naturalist finds in the Brazilian jungle, he can hardly fail to be interested and he is certain to be instructed, for though the only method that is observed throughout our chapters is a rough alternation of interest, now in mammals, next in reptiles, then in birds, fishes, insects, each chapter of this work is written either by one of the leading specialists on his subject or—where expert knowledge is less needed than vividness of descriptive style—by a popular author.

A glance at the list of contributors, their scientific and literary credentials, and the subjects allotted to them in our scheme, will indicate to the reader that though WONDERS OF ANIMAL LIFE is designedly popular in its appeal, it is not the less authoritative in being more entertaining than the conventional sort of natural history.

Never before has there been brought together so representative and so varied a collection of photographic documents covering the whole range of animated nature. In the last decade, and particularly within the latter part of it, naturalists have acquired an immense amount of new knowledge, and marked progress has been made in recording the wild life of the world by means of direct photography.

The exploits of the camera experts employed by the organizers of some of the great 'nature and adventure' films—'Simba' is a fine example—that have fascinated millions throughout the world in these years have produced so rich a body of material for illustrating such a work as this that editorially we are in a more favoured position than any of our predecessors in the same field and we hope the reader will agree with us in thinking that we have taken advantage of that fortunate circumstance for his entertainment and instruction.

J.A. HAMMERTON

Publisher's Note

We are happy to present the illustrated encyclopaedia—Wonders of Animal Life—to the learned readers. As its title suggests, it attempts to enquire into the astonishing realities and the mysterious ways of life of the animal kingdom—mammals, reptiles, birds, fishes and insects.

Presented in eight volumes, each chapter of this work is written either by one of the leading specialists on the subject or—where expert knowledge is less needed than vividness of descriptive style—by a popular author. The text is enriched with a representative and varied collection of photographic documents covering the whole range of animated nature. Our other notable illustrated encyclopaedias include *The Living Animals of the World* (4 volumes), *The Wonders of the World* (4 volumes), *Peoples of All Nations* (14 volumes), and *The Earth and Its Inhabitants* (8 volumes).

TABLE OF CONTENTS

Volume One

List of Colour Plates

Volume Two

List of Colour Plates

Volume Three

List of Colour Plates

Volume Four

List of Colour Plates

Volume Five

List of Colour Plates

Volume Six

List of Colour Plates

Volume Seven

List of Colour Plates

Volume Eight

List of Colour Plates

Chapter LXXXII

Nature's Busy Miners and Tunnellers

By W. Percival Westell

Author of "The Book of Nature"

So many of the inhabitants of the busy world of animal life work unheard and unseen that the ordinary observer has little, if any, conception of the marvels and mysteries that encompass us. Even the skylark that soars and sings well within sight is rarely seen performing its domestic duties, its apology for a nest being hidden among summer's wealth of grasses. Bees and butterflies may be watched at close quarters during their sweet pillage among the flowers—gay buccaneers as many of them are—but few have any idea of their life histories, and of how the perfect insect came into being. Only the Nature student gets behind the curtain, or has a peep behind the scenes.

If, then, it is only possible to get fleeting glances, as it were, of Nature's children who share with ourselves the glorious heritage of Mother Earth, what shall be said of the army of miners and tunnellers who work and play out of sight and hearing? A wasp may be seen rasping from a fence, post, or gate a tiny strip of wood wherewith to commence or enlarge its nest, but no human eye is able to watch the creature underground, the entrance to whose home is just a small hole in a bank. Tree wasps and their fellows can be watched at their operations. One tree wasps' nest that came under my own observation was suspended in a gooseberry bush and resembled a grey Chinese lantern deftly hung among the ripening berries, but the wasps that place their citadels underground are subterranean workers the result of whose labour is only observable when the finished product is extracted for us.

Some of these navvies work desperately hard to attain their ends, others adopt the method of "slow but sure." Some work only at night, irrespective of the fact that their holes, or burrows, are in the dark. Some of the holes or tunnels that are made are merely used for one season and are then deserted. On the other hand, certain animals, such as badgers and foxes, resort to the same underground dwelling for many years, enlarging or altering as occasion and circumstances demand. A deserted or even tenanted hole made by one kind of animal is often eagerly taken possession of by another. The kingfisher, for example, will frequently commandeer the tunnel made in a river bank by the trim and elegant water vole, and at the extremity of the tunnel this bright-clad bird and expert fisherman places its pure glossy-white eggs. Once having obtained possession of the tunnel, the kingfisher continues a tenant by right of occupancy, and the water vole must, of necessity, set to work to make a fresh retreat.

A. H. Willford

KINGFISHER AND THE TUNNEL IT MADE

Cautious observers may track the kingfisher to its nesting place and will find that the young are reared at the end of a tunnel in the river bank. Often the burrow of a vole or "water-rat" is utilised, but otherwise the bird is very well able to make its own tunnel.

The holes made by the water vole—known by sight to anglers in our sluggish waterways—are not used for rearing the young. They are bolt holes, or hiding-places, into which the animal can escape from its enemies. The nest, a globular homestead about the size of a football, is composed of dry grasses and other materials, and is placed among aquatic herbage, as a rule well out of harm's way.

The prairie marmot is an inhabitant of the dry, desert regions and open plains of the Rocky Mountain plateau. Another species is found in Mexico. One species, the Columbian prairie marmot, is more of a mountain dweller than its cousin of the lower regions. These are social dwellers, and the common species takes possession of many acres of country and riddles it with burrows. Each burrow is tenanted by several animals. There is a funnel-shaped entrance made of earth thrown out of the burrow, and this forms a look-out place. When danger threatens these little prairie

F. Vear

YOUNG RABBITS UNEARTHED AT THE END OF THEIR UNDERGROUND HOME

Sharp steel spades, wielded lustily, have discovered the precious secret that the mother rabbit hoped the earth would keep. The family of young rabbits in their nursery at the end of a long burrow has been brought to the unwanted light of day for the purpose of photography. The warren where it lives has tunnels which ramify something like those of a coal mine and these tunnels are altered and adapted to changing conditions from time to time according to the fortune of the warren.

folk utter a shrill whistling sound, whereupon all within hearing of the danger signal disappear very rapidly underground.

With four-footed animals, such as the badger, fox, marmot, mole, rabbit, and others the navvying is done with the feet, and it is astonishing at what a rate the excavating is accomplished and the distance soil has to be moved where the tenant makes passages far underground. Rabbits, as all country dwellers know, are expert diggers. Their warrens, in districts where these rodents abound and where the soil is easily worked, are a familiar sight in rural England, and a great many inhabitants are found in one community. Early morning and late evening are favourite times for Brer Rabbit to steal warily from his hiding-place beneath the soil, to feed. The rabbit nibbles grass and other herbage when the dew is upon it, and is more fond of drinking than is generally supposed. It depends for protection on its fleetness of foot and its invariable habit of skulking in the undergrowth, if its underground dwelling cannot be reached. The white upturned tail serves as a warning to its fellows. The young are nearly always born underground and are blind, naked, and helpless for several days. Where a rabbit warren is well established it is used by succeeding generations, and is a happy hunting-ground for fox, stoat and weasel. The former, however, rarely seeks his prey close at home, for I have seen Reynard pass, unheeded, whole companies of rabbits not far from his very own "earth."

Fox and badger sometimes share the same abode, but it is not a good arrangement for Brock, the badger, as he is clean and tidy in his home affairs, whereas Reynard has yet to learn the ethics of good housekeeping. An old haunt of the badger will be tenanted over a period of many years, and in course of time, as new apartments are made and débris is brought to the surface, huge mounds of earth are accumulated. Trees of large dimensions spread their tapering roots below ground and among these the hidden ramifications of the nocturnal wanderer's home are situated.

THE brown rat, and that happy-go-lucky little fellow, the wood mouse, are both burrowers, but the velvet-clad mole is one of our most industrious, if somewhat destructive, tunnellers. It is partial to damp meadows and pastures where, when the miner has been busy during the night-watch, many hillocks

W. S. Berridge

GOLDEN MOLE AND A SECTION THROUGH A MOLE-HILL

Distinguished by its beautiful coat the golden mole (bottom) has the same habits as its relatives save that the tunnelling operations which it undertakes are not betrayed at a few places by mole-hills but throughout their entire length by reason of their being dug only just below the surface. Thus their presence is shown by the ridges in the turf which are the roofs of the tunnels. A careful section through the "hill" of a common British mole (top) reveals the nature of this busy little miner's home and nursery.

A. Brook

THE FOX FROM HIS LAIR IN THE MORNING": YOUNG REYNARD COMES ABOVE GROUND

Foxes are by no means the most energetic or enterprising of Nature's miners and tunnellers for they like some other animal to do as much of the work of making the underground home as possible. The fox's earth is usually in the burrow of a rabbit or a badger, and this the little red raider adapts for his own purposes. But sometimes Reynard digs his own earth. In the summer time, however, a dry ditch often serves as a sleeping place, while hollow trees and clefts in rocks are freely used, for, of course, such a bundle of craft and cunning is an opportunist of the first order. These photographs were taken in the Welsh mountains and show a young fox preparing to leave his earth but looking cautiously round first.

A. Brook

SUNSET DISCOVERS SOME FOX CUBS PLAYING ROUND THEIR EARTH

After sunset it is that the fox cubs come up out of the dark where they have spent the day to play in the twilight which, ever becoming deeper, emboldens them with the nearness of the night when all foxes can go fearlessly into the open. At the moment of the photograph the light was still good and the cubs, therefore, did not care to go more than a few jumps distant from the mouth of their earth. This is dug in the bank which divides two fields and is directly under the wire of a fence.

of soil spell industry. The pointed head of the mole, its rounded body, soft fur, and fine digging forelegs armed with strong, sharp nails, are admirably suited for the life it leads, and though it can move fairly quickly above ground, its movements beneath the soil are prodigious. When one remembers that this creature of the wild has to force its way through the ground and often has no time to clear a passage as it goes, its progress is little short of miraculous, as those who have disturbed a specimen on the surface and watched it disappear as if by magic, will be able to testify.

IN the nature of its food the mole is a friend of the agriculturist, but in some fields and gardens its tunnellings become a nuisance. It acts, in a way, as a natural drainage producer, but there are a few fields known to me which are almost uncultivatable because of the great number of hillocks of soil that are thrown up daily all the year round. Even in hard, frosty weather the mole still pursues its active operations beneath the surface, and knows no rest.

The curious duck-billed platypus, one of the few egg-laying mammals of the world, is of aquatic habits, and lives in pairs in burrows made in the banks of fresh-water rivers in Australia and Tasmania. It is very shy, and will submerge its body as soon as it is spotted. The burrow is an ingenious affair, there being two entrances, one above and the other below the water-line. At the extremity of the burrow—often extending to fifty feet—the platypus makes a cosy nest in a widened terminal chamber. In this nest two white eggs are deposited. The food secured by this remarkable mammal is not eaten straight away, as it is first stored up in large pouches situate on each cheek, and then consumed as required.

The aard-vark is another mammal overseas that may be included in our present census of miners and tunnellers. Its Dutch name means "earth pig," and to the colonists in South Africa it is known as the ant bear. It is not by any means a nice-looking animal, having a small, pointed head, very long ears, large body, stumpy legs, and a long, tapering tail. It also has a long tongue. On the front pair of legs there are four toes armed with powerful nails, whereas the hind feet have five toes. The skin is thick. Nocturnal in habits, the aard-vark makes a deep burrow in the soil, and there, during the day, it passes the time asleep, coming out under cover of darkness to feed on termites and ants which it

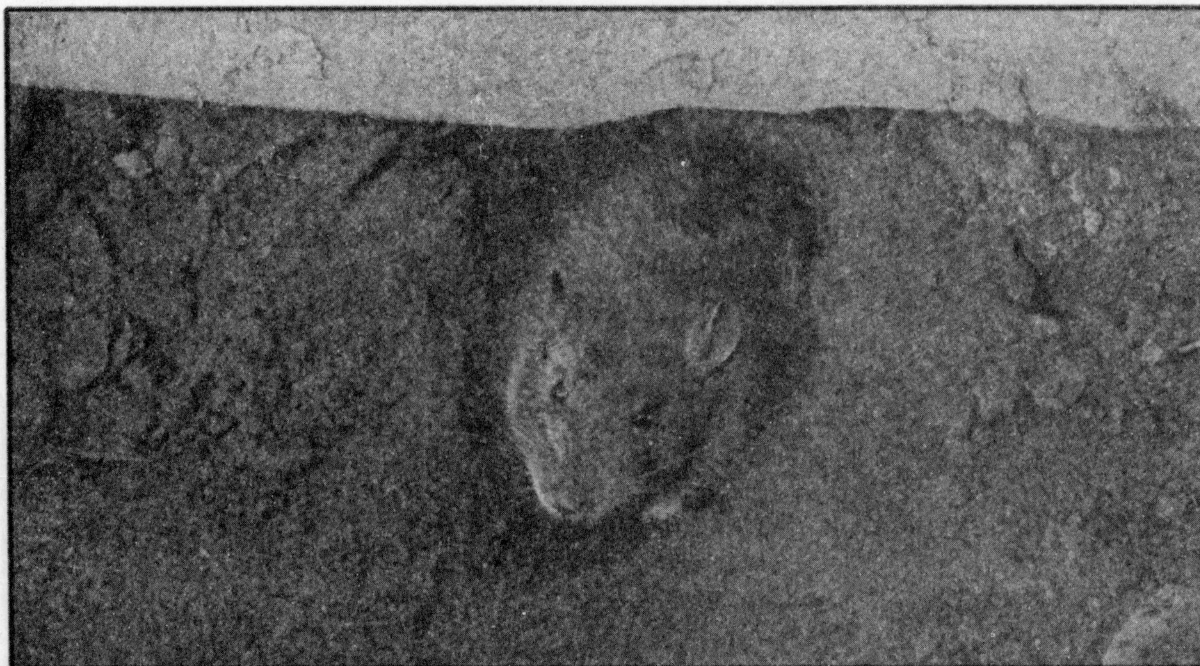

S. Crook

W. S. Berridge

TWO MINERS: PRAIRIE DOG AT ITS "PIT HEAD" AND THE RAT

That the communities of prairie marmots or prairie dogs are called "towns" is sufficiently indicative of their impressive capacity for mining. Areas measured by the square mile are tunnelled and at the entrance to each home is a kind of look-out tower. The upper photograph shows another industrious miner—the rat

secures by means of its extensile tongue. The burrow is usually near the termite-hills, so that an abundant food supply is assured close at hand. It is a strong, powerful animal, endowed with great digging propensities, and although it measures as much as six feet in length, the whole body can soon be buried, even in hard ground. The front feet are used for digging and the hind ones for throwing out the soil.

Several kinds of birds are to be numbered as miners, tunnellers, or burrowers. Among the latter is the burrowing owl, which inhabits regions similar to the prairie marmot already referred to. It differs from many others of its race by being diurnal in habits, standing on guard at the entrance to its burrow for hours at a stretch. It often usurps the burrow of the marmot, as also does the rattlesnake. It is not a happy arrangement except for the bird, as this small owl is a match both for the mammal and the reptile. Sometimes, it is said, the burrowing owl will take up residence in the "earths" of badger, fox, viscacha, wolf, and other underground animals, but it is an open question whether, in spite of its popular name, it burrows to any very great extent.

The puffin is a British bird well known to residents in coastal districts. This can confidently be called a burrowing bird. Grotesque in appearance, with a lurid-coloured sheath over its beak in the breeding season, the puffin, or sea parrot, as the fisherfolk call it, places its one egg in a burrow in the ground. In St. Kilda the burrow is made in the soft peat, or a cleft in the rocks may be chosen. The white egg is sparingly marked with brown and grey spots, and it is suggested that it is comparatively recently that this bird has adopted the habit of depositing its egg in burrows, as the eggs of birds which lay in holes are usually white and unmarked

One of the species of shearwater, a sea-bird of much interest, has been called mutton bird by sailors, apparently because the young are so very fat. The other name is perhaps obtained from the habit this bird has of shearing the water. However that may

A. Brook

BADGER EMERGING FROM ITS HOME BENEATH THE ROOTS OF A TREE

If undisturbed a colony of badgers may occupy the same site for centuries, and badger earths have been found fifteen feet below ground and dug the whole distance through solid chalk. Favourite sites are thick woods and the burrows are made under the roots of trees. The badger seen above has such a home with the burrow coming to the surface just where two projections from the bole of the tree make a frame for the entrance. The cautious animal, very seldom seen in daylight or indeed at all, exists even in the grounds of Ken Wood on Hampstead Heath.

W. S. Berridge

W. S. Berridge

F. W Bond

W. S. Berridge

FOUR MAMMALS THAT ARE MINERS: FENNEC, MOLE-RAT, AARD-VARK AND ARMADILLO

Living in burrows in the deserts of North Africa the fennec (bottom left) is a small, fox-like member of the dog family and distinguished by its enormous ears. The mole-rats, of which we have a specimen here (bottom right) known as Zech's mole-rat, are found in East Africa, south-eastern Europe and in Asia. They live on roots which they obtain by tunnelling. Notice the well-developed teeth and efficient-looking jaws. In the upper left hand photograph we have a giant among animal miners, the aard-vark, which is six feet long but can bury itself, even in a hard soil, in a very short time. It has strong nails and lives in a deep burrow. The nine-banded armadillo (top right) of South America is also a very quick digger.

Martin Duncan

be our interest lies in the fact that all shearwaters deposit their one pure white egg in a hole underground. Previously their numbers were enormous off the Australian coast, but when it is stated that as many as sixty thousand breeding birds have been destroyed in one season, small wonder need be expressed at its partial disappearance from the list of the world's avifauna.

A familiar visitor during the English summer, the sand martin—a member of the swallow tribe—is characterised by its unfailing habit of tunnelling into sandpits and cliff faces. For so small a bird, provided only with a short, sharp beak, the long tunnels that are mined—just beyond arm's length—are truly remarkable. Little colonies of these energetic birds nest together, and at the extremity of the aperture the nest is placed. The small pyriform eggs are pure white. The mouse-coloured plumage of this useful little species—it is entirely insectivorous—at once distinguishes it from its larger cousin which nests under the eaves of the houses and also from the swift-winged swallow.

Bastin

A DESTRUCTIVE BURROWER BENEATH PLANTS

Mole crickets are quite common in the British Isles, but are rarely seen because they spend their lives underground, burrowing like moles and feeding upon the roots of plants. The eggs are laid in a cavity made at the end of a burrow. The lower photograph shows the insect as a man sees it, from above, while the top illustration gives us a side view.

The Elegant tortoise of South Africa digs a shallow pit in the earth in which to deposit its eggs, sealing up the hole with the soil excavated so as to hide the treasures completely. Another species, the familiar Grecian tortoise, not only places its eggs in a hole in the earth, but excavates a burrow in which to pass the winter, the strong fore limbs being used.

Snakes use the holes or burrows of other animals in which to conceal themselves during the period of hibernation, as also do frogs, toads, newts, and other creatures which are inactive during hard weather, but they hardly come within our category.

On the other hand, there are many marine animals that are expert miners and tunnellers, some of which will have come under the observation of the reader. Perhaps the crab found promenading on the seashore is the most typical example that may first be mentioned, as, although it does not live in a burrow, the incredible way in which the creature can disappear under sand or shingle will have been witnessed by all visitors to the seaside. Whilst the crab can and does amble above ground at quite a good speed in order to escape its pursuer, it is rather by rapid self-burial that it avoids detection and depends for its survival, at least from human enemies. If seen in one of the pools left by the tide the crab disappears in double-quick time, its legs moving with mechanical precision as it hastens to cover itself with sand, and then remains motionless. Even if a leg is lost, little ado is made of such an accident, as another one is grown to take the place of the missing limb in the same way that the lizard grows another tail.

Wandering along the shore making, perchance, a collection of the different kinds of shells thrown up by the sea and from which the soft bodies of the owners have disappeared, one may almost certainly

Otho Webb

SHEARWATER OF THE BARRIER REEF ISLANDS

The wedge-tailed shearwater used to nest in its thousands on many islands of the Great Barrier Reef, although persecution has since led almost to its extinction. It burrows and at the end of its tunnel lays its eggs. An egg (bottom) has been brought to the mouth of the tunnel so as to be visible to the camera. Above is a general view of a honeycombed island haunted by shearwaters.

pick up two kinds of shells of common occurrence. One is the well-known razor shell, having two halves joined together with an outside hinge in the centre, and the second is a pure white-ribbed shell, tapering almost to a point, known as pholas. Both these sea dwellers are capable burrowers, as we shall now discover. The razor shellfish is the possessor of a large and powerful foot with which it burrows deeply in the sand. Not only does this species bore a great depth in the sand, but it does so with much rapidity. It is not often that the animal can be obtained alive, and its shells are usually the only reminders of its one-time life in the sea.

Walking one day on a sandy shore in Lincolnshire, I was interested to find many pieces of hard clay and nodules of chalk worn smooth by the action of the water. In these pieces of clay and chalk there were several symmetrical holes running right through, and I was puzzled as to the cause until I discovered several pairs of pure white shells tightly wedged in some of the holes. Here, then, was a solution of the mystery. The owner of the shell was *Pholas dactylus*. The shell is thin, but of much strength, and is used, in conjunction with the foot, for boring purposes, the former acting as a file to enlarge the hole as necessity arises. Many species of pholas are phosphorescent.

The teredo, or ship's worm, is a close relative of the last named, and does immense damage by boring into submerged timber in jetties and breakwaters.

W. S. Berridge

INDUSTRIOUS DIGGERS AMONG THE BIRDS: SHELD-DUCK AND PUFFIN

The common sheld-duck (bottom) seeks out a hole in the nesting season and makes its nest there. Often a rabbit hole does for the purpose, but the bird can dig a tunnel eight feet long in a sand dune if necessary. Above is a common puffin. This sets to work in the breeding season to dig a hole in the sand or peat. This underground gallery it excavates usually for about a yard or four feet, and at the end is a cavity where the eggs are laid. Chinks and crannies in the rocks are sometimes used, however, for it is not every puffin that digs a tunnel.

W. S. Berridge

BURROWING OWL WHOSE HOME IS UNDERGROUND, AND THE TUNNELLING SAND MARTIN

In both North and South America there are burrowing owls. These indeed cannot take very much credit for their ability as sappers, for they merely adapt some other creature's burrow to their own purposes. Badgers, prairie dogs and foxes may find their earths suddenly shared by these bold intruders, and it is believed that, in some cases, the owl attacks the offspring of its hosts and even the hosts themselves if they be of the vulnerable sort. The right-hand photograph shows a sand martin at the mouth of the hole in a cliff which the bird has drilled out. The passage leading to the nest cavity is often three feet long and the cavity itself is furnished with hay or straw and a feather lining.

Another marine creature known as Rocellaria bores into solid rock, and one species at least is capable of successful operation even into such a hard substance as granite.

Date shells may be aptly termed stone-borers, master navvies of marine life. The shells are thin, and shaped something like the favourite date fruit. The boring is performed by the foot, and Lydekker mentions the interesting fact that the columns of a temple at Puteoli are impregnated with holes caused by a species of date shell at a time when these wonderful ruins were lying submerged beneath the sea.

One would hardly associate sponges with boring animals, but some species of burrowing sponges are capable of riddling blocks of limestone rock until the latter is almost honeycombed with their ravages. They also perpetrate damage among oysters.

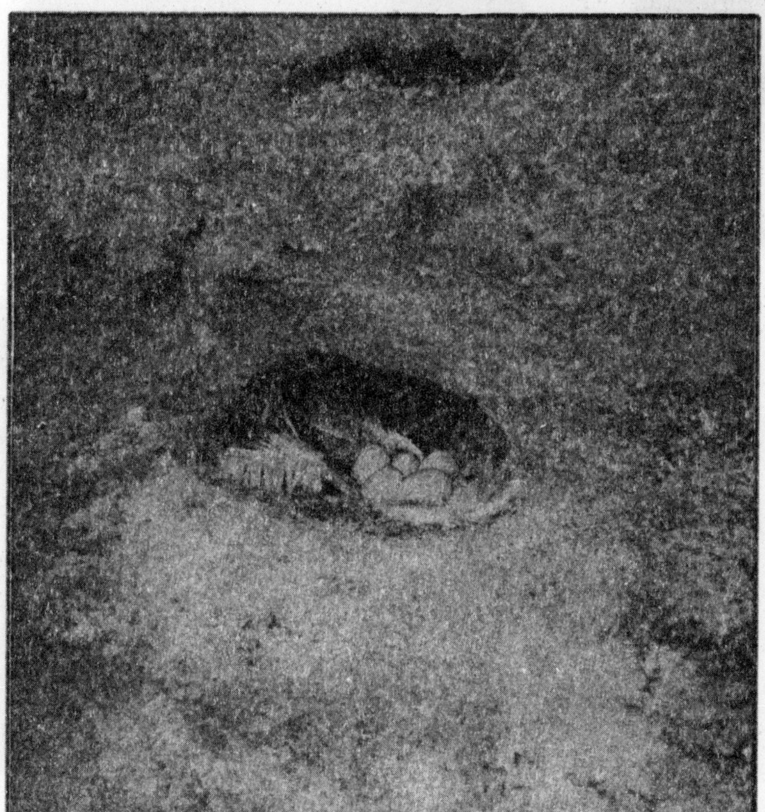

A. H. Willford

SUBTERRANEAN NESTS DISCOVERED TO THE CAMERA

Here are two photographs discovering nests which are built at the end of subterranean passages. The sand martin (bottom) lines her nest comfortably with feathers as we see. The young burrowing owls photographed in their burrow (top) are probably only a few inches from the surface in spite of their apparent seclusion.

Among the lower forms of life the common earthworm is one of the best-known examples, and its work as a tunneller in the soil is familiar to all. When excavating a Roman cemetery site at Baldock, Herts, I was much struck, not only at the enormous size of the earthworms there encountered and their plentifulness, but also at the great depth at which these soft-bodied animals were found and the hard chalk rock and rubble through which they were able to make their way with ease and facility. Earthworms are night roamers, coming above ground to deposit their castings and to feed. They are vegetarians, feeding upon dead and decaying leaves and other vegetable matter. Quick of movement when on terra firma, retreating within their holes with much rapidity, these beneficent creatures, as Darwin has shown, have been of prime assistance in helping through the ages to make the soil fit to till. They also supply hungry birds and other creatures with food, including our homely friend the robin, which, it is computed, devours several feet of earthworms per day.

Date-shells boring in stone

Great, medium, and short piddocks

Timber honeycombed by the teredo

Burrows of a miner bee in sandstone

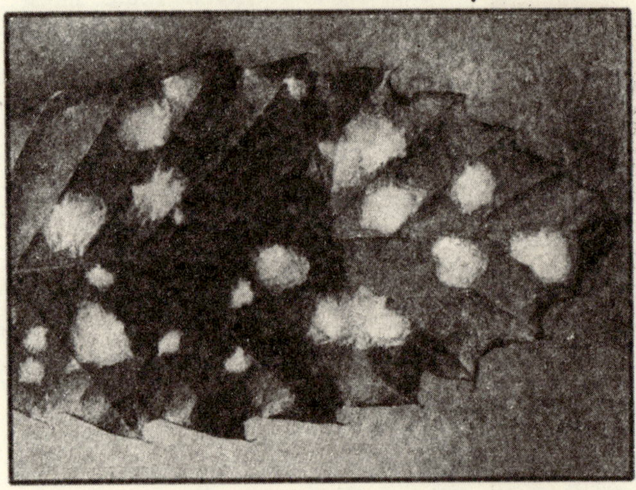

Chestnut leaf mined by a small moth

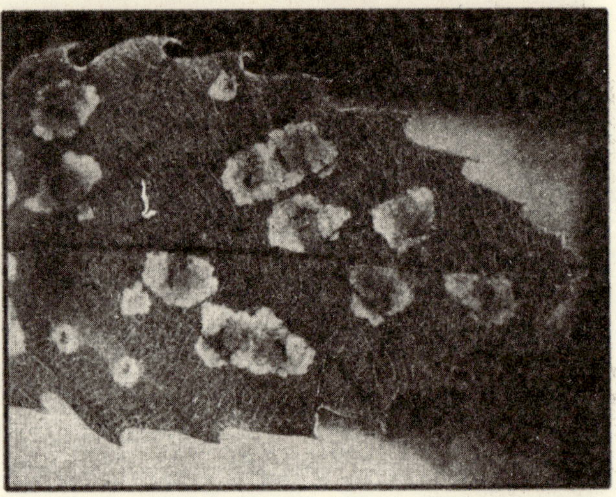

The moth caterpillars seen in the mined areas

LITTLE BURROWERS AND BORERS IN LEAF, WOOD AND STONE

About the most subtle mining in the animal kingdom is done by the larva of a micro-moth—*Lithocelletis messamella*—the little grubs eating out a space within the thickness of the leaf of a Spanish chestnut (bottom left). The bottom right-hand photograph gives us the same leaf photographed against the light to show each tiny caterpillar in its "mine." The date-shells (top left) are little sea molluscs with a special "foot" which bores through stones. Photos by E. J. Manley, M. Duncan, J. J Ward, and H. Bastin.

Green shore crab digging itself in

The crab nearly buried

Alder fly larva on a stone in the water

The larva burying itself under the stone

European burrowing toad digging itself a shelter

QUICK DIGGERS AT WORK IN TIME OF DANGER; BURROWING TOAD, FLY LARVA AND CRAB

The burrowing toad (bottom) has spade-like projections on its feet by means of which it is able to bury itself. One African species uses this digging ability to attack the nests of termites, for it has a partiality for these "white ants" as food. The larva of the alder fly (centre photographs) develops under water and in times of danger buries itself. One of the quickest diggers is the green shore crab (top) whose legs operate with the precision of a steam shovel. Photos by W. S. Berridge, S. C. Johnson, and M. H. Crawford.

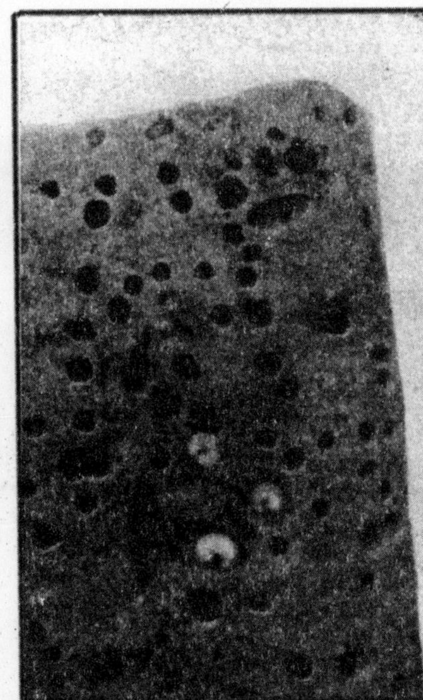

I. J. Ward

"DEATH-WATCH" THAT BORES WOOD AND A WEEVIL THAT BURROWS IN BISCUITS

Grubs of the so-called death-watch beetle do enormous damage to woodwork unless quickly and severely dealt with. The photograph on the left shows the wooden plate used for fastening a gas bracket to a wall, and it is riddled with the little tunnels made by busy grubs. The other illustration is of a piece of ship's biscuit which has been attacked by the weevil *Anobium paniceum*. This is an ancient foe of mariners, and a bag of biscuit, once infected, is very speedily destroyed

There are numerous beetles which make the ground beneath our feet their dwelling-place. The cocktail beetle, or devil's coach horse, is one of these. It is an all-black, flat-bodied creature, and has the habit of quickly erecting its hinder parts when disturbed and assuming a threatening attitude. When digging in the garden other beetles—some jet-black, others dark green and violet coloured—will be disturbed from their hiding-places. They soon disappear again, but it is rather amazing to discover how clean their bodies are when one reflects that the soil is their constant abiding place.

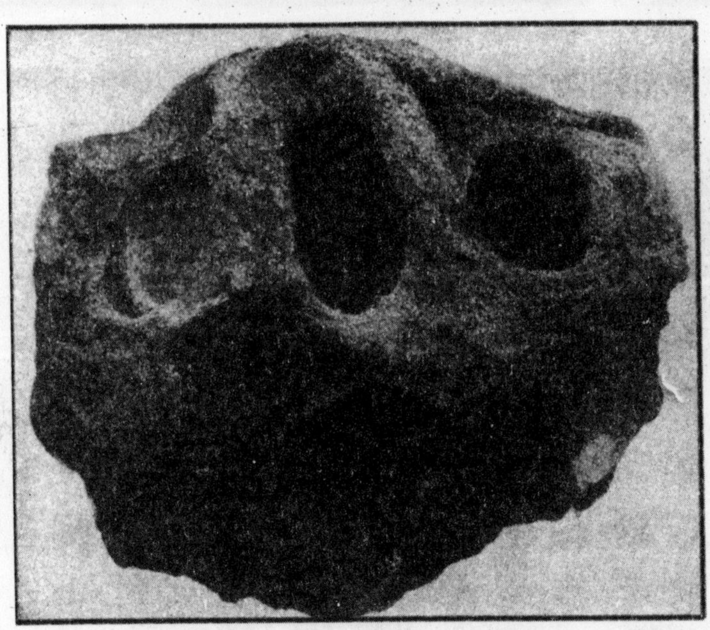

H. Bastin

BURROW HOMES OF SOLITARY BEES SEEN AT CLOSE QUARTERS

Among the various kinds of solitary bees, as opposed to the social bees which live together in hives, are the flower-bees or *Anthophora*. They look much like humble bees and burrow in the ground to make their solitary homes. The cells (left) in which the eggs are deposited are constructed from the soil or, if the home is made in the cleft of a tree, out of wood. The right-hand photograph shows some burrows of a species of the same genus, *Andrena*, seen from above. The burrow on the right has freshly excavated earth round it.

LITTLE ARMADILLO, A WONDERFUL TUNNELLER OF THE NEW WORLD

Provided with strong claws, the forelimbs of the armadillo are very efficient shovels. These little animals—most armadillos are about the size of a rabbit—can bury themselves with surprising speed, especially those that live in the sandy pampa country of South America or in the deserts of Texas. Some localities are positively honeycombed with the burrows of these armoured miners of the New World.

Chapter LXXXIII

Animals that Live Upside-Down

By Frank Finn

Author of "Birds of the Countryside"

AMERICA has never been backward in advertising, and her native live stock, even from the earliest times, have enjoyed a "good Press." The sloth has thus long been well known, but not accurately known, for all sorts of stories have been told about it, from the old one which credits it with being a monstrous, imperfect creature which could only crawl at the rate of three yards an hour and descended from a tree, eaten bare, by tumbling down with a whack and a wail, to the modern ones which credit it with bounding from tree to tree, or with all the paces of other kinds of quadruped, including even the gallop.

It does indeed deserve its notoriety, for, being as big as a small dog, it is the largest of the large number of animals which live upside-down.

This accounts for the tales about its imperfections, for on the ground, and from our point of view right-side up, it can only haul, sprawl, and crawl ; but when it gets to a tree and has clambered on to the boughs, it is in its right element and reverses itself joyfully, clinging with no effort to the boughs by its long, hook-like claws, which also serve, in the case of the long fore-limbs, to drag branches within reach when the beast wishes to devour their leaves. Unless deficiency of arboreal accommodation, very unlikely in the New World tropical forests in which it lives, forces it to the ground, the sloth does everything suspended, "in fact, passes its whole life in suspense, like a young clergyman distantly related to a bishop," as Sydney Smith, with a cynical imputation of Simonism to his cloth, said when reviewing Charles Waterton's "Wanderings in South America."

THE proverb "It's an ill wind that blows nobody good" would be appreciated by the sloth if he could understand it, for windy weather gives him a chance of changing quarters without descending to the hated earth, since when the boughs of an otherwise inaccessible tree sway near those of that which is his base for the time being, he can claw out and shift over. He can do quite well without drinking, like so many vegetarian mammals, but will take to water and swim if necessary, his haul, sprawl and crawl method of progression, when on the ground, lending itself naturally to swimming, as indeed does the gait of most land animals. The biped gibbon ape cannot swim, any more than we can if untaught, because its land movements are unsuitable, and the throwing up of the arms does more harm than good.

The baby sloth, clinging to its mother's shaggy breast-fur, perforce lives right-side up for a time ; and about the sloth's fur there is a very remarkable point—it is minutely fluted, and in the beast's native home affords congenial lodgment for minute plant-growth of the type which colours green old walls and woodwork in England. Thus the sloth in the wilds is a green beast, but under the changed and drier conditions of captivity, or in the preserved skin, the green growth disappears. It must be of some service in protecting the beast, which is really not a very brisk mover at the best of times, from its natural enemies such as the harpy "eagle"—the giant of the hawks—and the jaguar, the American improved edition of the leopard. But the sloth also seeks security from such foes by keeping well up and out among the twigs, where a heavy beast could find no foothold, and a bird might get "hung up" in endeavouring to help itself with its wings.

In captivity the sloth does well enough, but is rarely seen, as it has about as poor recommendations for a cage, except as a scientific exhibit, as any beast well could have. There are several species, some with two toes only on the forefeet, and some with three ; and, what is really most remarkable, in these two types of this humble group of beasts, the standard specification for mammalian neck-vertebrae is twice departed from. Seven is the rigid rule for practically neckless whale as well as for over-necked giraffe ; but the three-toed sloths have nine, and, lest it should be concluded that the extra allowance is needed by an animal which from its position needs to twist its neck a lot, and does so, we find the two-toed sloths showing the normal seven in one species and actually one less than the normal in another.

BATS, as everyone knows, hang up by their heels when in repose, but as they pass so much of their time on the wing, can hardly be said to live upside-down, except in the case of the fruit-eating flying foxes, which do not usually fly except to reach their feeding trees, and when there scramble about back downward in a very sloth-like fashion, besides hanging up at their roosts in the usual topsy-turvy bat fashion.

Birds dislike being upside-down even more than most beasts, though some, like many beasts, will roll over readily enough in fun or for fighting, like parrots and birds of prey ; many also, as everyone has seen with tomtits, reverse readily when feeding. But the only birds which spend most of their time in a reversed position are the pretty East Indian hanging-parrakeets, or bat-parrots, to give them a better and a briefer name. These are little green, bob-tailed, sparrow-sized parrots, very like the "love-birds" ; but while those are seed-eaters, the bat-parrots live on the nectar of flowers and on soft fruit. To get food like this, they need to reverse as often as tits ; but when they rest or go to sleep at nights, they always hang up by their feet bat-fashion, so that on the whole, they must spend more time head-downward than the right way up. They are not common in captivity, but a few turn up at the great bird shows.

Living Upside-Down

W. S. Berridge

SLOW LORIS OF TROPICAL ASIA TAKES A REST IN A CHARACTERISTIC POSE

Inhabiting northern India, the Malay peninsula and the Dutch East Indies, the various kinds of loris form a group of tropical lemurs. The one above is known, from its very deliberate movements, as the slow loris. It has the large eyes of the nocturnal animal and gets a living by crawling with extreme stealth about trees at night and grabbing any insect or small bird it comes across. The birds are preyed upon while they are asleep. The animal always rests upside-down, as we see it here.

The larger honey-eating parrots belonging to the distinct group of lories are also fond of hanging head downwards, if not actually sleeping so ; and squirrels may often be seen doing the same thing, so that here we see the beginnings of a possible topsy-turvy habit in both beasts and birds.

Lories, by the way, will roll over on their backs in play more readily even than other parrots, and the large Indian flying-squirrel sleeps on its back, like some of the armadillos—a very rare habit, for nearly all animals, even if upside-down, do not lie with their limbs free, but like to be in touch with their base ; the statement that man is the only animal that lies on his back from choice is nearly correct, if by lying one understands sleeping.

The geckos among the lizards, which climb on any surface, horizontal or perpendicular, by means of the rows of transverse sucker-plates on their broad toes, must often live upside-down, when their hunting-ground is the ceiling of a room or cave, and they often repose head downwards ; but as a group they are not specialists in topsy-turvy life, but simply ignore orientation and travel and repose anyhow. Otherwise, reptiles as a class have a stronger objection to the upside-down position even than birds ; and as to fish, it is well known that a fish upside-down, if not a dead fish, is a very sick one. There are, however, two very remarkable cases of fish which affect this position. One is that of some African fish of the genus Synodontis, which belong to the curious whiskered family of cat-fish, well known to aquarists in the person of the commonest American species. These fish have many eccentric habits, but the speciality of Synodontis is swimming upside-down ; to this, two species found in the Nile are especially addicted, and the ancient Egyptians, who missed very little in the way of natural curiosities, have so represented them in their art. These two are noticeable for having the usual fish-coloration reversed, for they have the under parts darkened and the upper silvered ; this is no doubt an adaptation to the upside-down position, for a silvery surface exposed to the light would be simply asking for trouble from winged enemies which are only too quick to provide it for fish in any case.

The other case is that of the well-known Remora, or sucking-fish, which has so long and wide a reputation as a stuck-on stowaway with any craft, man-made or animate like shark or turtle, which may

give it free passage. The attachment is effected by a patch of sucking-plates somewhat like those on the toes of the geckos, and as this patch is on the top of the head, the fish must be often actually upside-down, and in any case has its back to its base and its underparts exposed to the outside world of the sea it traverses. The ancients, by a mistake not easy to understand, credited it with being positively able to stop any ship it joined.

WHEN we come to the great rivals of the back-boned animals, the arthropods, or armour-plated tribe, we have no difficulty in finding lives lived in reverse. The cockney sparrow has not much opportunity for Nature-study, and knows so little about his own feathered class, that the writer has seen a specimen snapped up by a gull, which he evidently did not classify apart from ducks ; but he is rather a good practical entomologist, and knows quite well that insects are to be looked for underneath leaves, and therefore hanging on upside-down. Caterpillars, it is true, will turn into flying creatures which will pass most of their lives right side up, but they are scarce compared with the myriads of aphides or plant-lice found under leaves, that produce several generations before winged forms appear, which must be upside-down livers all their short lives. The advantage to such little creatures in living in this way is obvious : a shower of rain would exterminate them wholesale if they did not take cover quickly

W. S. Berridge

CHARACTERISTIC SLOTH ATTITUDES

Another name for the two-toed sloth, of which the above are examples, is the unan, and it lives in Brazil. The epithet two-toed applies only to the fore-feet. It habitually hangs upside-down, and its eyesight and hearing are both said to be remarkably poor.

W. S. Berridge

SLOTH WHICH HAS A STRANGE NECK STRUCTURE

Hoffman's sloth, which belongs to the same family as the two-toed sloth, is distinguished by the fact of its being the sole mammal which has only six vertebrae in its neck instead of the usual seven. Like the other sloths, it is nocturnal, and spends the day curled up in an inverted, though to it, a perfectly natural position.

One of the most interesting insects is an exponent of a much more interesting upside-down existence, the water-boatman, which is about as large as a wasp, and can sting nearly as badly, only the point of offence is at the opposite end, for the creature is one of the bug family, and wounds with its strong proboscis. Its ordinary victims are small water-animals up to little fish and tadpoles, in search of which it rows about upside-down with its long hind-legs feathered at the end, looking, with its boat-shaped body, uncommonly like a sculling-boat. Sometimes it basks in the sun, turning right-side up and half-opening its wings ; and it has a most original way of launching itself on its strong buzzing flight, by taking a dive and then fairly firing itself out of the water by vigorously rowing upwards.

The insects' subtle enemies, the spiders, furnish an excellent and easily observed example of upside-down life in the case of the familiar web-weavers like the common garden-spider : these rest head downwards on their webs, and travel about them and their supporting rigging back downwards just like miniature sloths—a great contrast, in their wonderful activities, to those dullest witted of mammals.

The crustaceans furnish us with some of the most striking examples of what may be called supine activity in the little shrimp-like creatures known as Phyllopods, or leaf-feet, their feet, which number many pairs, being broadened and leaf-like, and serving alike as carriers of the breathing organs and as propellers, as well as entrapping articles of food in the groove between their two ranks, and driving the captures forward to the mouth. To this tribe belongs the beautiful fairy-shrimp (*Chirocephalus*), a fresh-water creature rather over an inch long and with a glass-like body adorned by the red and blue hues of the appendages. Another infinitely more abundant form is the brine shrimp (*Artemia*), less interesting in its appearance, as it is merely a little reddish creature about half-an-inch long, but with the remarkable eccentricity of positively enjoying being pickled alive. Ordinary salt water is not strong enough for it, and it thrives in the brine of salt-pans wherein the salt is a quarter-pound to the pint, often colouring their contents pink by its numbers. These little creatures lay their eggs in the mud, and thus get them transported by birds, some species of which are certain to visit any piece of water sooner or later, wet their feet in it, and so pick up some of the eggs.

Most remarkable of all are that numerous and familiar tribe of crustaceans which not only stand on their heads but cement themselves down in that position and then, as Huxley said, kick their food into their mouths. These are the barnacles and acorn-shells, so familiar as adhering to any hard substance, fixed or floating, found at sea. They begin life as little, active, shield-shaped, brush-footed larvae, and then change into little creatures, still active and fringe-footed, but covered with a couple of shells—much like some water-fleas in fact. After attaining this stage they glue themselves down to some support by a secretion of special glands in the head, developing additional shell plates, and in the case of the barnacles, a flexible stalk. The legs still remain in vigorous action, their use now being to draw in atoms of food circulating in the water ; to act as casting-nets, in fact. These creatures, so strangely self-condemned to a fixed reversal of position, are one of the great successes of evolution ; their fossils occur in some of the earliest formations, and they are one of the standing nuisances of their vertebrate superiors. They grow too abundantly on ships' bottoms, infest whales till their irritation makes those leviathans leap like lambs, and have even been found growing on the toes of a penguin, which had lost some claws as a consequence.

Chapter LXXXIV

The Mystery Senses of Insects

By John J. Ward

Author of "Insect Biographies"

It is somewhat difficult to realize that all the marvellous instinctive actions of insects are merely responses to external stimuli. Experiments prove that the apparent intelligence of insects is really non-existent, although a few of the more highly-evolved types such as ants, bees, and wasps do occasionally provide a hint of something that seems to approach mentality.

The solitary wasp emerges from its pupa chamber and commences to build a cell in which it places an egg and a store of caterpillars, each one of which is first paralysed by the action of the wasp's sting. It has never seen a cell built, nor caterpillars captured and stung, yet its inborn instinct guides it with unerring skill to carry out the work of providing shelter and living prey for its offspring that it will never see. Likewise the butterfly, whose sole food consists of liquid nectar from the flowers, when the time comes to deposit its eggs seeks the green leaves of some plant which up to that time has had no interest for it. It has never laid eggs before, yet it finds the correct food plant for its leaf-eating, unborn young. Such clever actions seem to imply intelligence, but really they are nothing more than the insect's responses to impulses working on its complex sensory organs, its first movement suggesting the next as its various senses are stimulated to act just at the proper moment.

The senses of insects, other than sight, are largely associated with hair structures. On the proboscis of a blowfly four distinct kinds of sensory hairs have been recognized, but to connect these hairs with their particular sense-function of touch, taste, smell, or even hearing, presents enormous difficulties. All that the microscope reveals is that each kind of bristle, or hair, is associated with its own particular type of nerve-cell; from which we may infer that they serve different sensory functions. Experiments can, however, be made in less complex instances

Everybody has probably met with the "woolly-bear" caterpillar of the tiger moth, and touched its long, silky hairs. Even if only one or two of its hairs are very gently touched, the caterpillar is seen to shrink in response, and the chances are that it will coil itself up and fall from its food-plant to the ground. Then, if we try to pick it up amongst the grass blades its smooth, flexible hairs give beneath our touch and the caterpillar slips further down amongst the vegetation until it has reached the soil, when its legs then rapidly come into use. Obviously the sense of touch is very highly developed in those long brown hairs, but the caterpillar's actions do not indicate that it thought it must try to escape. More probably its escape was entirely due to a series of reflex actions commencing with the first touch of its sensitive hairs and ending with finding its felt in contact with the ground, and having no connexion beforehand in the creature's consciousness.

More complicated organs of touch are witnessed in the antennae, or "feelers," of insects, and not infrequently we may see these organs being used as feelers in the proper sense of that word, but that is perhaps the least of their functions, for their sensory uses are extremely complex in character. Circumstances seem to suggest that it is quite possible that some insects may smell, hear, and even perhaps receive radio vibrations by means of their antennae.

There is, for example, the curious fact that the newly-emerged female of many species of moths will attract a crowd of male suitors of her species from all points of the compass, though she herself may be enclosed in a box The male moths that seek the imprisoned lady of their kind are

J. J. Ward

EMPEROR MOTHS' ANTENNAE

To capture a male emperor moth one first catches a newly-emerged female and puts her in a box. The males soon begin to arrive, directed by some strange sense. The antennae of the male (bottom) are quite different from those of the female (top). Both photographs magnified.

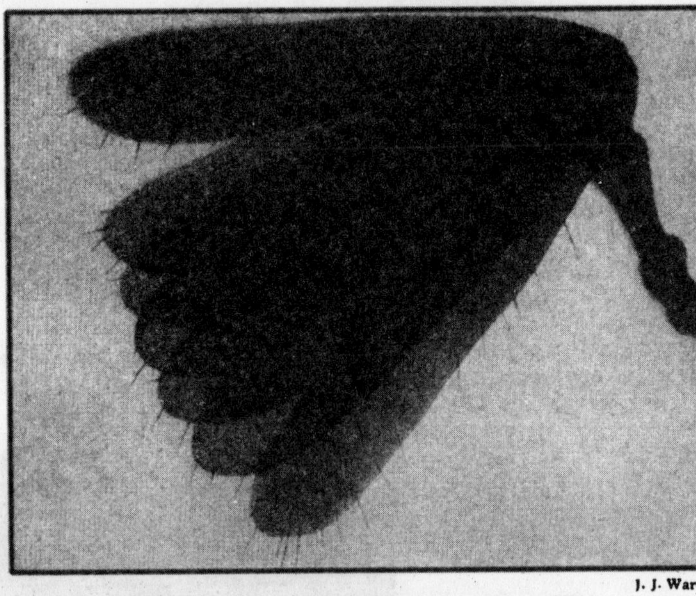

J. J. Ward

ANTENNAE OF COCKCHAFER AND MOTH

The lower illustration is of part of the antennae of a cockchafer much magnified, and shows the plates with their sensitive hairs. Above is the antennae (enlarged) of a male tiger moth. It is the caterpillar of the garden tiger that is known as the "woolly bear" and it is thickly covered with very sensitive hairs.

usually found to have very feathery antennae clothed with sensitive bristles and hairs of various kinds, while those of the female moth are of comparatively simple structure; and it is maintained by some authorities that the male moths can by means of their complex, feathery feelers scent from afar the object of their search. There may, however, be a quite different explanation, as I will here endeavour to show.

If smell is the means of attraction, it is a sense of smell quite beyond human comprehension, for to us "smell" means odour that is perceptible to human senses; yet the smell of the female moth is supposed to attract male moths from miles around, up or down wind indifferently. Henri Fabre, at the beginning of the century, made experiments with various moth species, and he found that when certain female moths were placed under a bell glass cover sealed with putty, or put in a well-closed box, they no longer attracted the males, and on his experiments is largely based the evidence of those who support the scent theory.

Fabre also found that objects against which the female moths had rested would, likewise, for some time afterwards, attract the male moths; which seemed a further proof that smell was the agent of attraction. Fabre endeavoured to mask this subtle smell with naphthaline, sulphuretted hydrogen, oil of lavender, paraffin, and so on, until his study had "become an odious laboratory," but still male moths continued to come as frequently as ever, and he then found that he could not believe that his own experiments had proved that it was smell. He realized that they left much unexplained, and finally he asked: "But what is materially emitted? Nothing according to our sense of smell. And this nothing is supposed to saturate an immense circle several miles in radius with its molecules.! However divisible matter may be, the mind refuses to accept such conclusions." Then, as a solution of the mystery, he added: "It does not emit molecules: it vibrates, it sets in motion waves capable of spreading to distances incompatible with a real diffusion of matter."

At that time Röntgen rays, or X-rays, had just been discovered, and our present knowledge of rays and electro-magnetic vibrations had scarcely commenced, yet by some marvellous intuition Fabre's great mind had surely provided the key to the solution of the mystery. If we apply the theory of wave emanation, and suppose that the female moths "broadcast"

Antennae and mouth of ground beetle

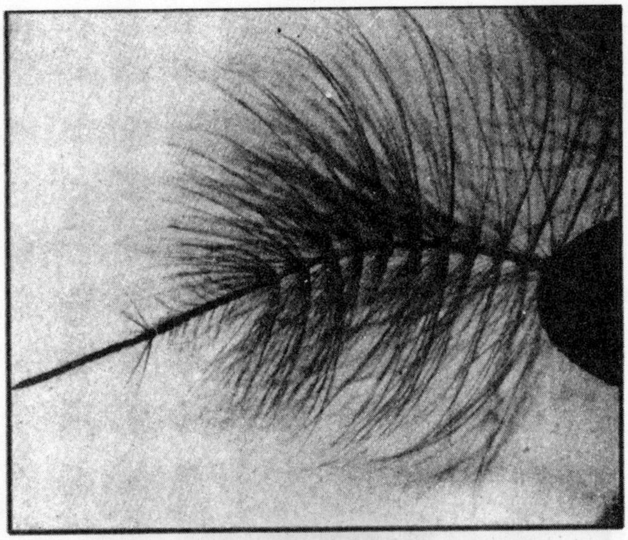

Antennae of male gnat

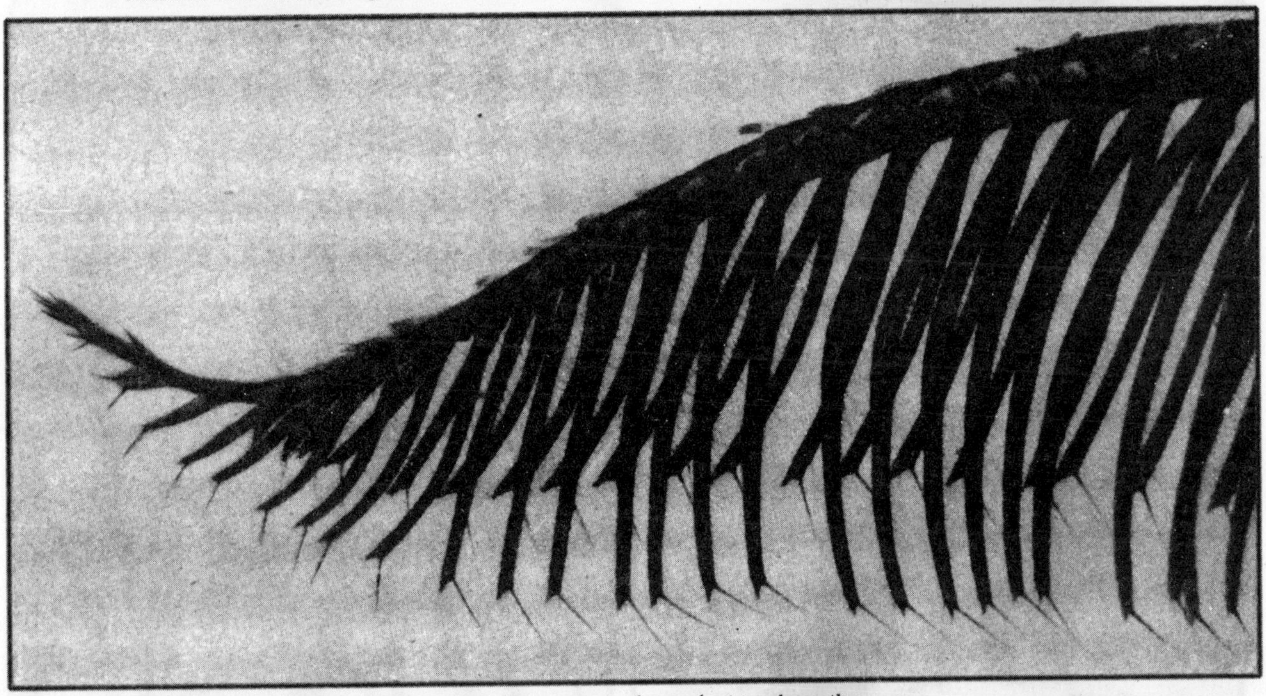

Part of the antenna of a pale tussock moth

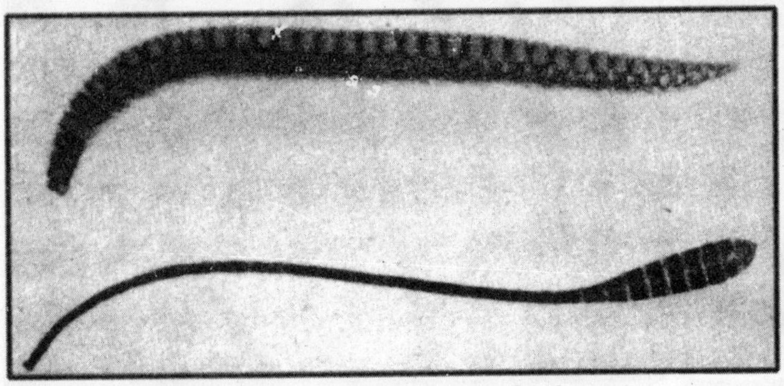

Antenna of moth (top) and butterfly (bottom)

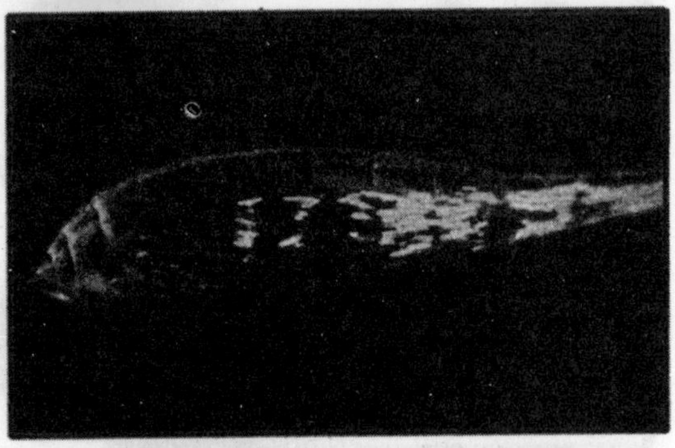

Tip of antenna of tortoiseshell butterfly

AERIALS FOR INSECT RADIO? INTENSELY SENSITIVE ANTENNAE OF VARYING FORMS

In the antennae or feelers of insects we have organs of remarkable sensitiveness, and, indeed, it is not yet certain what the limits of that sensitiveness may be. It seems possible that they may serve to convey to the insect what corresponds in man to the senses of touch, taste and smell, and perhaps the perceptive qualities of these delicate organs may be even capable of receiving some stimuli on a par with the waves that actuate a "wireless" set, and in the same way. These micro-photographs by J. J. Ward show a variety of patterns.

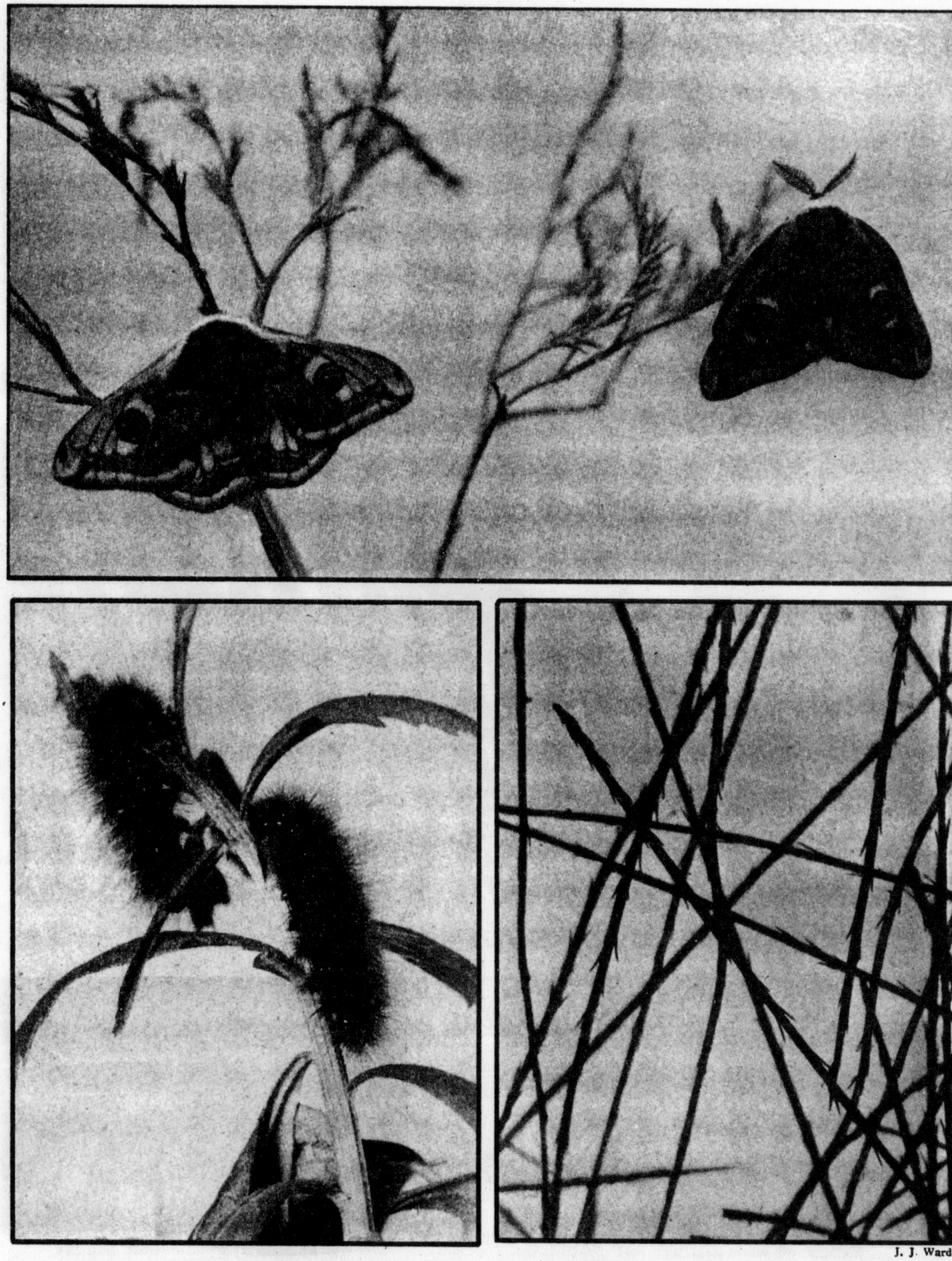

J. J. Ward

SENSITIVE HAIRS OF THE "WOOLLY BEAR" AND THE MOTH IT EVENTUALLY BECOMES

Familiar in most gardens during the summer, the "woolly bear" caterpillar (bottom) may sometimes be seen proceeding along the surface of the garden path in a series of rapid undulations of its hairy back. These hairs, when magnified (bottom right), will be found to possess barbed edges, and they are very sensitive. The lightest touch will make the caterpillar shrink. The top photograph shows, on the left, a female and, on the right, a male emperor moth. These are the creatures into which the "woolly bears" grow.

J. J. Ward

BRISTLES, HAIRS AND ANTENNAE THAT SERVE WONDROUS PURPOSES FOR THEIR OWNERS

Sheep ticks get in touch with their hosts by waiting on grass stems till a sheep walks by. The bristles on the tick's leg (bottom left) warn it that something has brushed against it, and the formidable grappling-hook of the foot comes into play. This photograph, and the one to the right of it, showing a gnat larva's head are greatly magnified. The gnat larva is equipped with hairs which pass currents of water to the mouth, which thus extracts nutriment. Above are two crickets getting their bearings by means of their antennae.

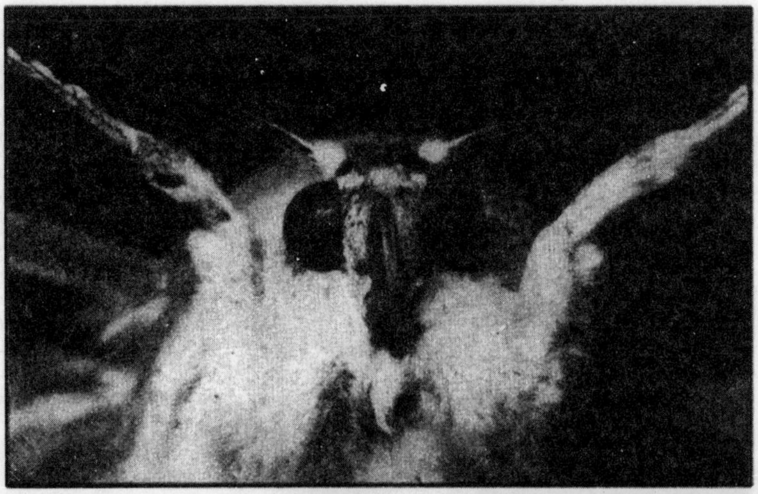

J. J. Ward

HEADS OF PUSS MOTH AND UNDERWING MOTH

In the puss moths both sexes have antennae that are bipectinated, that is, resembling two combs, laid back to back. The "teeth" of these combs are much larger in the male than in the female. Here we see a male with his antennae. Above is a full-face photograph of a broad-bordered underwing. Both photographs are magnified.

for a mate, it appears to offer at once a clear explanation of the whole of the phenomena. Even the fact of the male moths visiting objects on which the female moths have rested (one of the chief planks of the scent theory) is then no longer a puzzle, for it is the property of rays to penetrate, and often to leave a record behind.

The actinic, or ultra-violet, rays at the end of the known light spectrum, although invisible to our eyes, we know will affect our photographic plates. During the War period a street novelty was sold in the form of buttons coated with a paste made from sulphides of metals, as calcium, barium, and strontium, which, on exposure to daylight, would, at night, give out their absorbed light rays. Even a rock after exposure to sunlight will for hours afterwards give out invisible heat rays. These are rays of which we have knowledge, but those that are probably used by the delicate sensory organs of insects are far beyond detection by means of man's coarse instruments. I suggest that they are probably of very short wave-length, nearly approaching those of visible light—round about one fifty-thousandth of an inch—which, of course, are very rapid when compared with man's wireless waves of from hundreds of yards to some miles in length.

Recent American experiments in the making of a new transmitting valve for short wave-lengths of approximately ten centimetres have shown that the operators engaged on the work suffered with pains in their limbs, and that rats kept in a cage near the transmitting aerial became greatly excited. That at least indicates that animals can be influenced with such short waves.

Fabre's experiments with the moths under a sealed glass and in a tightly closed box when considered from the wave emanation aspect might easily fail. The moth itself may not have been "broadcasting" at the actual time of the experiment for the moth can instantly shut off the wave, as she does when she has found her mate. Also, the fact of interference, and shutting off the air supply, might, with her delicate senses, readily bring about that very result. Indeed, Fabre himself, although he could not understand why, recorded of the moth that: "Taken from her couch and placed elsewhere, the female loses her attraction for the time and becomes an object of indifference." In any case, Fabre shows clearly enough that the phenomena he had witnessed could not be accounted for by an air-borne scent; he fully realized that something still remained unexplained.

That an insect should produce an invisible ray is quite a possibility, for there are insects that emit light rays—as the familiar British glow-worm, and the fire-flies of tropical America, which, like the glow-worms, are really beetles; there are also tropical may-flies that produce light. And this brings us to a strange connection. Male glow-worms, of course, seek their mates by the sense of sight, the bright light of the female attracting them from afar. However, innumerable males are drawn from their course by artificial lights, and where such lights are exposed these amorous males quickly meet with their destruction. Here we have an instance of what in wireless is known as "interference"—a stronger transmitting station superimposing on a weaker one with most unfortunate results for the owner of the "set" interfered with.

Strange to relate, we find exactly the same thing taking place with regard to moths; the moth and

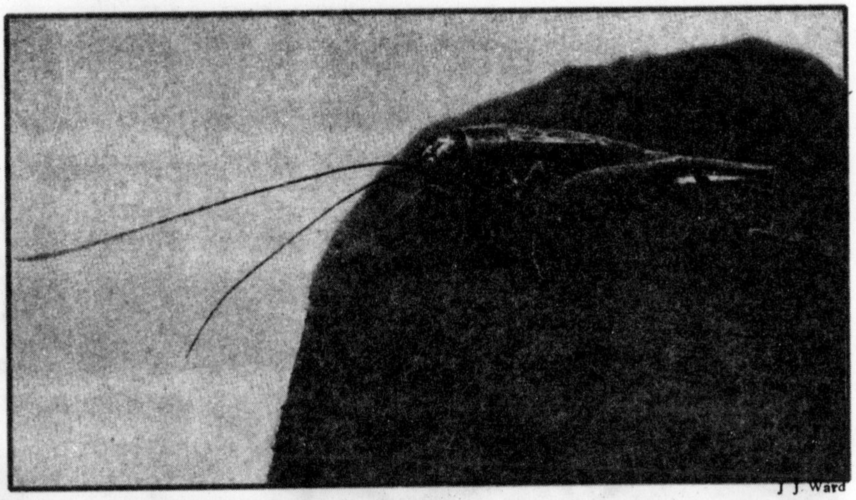
J. J. Ward

the candle flame have become proverbial. The moth in "tuning-in" to the invisible wave that is transmitted by its mate is likewise drawn from his course by artificial lights; surely the explanation is because he is using a wave-length very close to that of visible light, exactly as in the case of the male glow-worm. Similarly, we have beetles, such as the cockchafer, which do not emit light but which, like the moths, fly to the lights, and it is significant that the antennae of the male cockchafer are of a very complex structure, being formed of a series of leaf-like plates bearing sensitive bristles; they are quite unlike the ordinary eleven-jointed feelers of most beetles. The scent theorist entirely ignores these allied phenomena when he proclaims that an ordinary air-borne odour as human senses perceive it is the means of attraction.

HOUSE CRICKET AND THE "EAR" ON ITS LEG

House-crickets hear with a special organ upon the foreleg (bottom). This is an oval opening, and by its means the house-cricket (top) hears the chirping of its mate. To human senses the sound is most deceptive, and seems endowed with some quality as of ventriloquism, so that it appears to come from some other quarter than the real one. But the mate is not deceived.

THERE is another strange phenomenon with regard to moths. The collector goes out into the woods on an ideal night for making captures, when there is a warm thundery atmosphere, and it may even be raining at the time; a bright moonlight night is generally hopeless. Sometimes the ideal night yields nothing, while perhaps the next night, which may be cold with moonlight, will provide abundant specimens. With the light as a lure to effect his captures the same thing happens; on what appears to be a most favourable night nothing is attracted, while another night when conditions seem altogether unsuitable there is a swarm of moths of many species round every lamp. Here, surely, we are up against what in wireless parlance is known as "atmospherics." I suggest that the moths are using a miniature long-distance transmission. All who have wireless sets for long-distance reception will know full well that on some nights the transmission comes over quite well, while on other nights it is hopelessly bad.

When we examine the antennae of the male moths who respond to the "wireless" calls of their mates, we find that each species has an entirely different "wireless set." That must be so, for their instruments are not provided with a series of knobs to tune in to different stations. Their sensory organs necessarily have to be adjusted solely for the wave-length used by the female of their species.

From the evidence here adduced, surely there is a case for showing that the moth's sensory feelers are organs specialised for receiving delicate radio-vibrations, probably of the nature of the infra-red, or heat, rays, which in the wave spectrum come just below those of visible light. The value of such organs as a means of finding a mate is demonstrated in a very curious fashion. It has proved so effectual that we find the wings of many of the female moths that "broadcast" have become more or less atrophied and in some species they have entirely disappeared. Here, too, it is well to remember that the female glow-worm, that emits light, is also wingless, while the males have good flying wings, exactly as in the case of the moths. Some species have gone even further and lost the use of their legs, and are without mouth-parts, so that they cannot fly, walk, or feed. It is therefore essential that no time whatever should be lost in finding their mates.

J. J. Ward

OPERATIONS OF UNCOILING AND RECOILING THE AMAZING PROBOSCIS OF THE CONVOLVULUS HAWK MOTH

So huge is the proboscis of the convolvulus hawk moth that, in the chrysalis stage, the tongue case forms a projection at one end which rather resembles the handle ot an earthenware jug. The suggestion is further strengthened by the fact that the chrysalis is of a brownish-red tint. When the moth crawls out of its case the proboscis is found to be about twice as long as the whole length of the creature's body. This enormous organ is kept coiled up like the mainspring of a watch, and we see it here in the process of being uncoiled (left) and recoiled (right) after the feeding process has been finished. These photographs are, of course, both considerably magnified.

J. J. Ward

CONVOLVULUS HAWK MOTH AND ITS EXTRAORDINARILY LENGTHY PROBOSCIS

In the left hand of these two photographs, which are both much magnified, we see how the convolvulus hawk moth withdraws its tremendous proboscis into the lower part of its head. This is the position in which it carries the proboscis. When the moth arrives opposite a flower the coils are unwound and the whole affair thrust into the heart of the flower to sip the nectar that lies there. It especially visits plants with long tubercles, such as the tobacco plant and the petunia, and does not alight but feeds while hovering. It commences operations at dusk and continues well on into the night. The right-hand illustration shows the moth at rest upon a plant.

Senses of Insects

observed to show a sympathetic jerky movement with the whistling of a railway engine a mile away. If we think of the shrill piping note of the female gnat and mosquito, we begin to understand that probably the distant sound of the engine's whistle may approach the gnat's range of sound. The male gnat has beautiful feathery antennae, and Mayer, who made a series of experiments, says: " The hairs on the antennae of the male gnat vibrate in unison with the notes of a tuning-fork within the range of sounds emitted by the female. The longer hairs vibrate sympathetically with the graver notes, and the shorter with the higher ones." So that insects may be said to "hear," or at any rate perceive, sound, although they have no apparent "ears."

The variations in the antennae of the various orders of insects are really amazing, and they doubtless serve very different functions in each type. Butterflies do not exhibit any of the phenomena referred to above in the case of the moths, and their antennal functions are somewhat of a puzzle. It is possible that they have something to do with the locating of the particular food plants required by their caterpillar offspring; for the butterfly itself feeds entirely on the fluid sweets from the flowers, and cannot have the very least idea of the meaning of green leaf food.

J. J. Ward

STRANGE EARS AND EYES

The short-horned grasshopper (bottom) has its " ears " in the first ring of its body, near the thorax, and by this means hears the stridulating of its mate. Above is a queen wasp's head with two kinds of eyes, single and compound. The single eyes are called ocelli

THAT insects do possess a very highly-developed sense of smell nobody can doubt. One may witness the speedy arrival of the wasp the moment the sweets are placed on the dining-room table; or the advent of the blowfly eager to deposit its eggs on a dead or injured animal; or the early visits to the crocus blooms of tortoise-shell and brimstone butterflies, although it may be a day in early March when perhaps an hour before those same insects were snug and dormant in their winter hibernating places. Possibly, too, scent plays a part in the courtship of many of our common butterflies, for when we see them fluttering around each other in mid-air it is probable that the male is wafting sweet odours to attract the lady of his species; for on his wings are peculiar scales known as plumules, or androconia, which are associated with scent cells, producing such perfumes as lemon, sweet briar, violet, and other flowery essences quite perceptible to the human olfactory organs when the scales of the butterfly are disturbed.

Recent experiments have shown that honey bees have a similar sense of smell to that of man so far as it is associated with floral perfumes. Also that they can absorb a particular food scent, and, in the hive, by dancing movements, convey that scent to the other bees so that they can go out quite independently to seek that food supply.

If we turn to the sense of hearing, we again find the antennae playing a part. Swarms of gnats have been

We should remember, too, that probably they make and hear sounds quite beyond man's sense of hearing; ordinary noises have little or no effect upon them, but when imitations of their own sound productions have been made with suitable instruments they have been shown to be both excited and alarmed. Some insects, however, have ears similar in mechanism to our own, and such ears may be found in various parts of their body and limbs. Crickets and long-horned grasshoppers, for example, have their ears situated in their fore-legs, just below the " knee "; while in the short-horned grasshoppers a different arrangement prevails, their ears being found one at each side of the first ring of the abdomen, close to the thorax. The chirping of the male cricket attracts the female, and it has been demonstrated that when a chirping male has been placed against the mouthpiece of a telephone a female cricket in another room was at once attracted and made her way rapidly to the telephone in response to his call made in this quite unusual way. Of the sense of sight little need be written here, as

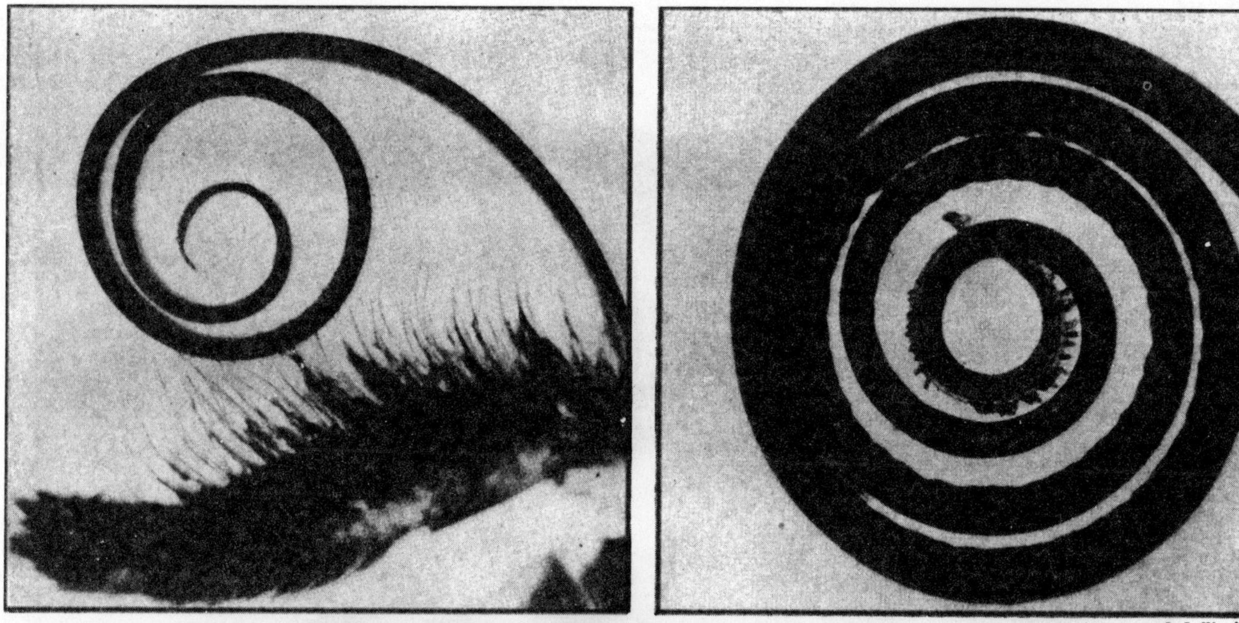

J. J. Ward

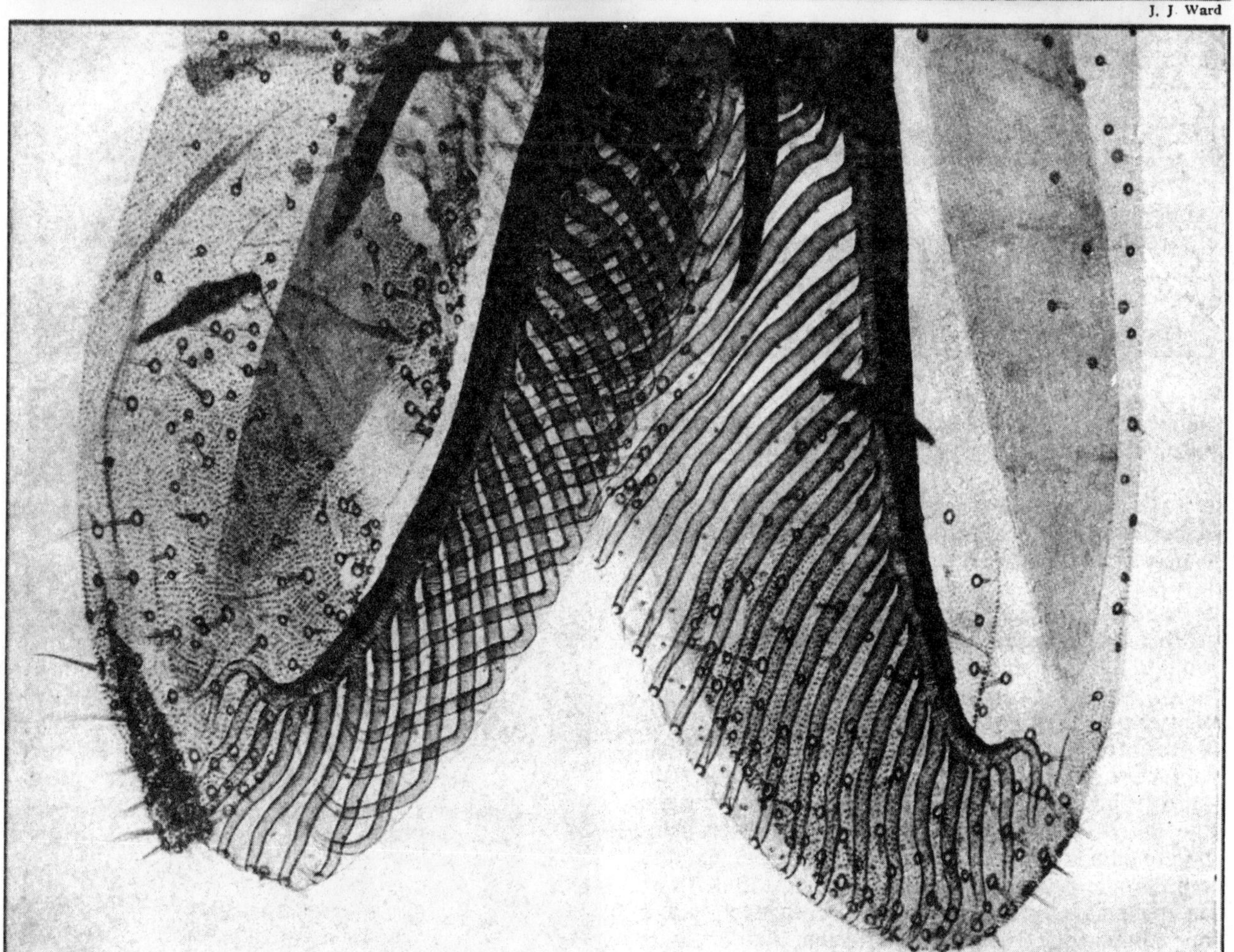

E. A. Botting

FORMS OF PROBOSCIS POSSESSED BY DRONE FLY AND BUTTERFLY

The proboscis, or trunk, of insects is the organ by means of which food is conveyed to the mouth. Below is the proboscis of a drone fly much enlarged, while the top photographs show (left) the proboscis of a butterfly with the mouth palps and its special sensitive hairs and (right) a butterfly proboscis more highly magnified to show details. The proboscis consists of two tubes which are joined by interlocking hairs. This join makes a third tube, between the others, and it is through this that the nectar from the flower is sucked. The outer tubes supply air.

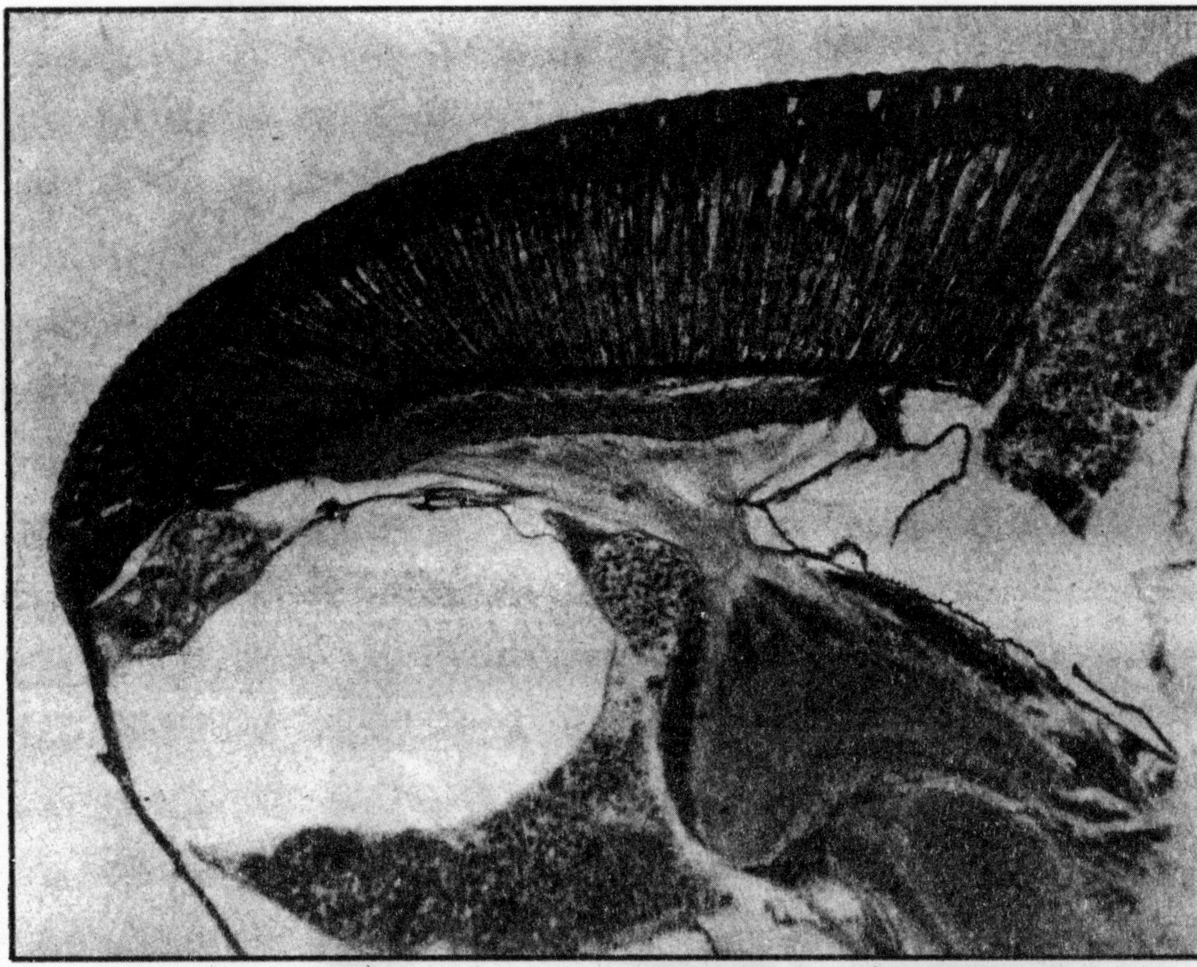

an account of the ocelli, or single eyes, and the compound eyes of insects has previously been given in this work (pages 192—204). It is interesting to learn, however, that some recent experiments by a German biologist, Professor von Frisch, have shown that the ultra-violet rays, invisible to the mechanism of the human eye, but which, as previously mentioned, affect a photographic plate, are visible to honey bees, although of what colour they represent to them we have no possible conception. Also, that while the bees could appreciate the ultra-violet rays, they failed at the other side of the light spectrum; they could not recognize red at all; red and black were to them of equivalent values. Surely an interesting fact when we remember that the same applies to a sensitive photographic plate. It may also account for the absence of black and pure red flowers in temperate climes. In the tropics a few spectral, or pure red, flowers occur, and it has been found that these are pollinated by birds. It is the green, blue, violet and ultra-violet side of the spectrum that attracts the bees; the red side is to them a blank, just as the ultra-violet is to us.

Finally, there is the sense of taste. Groups of cells associated with taste, in the higher animals are in insects represented by wonderful tongues with very complex sensory functions specialised for fluid food.

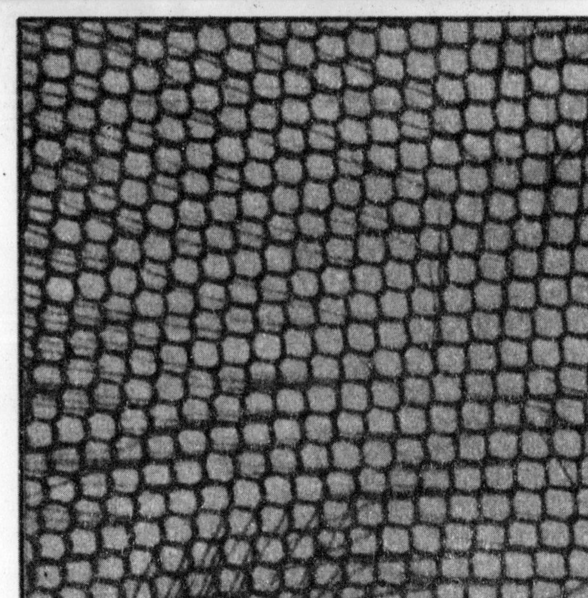

J. J. Ward

FLIES' EYES IN DETAIL

Below are a few of the four thousand or so of facets which go to make up one of the compound eyes of the house fly. A picture of the fly's head with the complete eyes is given on page 192. Above we have the compound eye of the blow-fly in section. Each facet is connected with the optic nerve centre.

Chapter LXXXV

The Marvellous Angler-Fishes of the Ocean Depths

By C. Tate Regan, F.R.S.

Director, The Natural History Museum, South Kensington

It is believed that no light rays penetrate the ocean to a depth of more than 250 fathoms, yet at this depth, and in the still deeper waters, down to a mile or more below the surface, there is a great diversity of living creatures.

The fishes of these ocean depths, that pass their lives in complete darkness, differ in colour from those that live at the surface or in the coastal waters; they are generally uniformly blackish, without that gradation from dark on the back to pale below which is characteristic of fishes that live in the light, and counteracts its effect. Many of these fishes, but not all, are provided with luminous organs. In one group, known as the Stomiatoids, there is a double series of small luminous organs along each side of the body; these must look like the shining port-holes of a ship in the night, and may help the members of a shoal to keep in touch with each other; a larger organ is placed in a pocket just behind the eye, and is so arranged that the luminous surface may be turned inwards into the pocket, or may be exposed, giving light for the eye to see; finally, there are luminous appendages — barbels — depending from the chin, which may be used to attract prey.

All the fishes of the ocean depths are carnivorous, living on each other, or on the prawns and other sorts of small creatures that inhabit these regions. In the absence of light there is no plant life, and one wonders what the primary source of food may be. It is generally accepted that this must be organic matter falling from the upper layers, and that the minute floating plants of the surface are the ultimate basis of the life of the fishes of the depths. This seems almost incredible, but is not more wonderful than that the small amount of carbon dioxide in the air should supply the carbon for the growth of trees.

The pressure of the water at depths of 200 fathoms or more is enormous, but fishes that live at these depths appear to need no structural modifications to enable them to withstand it. Moreover, if the nets in which they are caught are brought slowly to the surface, so that the alteration of pressure is gradual, they arrive intact and in perfect condition. What would happen if they were hauled up quickly is shown at Madeira, where there is a fishery for wreck-fish (*Polyprion*) by long baited lines fished on the bottom at about 200 fathoms; as the hooked fish ascend the gases in them are liberated, they gather speed and shoot out of the water, considerably distended and with eyes protruding.

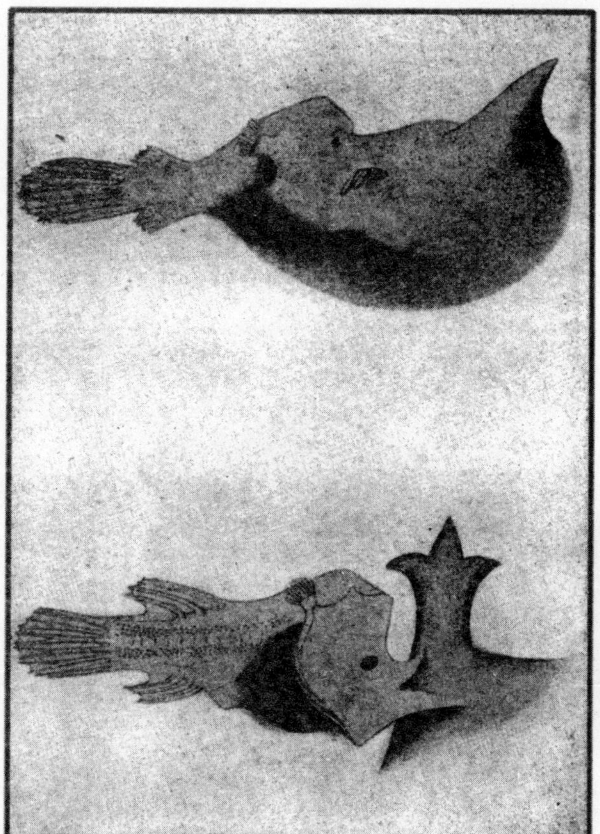

LITTLE CANNIBALS OF THE DEEP

Most of the angler fish are very small indeed, and of the two here the one below, *Edriolychnus*, is seen four times its natural size and the one above, *Photocorynus*, five times its real dimensions. The illustrations are given by courtesy of the British Museum (N.H.).

One of the most interesting groups of fishes that live in the ocean depths is that of the anglers, so named because the first ray of the dorsal fin is placed on the head and is modified into a line and bait. The anglers of the coastal waters generally lie in wait for their prey at the bottom, and their coloration harmonises with that of the ground on which they lie, or the rocks and weeds among which they lurk. Their bait is a skinny flap or a tassel at the end of the line, and is waved about to attract other fishes. The anglers of the ocean float about in the darkness of the depths, they are uniformly blackish, and at the end of their line is a bulb-like swelling that contains a gland with a luminous secretion; there is some evidence that the light can be switched on and off; when turned on it acts as a lure, which is not meant to be seized but to bring other fishes near the angler's mouth.

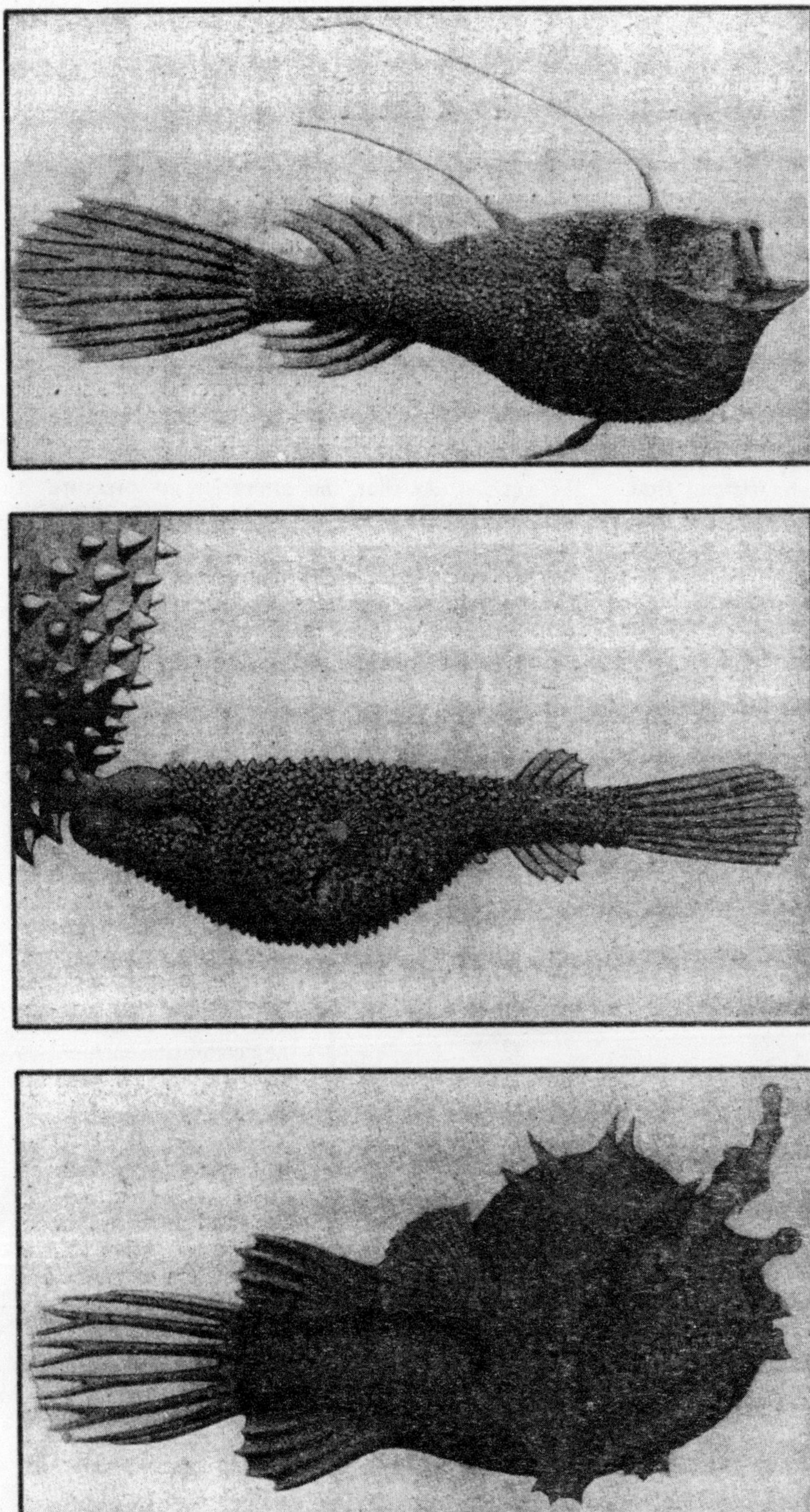

British Museum (Natural History)

FEMALE FISH WHOSE MATES ARE MERE PARASITES

Belonging to the family of the Ceratoids, or angler fishes, are some sixty known species, of which we have two here. *Photocorynus spiniceps* (bottom), enlarged to nearly twice natural size and *Ceratias holboelli* (centre and top). The males are mere parasites, attached to the females for life. The centre illustration shows a male, natural size, and above we see it with its female.

The oceanic anglers are distinguished not only by their black colour and the luminous lure, but by other peculiarities; they form a group apart, known as the Ceratioids. This group contains some sixty different known species, some of which are figured in these pages.

Most of these oceanic anglers have enormous mouths, provided with sharp teeth that are depressible, allowing their victims an easy passage inwards, but becoming erect and holding if one attempts to escape. They are also remarkably distensible, swallowing fishes many times their own size and simply stretching to accommodate them. Two genera, Melanocetus and Linophryne, are particularly noteworthy in this connexion, for specimens have been found at the surface of the ocean, far away from their home in the depths, alive but helpless, swollen out by the much larger fishes they have swallowed. Each had seized her prey by the tail, and then held on—probably she was unable to let go—while the victim swam upwards. Every time he paused the angler would take in a little more of him, but by the time his struggles ceased he had brought his captor to the top, in no condition to make an effort to get down again. One Melanocetus managed successfully to swallow a large fish without being brought to the surface, and had just begun to digest it when she saw a bait on a hook, took it, and was caught; such greediness deserved no better fate, and she is now preserved in spirit in the Natural History Museum at South Kensington.

In some of the oceanic anglers the lure appears like a lantern placed directly on the head just above the mouth, in others it is at the end of a long and slender line and is no doubt moved about to imitate the swimming movements of a small luminous animal. The line, like other fin-rays, is attached to a bony support, and in some species this bone projects from the head, becomes long and flexible, and forms a rod. In one genus (*Lasiognathus*) the line ends in a triangle of hooks, and this fish, with rod, line, bait and hooks is certainly a complete angler, and should, perhaps, have been named after Izaak Walton. Only one specimen is known, and as the stomach is empty we cannot say what sort of prey is hooked.

In the preceding account I have once or twice referred to a fish as "she" and this is of set purpose, for all the Ceratioids that swim freely in the ocean are females, and the only males known are dwarfs parasitic on the females. Males are rare and so far have been seen in only three genera, Ceratias, Photocorynus and Edriolychnus.

Ceratias is remarkable for the spiny skin and the very long and slender rod bearing a short line. The fishes of this genus grow to a larger size than others of the group, and, when large, find insufficient food in the open ocean and make for the banks where cod abound. Thus, two examples, each about forty inches long, have been taken by trawlers to the south of Iceland; one had two males, each three inches long, attached close together on one side of her abdomen, the other had a single male, measuring four inches long, which was placed in the mid-ventral line a little behind the head.

The other females with males are quite small, less than three inches long; one was caught in the Atlantic, the other in the Gulf of Panama. The males are adults, but one, placed on the top of his wife's head, just above her right eye, is only two-fifths of an inch long, the other, spending his life upside down attached to the side of his mate's head, measures three-fifths of an inch. Thus in weight the wives are about

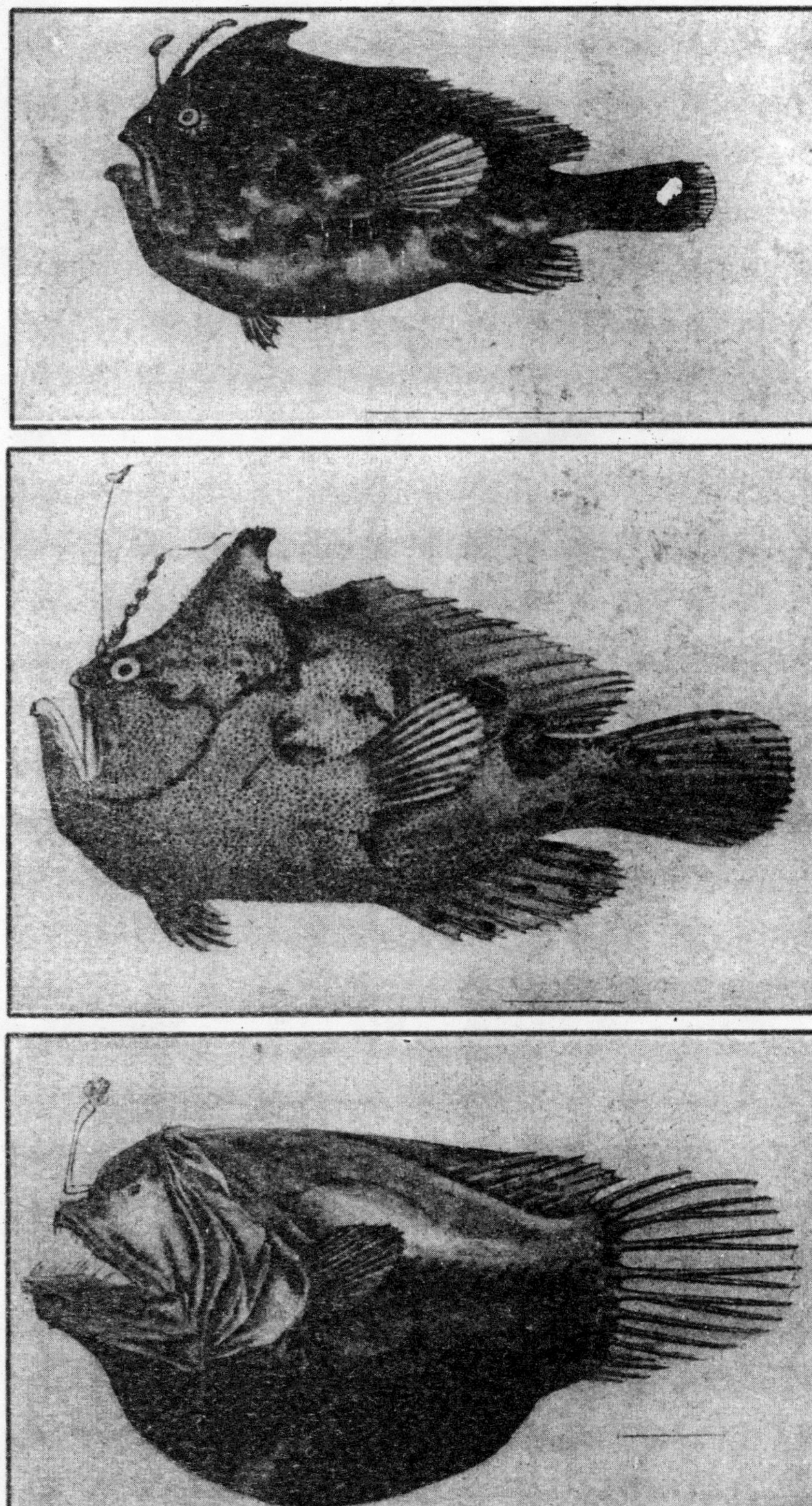

U.S. National Museum

MINUTE MONSTERS FROM THREE HUNDRED FATHOMS DOWN

The small lines in the above photographs indicate the actual size in life of the fish shown. It is only by enlargement that it is possible to get a convincing illustration of these tiny ogres of the deep which, one might imagine, were huge things. But they make up for their size by having widely distendible stomachs in which they can accommodate fish their own size.

British Museum (Natural History)

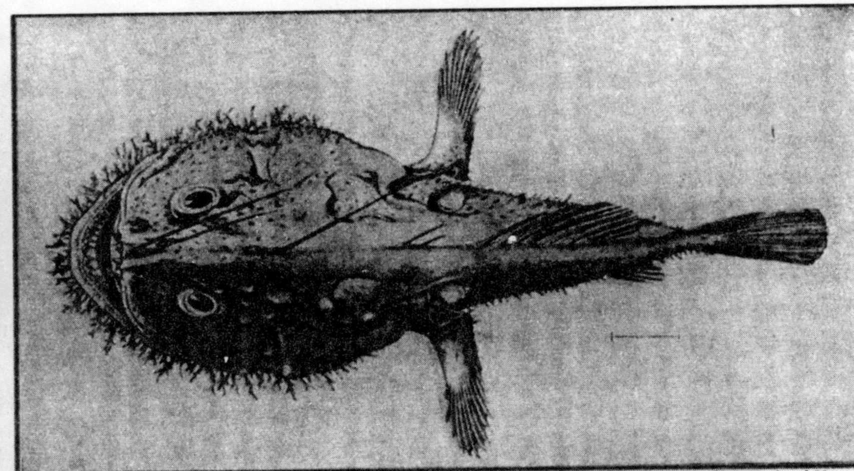

U.S. National Museum

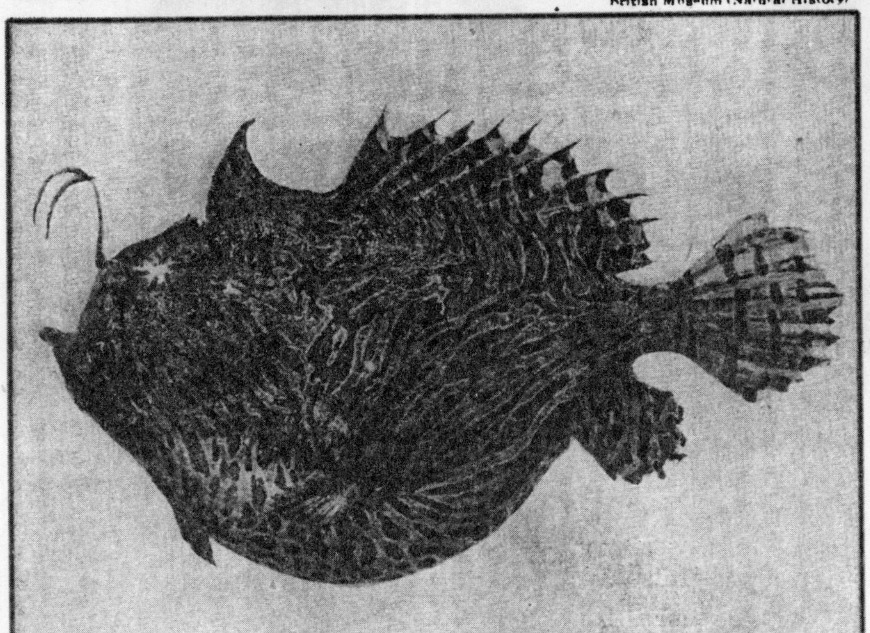

Australian Museum, Sydney

UGLY ANGLER FISH WHICH HAVE SHORT BODIES AND VERY LONG NAMES

Angler fish, for the most part, have names almost as fearsome as their appearance. In the waters of the Middle Harbour at Sydney swims *Antennarius striatus* (bottom left). It is of a light brown, and is marked with irregular blackish stripes and, so attired, matches the seaweeds in which it lurks. Its food consists of prawns and small fish, and some of the latter it can swallow although they are much the same size as the swallower. The other fish seen above are *Aegoeonichthys appelii* (bottom right); *Edriolychnus schmidti* (top left), and *Lophiodes olivaceus* (top right), alarming and impressive both in appearance and nomenclature. **All of them entice their prey by angling for it with a special attachment on the head or back.**

one hundred to two thousand times as big as their husbands.

The males are permanently joined to the females. In Ceratias and Photocorynus outgrowths in front of the mouth of the male unite with a soft projection from the skin of the female, but in Edriolychnus the main connection is inside the mouth of the male. Other fishes that live in the darkness of the ocean depths pursue their prey actively and swim in companies; but the anglers are sluggish, they float about waiting for their prey to come to them. The males, as soon as they are hatched, look for the females, and if they are fortunate enough to find one hold on to her and from henceforth become parasitic.

As in many other fishes a female angler produces thousands of eggs at a time, which hatch into tiny larvae, of which, as a rule, not more than one or two would grow into mature fish; so that, when they are just hatched, the larval fish are much more numerous than the mature ones of the same kind in that region, and if at this time those of the male sex devote themselves to the search for females there is more chance that some of them may find one than if they waited until later, when their numbers had diminished. If a male finds a mate he must hold on to her by his mouth, it does not seem to matter much where; probably he nips a piece of her skin and so forms a papilla, with which later his lips and tongue unite, so that thereafter he is a mere appendage, as much a part of his wife as a finger is a part of a man. Whatever position he takes up he is sufficiently near to fertilise the eggs when these are shed.

These fishes have thus arrived at a strange solution of the sex problem. The husband's attachment is for life, and if his wife dies he dies with her. On the whole she seems to have the best of it

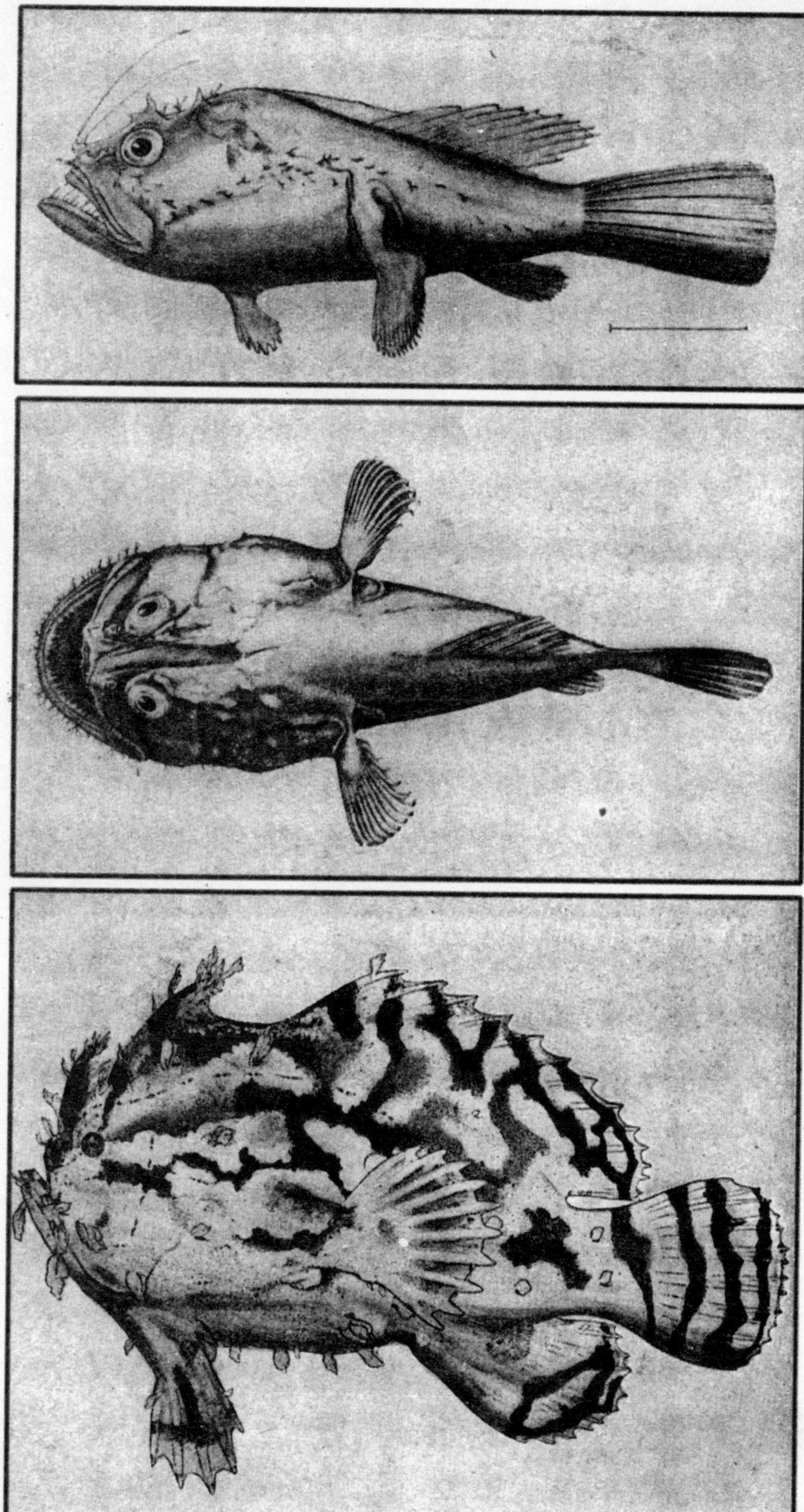

U.S National Museum & Australian Museum, Sydney

HUNGRY HUNTERS OF THE DARK DEPTHS

All the fishes of the ocean depths are flesh-eating, for there is no plant life at depths beyond two hundred and fifty fathoms, where the influence of light fails. At such depths the pressure of all this water above the fish is tremendous. If caught on a line and hauled too quickly to the surface they arrive distended and with eyes protruding from the sudden alteration in pressure.

MOUNTAIN SHEEP ON THE SKYLINE OF A ROCKY RIDGE IN JASPER NATIONAL PARK, ALBERTA

Animals living among mountains lead a more vigorous life than those of the lowlands, for not only have they their particular enemies to face but also exigencies of weather either unusual or unknown in the plains. Besides this, weather conditions, apart from their severity or otherwise, compared with conditions at lower levels, affect the surroundings of the mountain animals tremendously. The snow that hides all food, and the deadly avalanche, have all to be reckoned with. Mountain animals deal with their physical surroundings with an efficiency that is astounding and seem to know the weather before it has happened. On this faculty their lives often depend. The photograph is reproduced by courtesy of the Canadian National Railways.

Chapter LXXXVI

Have Animals Foreknowledge?

By H. Mortimer Batten

Author of "Habits and Characters of British Wild Animals"

WITHOUT entering upon such problems as migration, there can be no doubt that animals possess many faculties unknown to ourselves, which leaves us with a sense of profound wonderment as to the working of their minds. In dealing with such matters the word instinct is most convenient— instinctive knowledge, instinctive warning, and so on—and however inaccurately it may be applied, we need, nevertheless, to bear in mind that instinct is inherited knowledge, and it may be no more wonderful for an animal to preconceive a pending event than for it to obey more familiar faculties.

Let us seek out one or two examples serving to show how an animal's mind may, under certain circumstances, surpass the human mind. Some of the most remarkable examples have been furnished by that universally detested creature, the house rat. The saying that rats will leave a doomed vessel is, of course, world-wide, but that they will often forsake a doomed building is not so well known. An example of this was afforded during the War period, though at this time it passed without comment and almost unnoticed under the stress of prevailing circumstances. A lady living in an old house in Norfolk was much disturbed during the evening by the commotion among the rats in the walls. The house was filled with their squealing and scuttling, seeming to indicate that they were leaving the building, but eventually silence fell—the rats having apparently evacuated to the last tenant. An hour or so later an airship passed over the building, and dropped a bomb, which demolished part of it.

Those familiar with the world's great ports and dockyards can tell many strange stories concerning the conduct of these highly strung and sensitive animals, and it is common knowledge that when, a number of years ago, a great fire occurred among some warehouses on the Thames Embankment, the rats were seen to leave the building and to swim across the river some time before the fatal spark occurred.

NO comment can be made upon such occurrences as these, and there can have been no question of scent or sight or sound having conveyed the warning. Instinctive fear, instinctive dread, the preconception of pending calamity, must have been the moving force, and there are cases on record of human beings, particularly women, having similarly been forewarned. I remember a case of a young officer in the Indian Army cancelling his passage on a certain vessel to gratify an elderly relative, whose dreams had warned her. The vessel actually turned keel on the outward journey, and all on board were lost. But Fate had, nevertheless, placed her finger-tips on the young officer, for his train was wrecked on the up-country trip and he lost his life.

Examples of the human mind rising to these levels are, nevertheless, rare, whereas I believe that it is almost the common order among certain animals. May not the overwhelming and world-wide success of the house rat be partly due to its guarding instincts? We come across only occasional examples, but without paying undue attention to the many tall stories one hears about the cleverness of rats, the fact remains that the more closely one studies them, the more fully does one become convinced that they possess certain powers beyond our understanding. I used at one time to occupy an old house which stood a hundred yards or so from a rapidly flowing stream. During the summer months the rats left the village and took up residence along the banks of the stream which was literally honeycombed with their burrows, and if rain occurred back in the mountains the stream was subject to sudden spate, even though no rain had fallen locally. Thus for weeks of fine weather we would never hear a rat in the walls, then one evening the familiar scuttling would again occur, and someone would remark—"The rats are back. We're going to have a spate!"

This order of things was so regular that after a time it ceased to cause wonder.

I REMEMBER one other illustration. An old mill in Yorkshire had for years been overrun by rats, but one evening they were seen to forsake the building, a great army of them passing through the rushes towards the woods. Needless to say, the old mill had withstood many floods, but the flood which came a few hours later was such that the miller and his family had to flit for their lives. This flood was the result of a local cloudburst which had occurred some forty miles away.

Every trout fisher knows that trout are well aware when a spate is coming, and I have many times been able to prophesy the proximity of fresh water by the mood of the fish. There may have been no sign of rain, but one can never tell what has happened away back in the hills, where a single local storm sweeping a small area, from a certain quarter, may bring down a spate. Repeatedly I have heard something on the lines of the following conversation take place between an angler and a water baillie.

"Any sport, sir?"

"No."

"Nor anyone else. Judging from the fish they are expecting a spate."

Of course, the senses of fish may be very sensitive, for it is certainly a fact that when a spate is on its way they cease to feed absolutely, even though the fresh water is still many miles off; nor will they feed again till it actually reaches them, possibly eight or nine hours later.

Mondiale.

WEATHER-WISE CHAMOIS AMONG THE CRAGS OF THE SWISS ALPS

It often happens that the movements of the mountain animals warn those who have the faculty to understand them of the future behaviour of the weather. Here we have a group of chamois in their rocky feeding grounds on the Spietz Fluh, in Canton Fribourg. Living, in these rocky solitudes, is not always easy to pick up, and the older animals have a store of weather wisdom that seems instinctive. At any rate, it is surer than any meteorological instrument yet devised by man.

The sense of hearing of many animals is infinitely keener than our own, and their ability to catch up certain sounds quite inaudible to ourselves may at times mislead us. A farmer once told me that his dog always knew that he was coming home twenty minutes or so before he reached the door. His wife was forewarned by the dog rising from her place by the hearth and going over to the door, where she would utter a single bark for the door to be opened. Investigation revealed the fact that at the end of the occupation road remote from the house and almost a mile from it, was a swing gate, which the farmer was accustomed to bang behind his pony, and I decided that, unquestionably, the dog listened for and heard the gate. Thus I somewhat undermined the farmer's faith in his dog's astuteness, but there was a strange sequel to this. Some years later he came back to me almost triumphantly to tell me that the old dog was now almost blind and as deaf as a post, but that she still knew when he was nearing home!

On the matter of fine hearing we need to bear in mind that there are many sounds we cannot hear, but which animals can hear quite clearly. When at night-time we say that the countryside is absolutely silent, the probability is that it is filled with a host of insect and rodent noises too high-pitched for our ears to detect, but which those of that world hear as distinctly as we hear each other speak. Many people, particularly elderly people, cannot hear the scream of a bat, and the high-pitched scream of the mole is even further from the tuning-fork of human ears, yet such creatures as weasels are guided in their hunting by these sounds. The case of a stoat hearing the sounds of rats in a byre half a mile away came before my notice, and having regard for such exquisite senses, many mysteries vanish in connection with the conduct of animals.

But just as the smallest of them can hear these high-pitched sounds inaudible to ourselves, I believe they are totally unable to hear many deep sounds which we hear distinctly. I have fired shot after shot at a stoat, yet such was his conduct that one was almost justified in believing that he was quite unable to hear the deep report of the gun.

A GREAT deal concerning the strange movements of animals can be set down to the weather sense, which man does not seem able to acquire to the same extent as those animals whose movements are

governed by the weather. The Red Indian may be taken as the master of woodcraft, and though the best Indian is often a wonderful weather prophet, it will be found that his judgment is based solely on the movements of birds and animals. They are his barometer; he himself never becomes so weatherwise as the creatures of the wild.

Naturally, animals of Alpine habits are governed by the weather to a far greater extent than those of the low country, and every year one may witness the most astounding examples of foresight as to what the future holds from such creatures as deer, ptarmigan and mountain hares. Repeatedly I have watched the deer pouring down from the high ridges, albeit there was no indication of storms, the barometer standing high, and the sky clear. Perhaps two hours, perhaps twenty hours later the cause of the general movement has become evident. Similarly, in spring

S. C. Johnson

CREATURES WITH PREKNOWLEDGE: BROWN TROUT AND RATS

Of the many reasons—or excuses—given by anglers for not catching fish to-day (whereas yesterday they had done wonders) is the mysterious reason of the spate. Trout may be on the feed and rising gaily, when suddenly all signs of them cease. An hour, or six hours, perhaps, later the river suddenly rises and is in spate. How the fish knew of the spate is a mystery. Above is the familiar rat, apparently endowed with preknowledge of disaster to the place where it dwells.

W. S. Berridge

PTARMIGAN THAT ARE WISE BEFORE THE EVENT IN BAD WEATHER

Ptarmigan, a species of grouse, seem to have an uncanny knowledge of the future, not only as regards approaching weather but of conditions generally, for they will suddenly, for no evident reason, entirely forsake a locality where they were once plentiful and go elsewhere for four or five seasons. It will be often found afterwards that those seasons were all unfavourable, and the birds do not return until some instinct tells of a renewal of better conditions. Below is a hen ptarmigan and, above, a cock bird

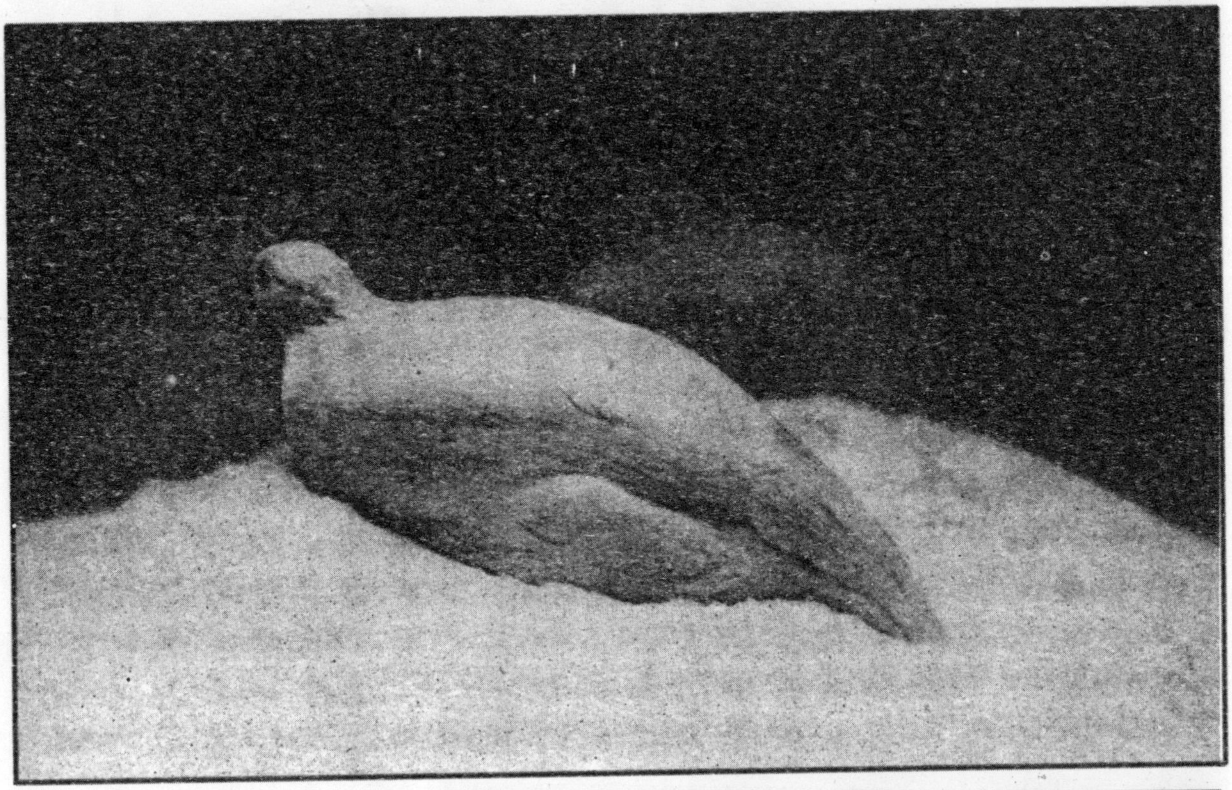

I have seen the hinds taking their calves out of the sheltered glens towards the sunning slopes when the weather conditions were so miserable that one might have thought that the sun would never shine again, but next day, or a few hours later, the calves were revelling in their sun baths under the peat hags.

W. S Berridge

MOUNTAIN HARE AND PTARMIGAN IN WINTER

When winter comes the mountain hare and the ptarmigan both change their coats. The ptarmigan is the only British bird which changes its plumage for protective purposes in winter. The mountain hare also has an apparent pre-knowledge of weather conditions leaving a district for several years together, in advance of inclement conditions

Mountain hares are still more mysterious in their movements. Often with them it is not merely a matter of local migration, but of migration on a wholesale scale. The hares at a certain time leave the entire slope of the range, forsaking it utterly for four or five years during a period of unfavourable winters, resulting perhaps in unfavourable food conditions. The movements of the ptarmigan are identical, and I cite these cases not because they have any bearing on the subject under discussion, but because they go to show how the power of seeing into the future governs the whole system of life where life is dependent upon the weather. My object has been to quote a few simple cases which I know to be proven, illus trating the wonder of animal foresight, and there from to lay before the reader some facts which may lead to a better judgement of such things It would not be difficult to dwell at length upon available examples proving that birds and animals *can* see into the future, and that, could we read their movements rightly, we should find in them a barometer far more sure than any human instrument But the reading of that barometer would demand years of intimacy with Nature's secret.

W. S. Berridge

CLEVER TRICKS PERFORMED BY THE WEAKER MEMBERS OF THE ANIMAL WORLD FOR SELF-PROTECTION

Among the most clever of Nature's "artful dodgers" is the hog-nosed snake of America. It is perfectly harmless but, when in danger, it imitates the action of the cobra. Raising the forepart of its body, it puffs out the skin of its neck into a resemblance of the cobra's hood (bottom left). But if this ruse is not successful the cunning thing writhes as though in the throes of its last moments and turns over on its back as though quite lifeless (bottom right). The horned lizard (top left) has the amazing habit, when alarmed, of swelling out its body until there is a rush of blood to its head and blood squirts from the corners of its eyes to a distance of five feet. The yellow-bellied toad (top right) feigns death when frightened.

Chapter LXXXVII

The Clever Tricks of Feeble Folk

By W. S. Berridge

Author of "Marvels of Natural History"

The life of the wild creatures that populate the earth may truly be said to be a continual struggle for existence, for every individual is faced with the problem of outwitting, evading, or overpowering its enemies. Nature has ordained that the carnivorous beasts shall live at the expense of other creatures, and even those that do not fall under this category are themselves potential victims of their more bloodthirsty kindred.

Many animals rely upon their strength to overcome the dangers that beset their path; others win safety by their extreme vigilance; while not a few resort to subterfuge, and may be said to live by their wits.

One of the most remarkable habits indulged in by certain mammals, birds, reptiles, and amphibians is that of "feigning death." This expression, however, implies a knowledge of death, and many people will assert that no animal is able to visualise that state, or can be aware that life is not without end. It has been stated that the phenomenon is due to a kind of paralysis caused by fright; while another suggestion put forward as an explanation is that the animals that act in this manner are thrown into a cataleptic state under the influence of hypnotic power.

Although it is not unreasonable to suppose that a snake or toad is not endowed with sufficient mental development to be able to realize the meaning of death, can the same be said in regard to the higher types of animals? We know, for instance, that a domestic cat will leave its home and go to some quite unwonted place to die, an act that surely points to some kind of knowledge on the animal's part of its approaching end.

But whether the creatures that feign death have, or have not, any idea of what their actions portray, there can be no disputing the fact that their behaviour is of a definitely defensive nature.

One of the greatest adepts at the art of deception is the hog-nosed snake, a harmless species, found in America, that grows to a length of about three and a half feet. When alarmed, this reptilian humbug assumes the pose of a cobra about to strike, raising its head into the air, and expanding the skin-folds of its neck. A person unacquainted with the snake might well imagine he was confronted by a venomous species, and would doubtless move off as soon as possible; but should he be aware it is harmless, and not be taken in by its attitude of defiance, the artful snake tries another ruse. Writhing upon the ground as if it were in the last throes of death, the reptile eventually turns over on its back and remains motionless, even allowing itself to be picked up without showing the least signs of life. But no sooner has the disturber of its peace departed than it quickly comes to life again, and makes off to shelter, gratified, no doubt, at the success which has attended its little game of bluff.

An amusing story is related by Mr. R. E. Ditmars in regard to one of these snakes. Travelling through a forest, accompanied by a number of native porters, he came across one of these reptiles, and, noticing the men were afraid of the creature, he thought he would make an impression upon them by showing off his powers as a snake-charmer. Approaching the reptile, he made a few magic passes over its body, with the result that it turned over on to its back and shammed death. Mr. Ditmars then picked it up, and, having shown it to his followers, invited them to watch him bring it to life again; a feat he accomplished by the simple expedient of replacing the reptile upon the ground, and remaining motionless and quiet a short distance away. But this display made rather too good an impression upon his audience, for they considered his powers to be bordering upon the supernatural, whereupon they disappeared one by one, and left him to continue his journey alone and in a very awkward predicament.

J. J. Ward

INGENIOUS PRETENCE

The Australian case moth has invented a most ingenious piece of trickery. The larva develops in a little case made of bark and leaf fragments, and this case serves also for a cocoon in the pupa stage. The creature thus runs little risk of discovery.

F. Vear

BLACK-HEADED GULL IN THE ACT OF TURNING ITS EGGS

Towards the middle of April the black-headed gull lays her eggs, usually three in number. These are about two inches long and vary considerably in colour between blue, olive or brown-green with brown and black markings. In this splendid photograph the bird is seen turning her eggs, a process which birds go through periodically during incubation in order that each egg may be properly aerated and receive the life-giving warmth on every side. This gull is found half way round the world from England to Japan.

Although many of us may not have had the opportunity of witnessing the artful behaviour of the hog-nosed snake, in Europe there are some very common toads, known as the fire-bellied toad and the yellow-bellied toad, that sham death at the least provocation When disturbed, they turn over on to their backs and lie motionless with their bodies contorted into the weirdest postures.

Although the attitude assumed renders the bluffers very untoad-like in appearance, and may well deceive other creatures into imagining them to be merely inanimate objects, the chief reason why they behave in such a manner is to display the red and yellow warning colours on the under parts of their bodies ; for as the toads are of a very unpalatable nature, the bright tints at once proclaim to those that have had previous experience of supping upon them that they are better left untouched

Another animal that has earned a reputation as a trickster is the Virginian opossum, and the expression ' to play 'possum " is proverbial. When captured, it immediately pretends to be dead, lying motionless upon the ground with its tongue hanging out of its mouth, and even allowing itself to be beaten.

But even greater endurance is exhibited by the South American fox-like animal known as Azara's dog, and also by the Australian dingo dog. The latter, when shamming death, has been known to allow a portion of its skin to be removed without flinching, and equally horrible stories have been related about the former beast.

One would hardly expect such an innocent-looking animal as a deer to indulge in subterfuge, but one of the mouse-deer or chevrotains, called the kanchil, will assume a deathlike pose when captured, a habit so pronounced that the natives will speak of a deceitful person as being " as cunning as a kanchil."

Most of the bees of the Andrena group, of which there are as many as sixty representatives found in the British Isles, will also feign death as a means of self-protection, and should a person pick one up it then emits a peculiar odour that some people regard as pleasant, and others as just the reverse.

Spiders, moreover, when dislodged from their webs, will often fall to the ground and lie motionless with their legs held tightly folded against their bodies, and in this attitude they look more like small stones than living creatures. At other times they will let themselves down suddenly, suspended by a thread, and then make off to safety; a trick also practised by certain caterpillars.

Even among lizards there is one species that will feign death when alarmed. Unlike the majority of its kind it possesses such short legs that it is incapable of eluding its enemies by running away; but by shutting its eyes and holding out its legs stiffly on either side of its body, it makes itself look as if it were dead—an artifice that is not infrequently successful and saves its life.

Another means by which some lizards will evade capture is by discarding the tail, or a portion of that member. But this act of self-mutilation is not of such a drastic nature as it appears to be, for many of the bones of the tail are divided across the middle and merely held together by a thin pad of gristle, the severance always taking place at one of these joints, without loss of blood. A discarded tail is eventually renewed, sometimes as a double structure, for the operation of this replacement is apt to be a little eccentric, but the bones of the new growth are only replaced by a rod of hardened tissue.

Arthur Brook

CAUTIOUS PEEWIT APPROACHES ITS NEST

The peewit never flies directly to its nest but alights some way off and then runs through the grass to the eggs. If man or beast approaches the cunning parent hops a little in front of the trespasser and pretends to have a broken wing, thus hoping to lure the enemy into pursuit. The bird draws her dupe well away from the nest and then flies off.

STARFISH and crabs will also surrender a limb when in difficulties, this act being accomplished by violently contracting the muscles at the base of the member about to be discarded; while spiders will jerk off their legs, and the long ribbon-worms that lurk beneath stones on the seashore will break into numerous pieces

A most remarkable method of defence is that adopted by the horned lizard, or horned toad, as it is sometimes called. When cornered or captured, it opens wide its mouth, swells out its body, and then spurts out jets of blood from the corners of its eyes to a distance of as much as five feet. This astonishing behaviour is due to excitement, and causes a rush of blood to the head, the eyelids then swelling out to such an extent that they may be as much as three times their normal size.

The ejection of a fluid as a means of defence, however, is not restricted to the horned toad, for we have in the llama and its kindred, the skunks, and the artillery or bombardier beetle other examples of creatures that act in this manner.

Those of us who have visited zoological gardens have probably at some time or other been brought face to face with the spitting habits of the llama, and as the animal aims with a precision that a

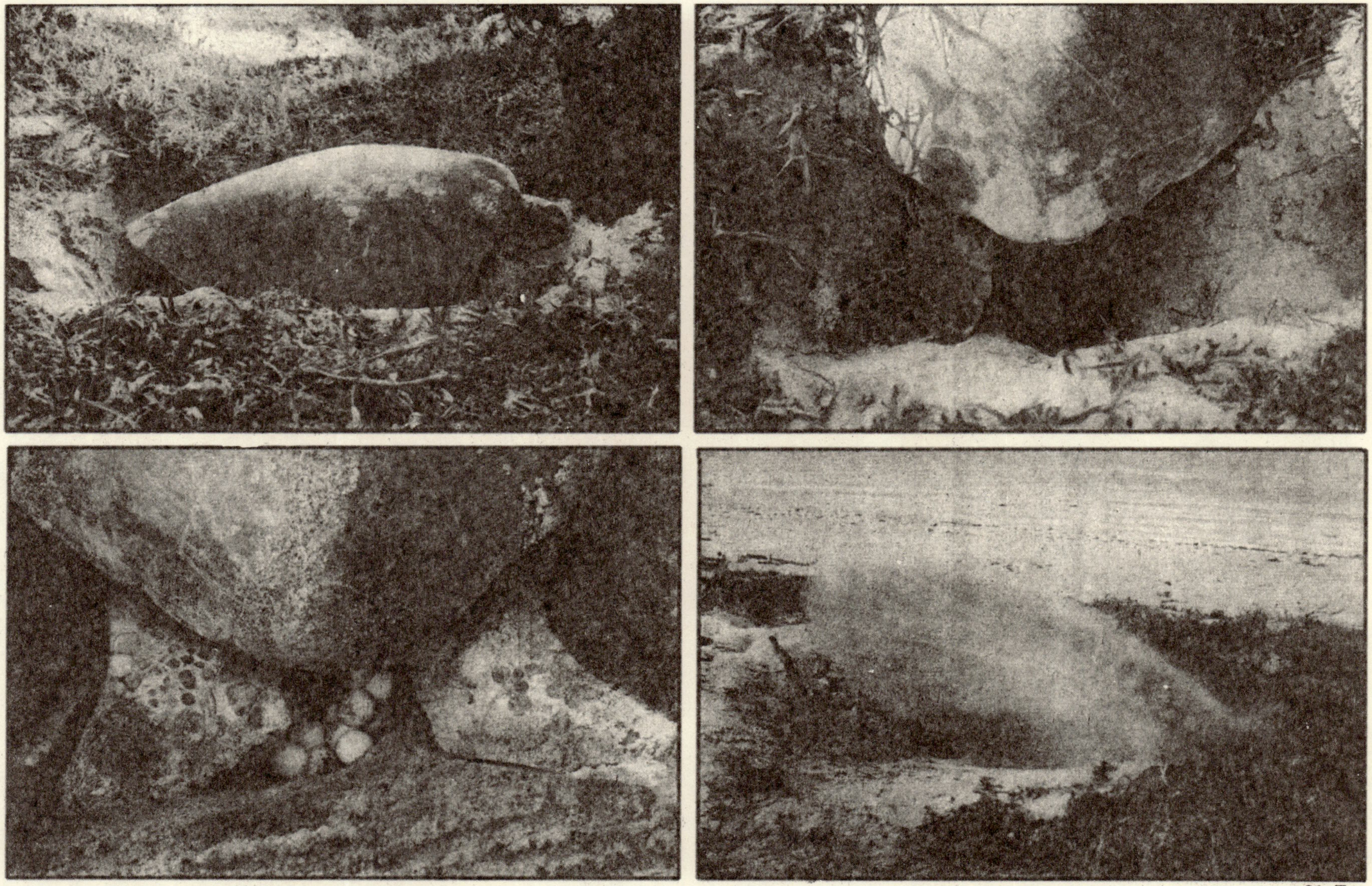

Otho Webb

GREAT PRECAUTIONS TAKEN BY A FEMALE GREEN TURTLE IN THE LAYING OF HER EGGS

When the time of the year arrives for the female green turtle to lay her eggs, she swims ashore and selects a suitable nesting site on the sand. This done, she scoops out a hole with her flippers (top left) for her body to rest in. She then deepens the hole, using her flippers alternately to dig and prevent the sand falling back into the excavation again (top right). She then lays the eggs (bottom left), from one to two hundred of them, in the hole which is about ten inches wide and eight inches deep. Finally she heaves herself out and throws back showers of sand until the site of her egg-laying is quite concealed, as we see in the bottom right-hand photograph, where a stick has been placed in the sand to mark the right spot.

human marksman might envy, its behaviour can be very unpleasant to the victim, though doubtless a source of amusement to the beholders.

But to be assailed by the evil-smelling fluid ejected by the skunk is a more serious matter, for one drop upon the clothes of a person would make his presence unbearable to others, and there would be nc alternative but to destroy the garment thus contaminated. The fumes arising from the liquid are so strong that were a man to inhale them without a large admixture of air he would not only become unconscious in a very short time, but his temperature would fall, and his pulse would weaken.

It is not only mankind that gives the skunk a wide berth, for experience soon teaches all living creatures to refrain from molesting it. Nevertheless, if the glands secreting the fluid be removed, the animals make

GREEN TURTLE CONCEALING HER EGGS

Below we see the egg chamber which a green turtle dug and where she deposited her eggs, excavated to show the hatching eggs inside. Above the turtle is packing the sand firmly down over the site after having piled it up as we saw in the preceding page. This prolonged egg burying is a remarkable instance of animal cleverness.

quite nice pets, and their presence in zoological collections is not then fraught with the danger of unpleasant consequences.

The conspicuous black and white fur of the creatures is much sought after for making up into ladies' cloaks and other garments, and in North America many skunk farms have been established where the animals are reared in captivity. Moreover, farms devoted to this purpose have been started in England, one being situated near the Kestor Rock, Devonshire, and another on the high and bleak part of Dartmoor.

Some beetles secrete an acrid fluid which they eject as a means of defence, and in one group the liquid volatilizes when discharged, and comes forth like a little cloud of smoke. The most familiar of this class is the bombardier or artillery

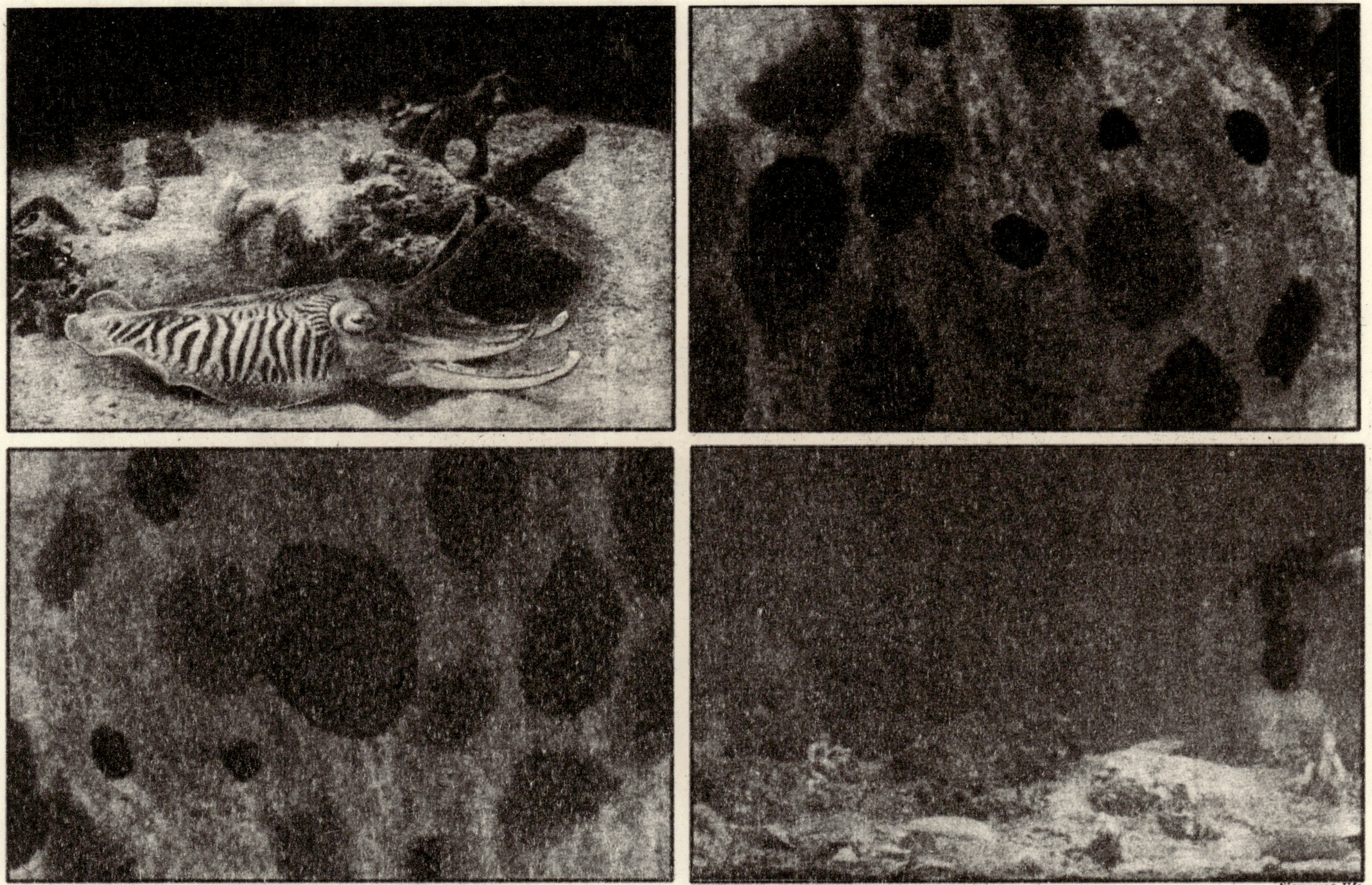

Siewersen-Ufa

CRAFTY CUTTLEFISH WITH MANY ENEMIES BUT WITH THE MEANS TO ESCAPE THEM ALL

For emergencies the cuttlefish keeps two protective tricks, the first a quick change, and the second a disappearing trick. The first is performed by the fish's ability to change colour to match its surroundings. This is effected by the contraction or expansion of a number of minute cells containing pigment and called chromatophores. The bottom left and top right photographs show magnified portions of the fish's skin with these colour cells in different stages of expansion. One of the cuttlefish's disguises is the zebra pattern (top left). Notice the tentacles, ten in number, the two longest being used for catching food. The bottom right-hand photograph shows the first stage in the use of the second line of defence (see also page 955).

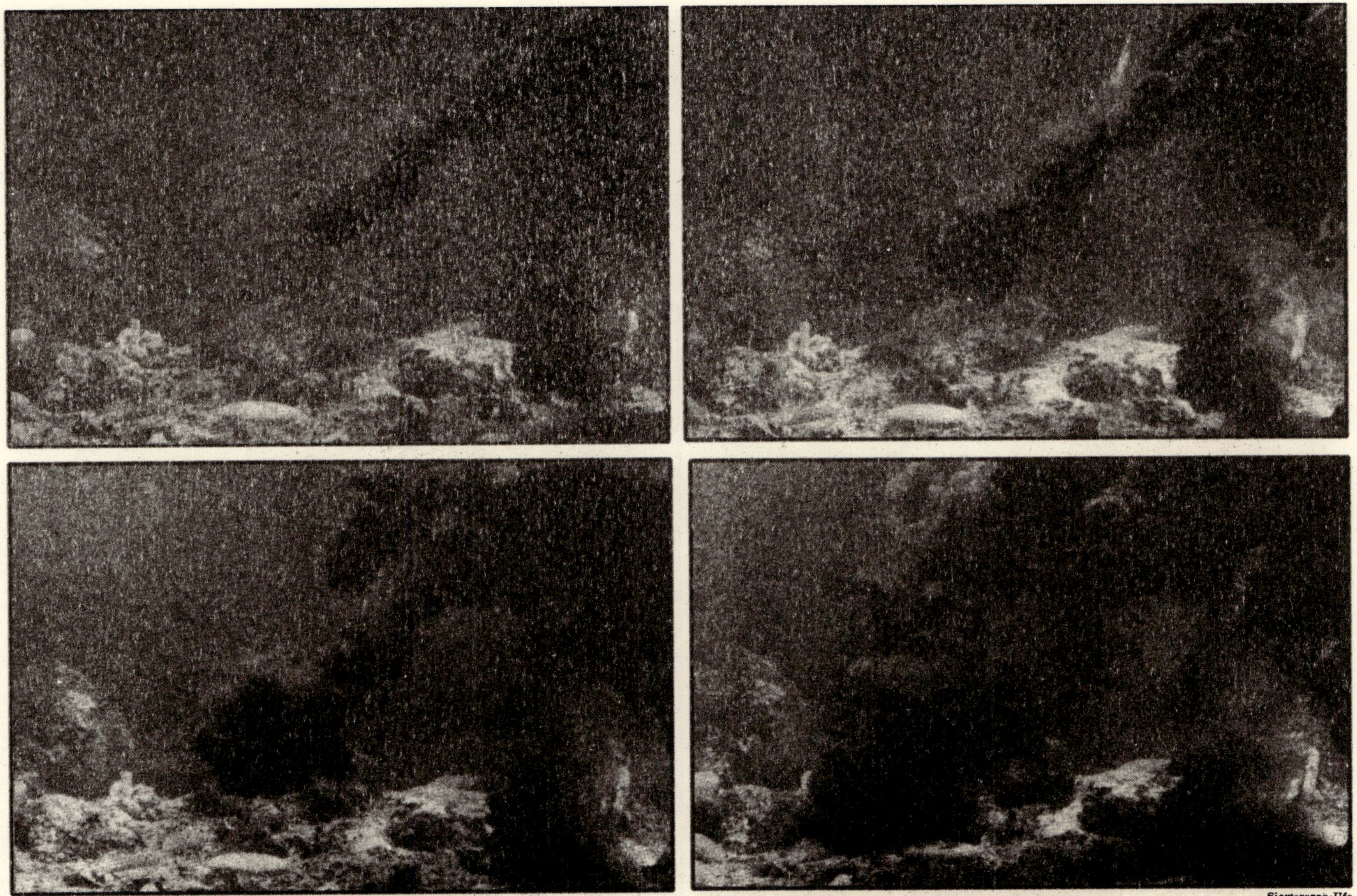

Siewerssen-Ufa

QUICKLY-ENVELOPING CLOUDS OF SEPIA DISCHARGED BY THE ESCAPING CUTTLEFISH

If the cuttlefish decides that mere imitation of its background has failed to deceive an enemy it empties the contents of a remarkable ink-bag into the surrounding water. We have, above, four stages of the development of one of these discharges which much resemble, both in appearance and in use, the smoke screens sent up by warships. Under cover of these inky clouds of opaque liquid the cuttlefish easily escapes. The liquid is collected commercially to supply the pigment called sepia. It colours the water for many yards around the site of the discharge and only dissolves slowly, and by the time this has happened the fish is far away.

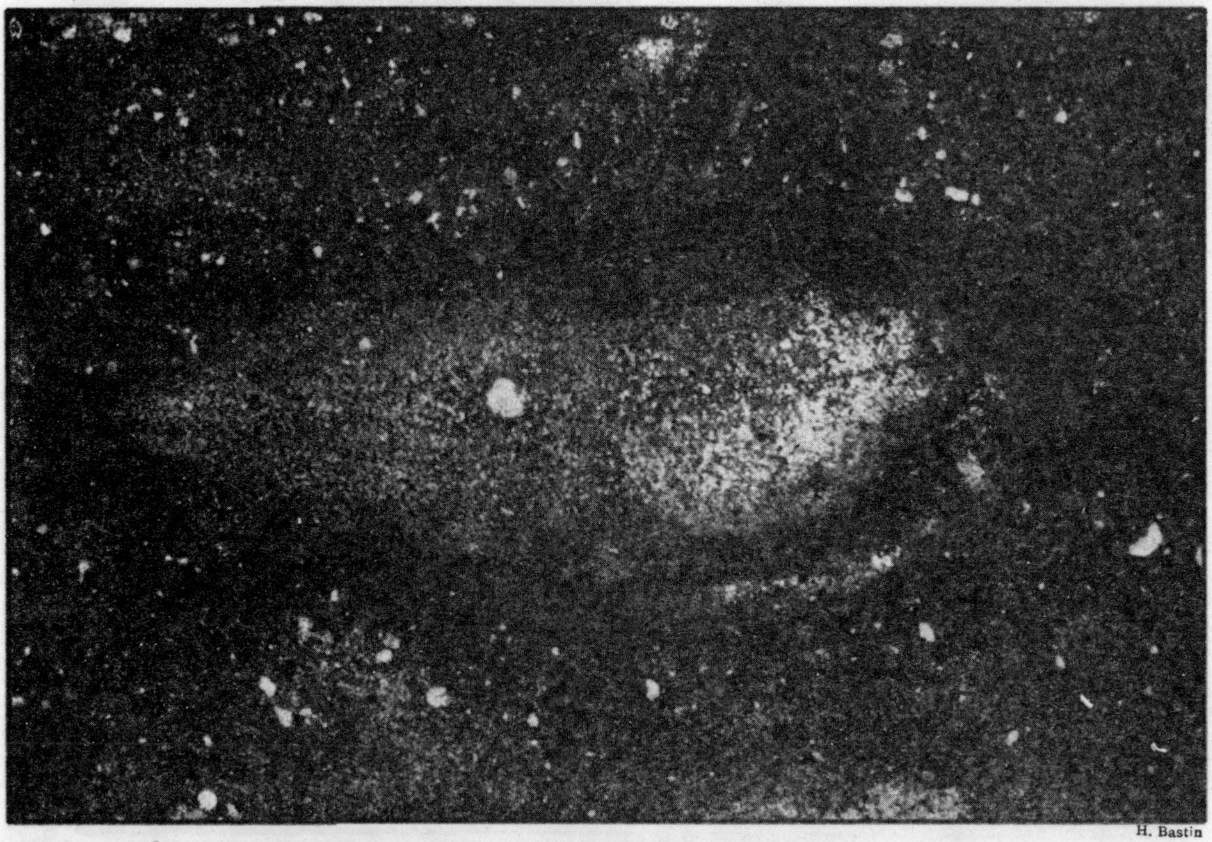

H. Bastin

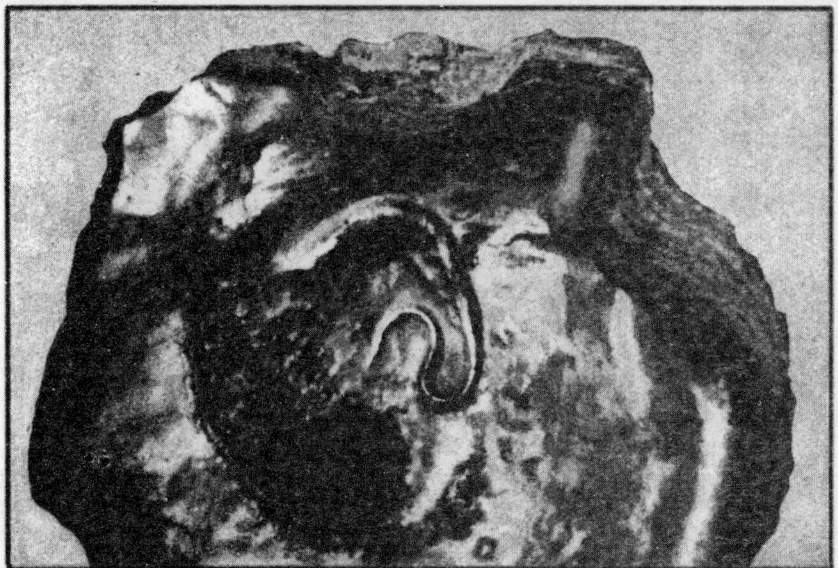

W. Saville Kent

HOW OYSTERS AND SOLES PROTECT THEMSELVES

Oysters make pearls for a very utilitarian reason. Should any foreign body—dead or alive—get by mishap within the oyster's valves the intrusive object is slowly covered over with a secretion which becomes a pearl. Here is one with a little fish inside. Above is a sole with its outline obliterated by the sand collected on the edges of its body when the fish settled down.

beetle, a creature very fond of hiding under stones, and one found in considerable numbers in the counties of Southern England.

Should a person pick up a bombardier beetle, it will immediately fire off its artillery, the discharge sometimes being accompanied by a slight noise. But some of the larger species found in foreign climes are able to produce quite an appreciable amount of sound, one kind found in South America having been known to crepitate two or three times in succession. Its emission is accompanied by a sensation of burning in the fingers that hold it, and a brown stain is left upon the spot that comes into contact with the vapour.

Somewhat similar behaviour is indulged in by the larva of the puss moth, which is provided with a squirting apparatus situated in the cleft of the neck. When the caterpillar is irritated it protrudes a curious organ, divided into four branches, and perforated by holes like the rose of a watering-can. The entomologist De Geer gives an interesting account of the behaviour of one of these caterpillars he found resting upon a twig. "As I was scrutinizing its appearance," he writes, "I happened accidentally to touch its body. Instantly there shot out, from a

spot near the neck, two streams of clear fluid, which struck me on the face, and partly entered one of my eyes, causing a very acute, but fortunately, not a very enduring pain."

But the puss moth larva has another curious arrangement on the hinder part of its body. The last pair of legs, or "claspers," have vanished, and are replaced by a pair of tubular organs containing two long, slender, and whip-like growths that can be protruded or retracted at will. Although the exact utility of these is unknown, it is generally assumed they are of a defensive nature. A writer in an old book, however, tells us that the caterpillar "possesses the power of lashing its sides with its tail, so as to drive away flies" but we need hardly state that the story is untrue.

Protective ejections are also emitted by certain kinds of millipedes which exude an evil-smelling and oily secretion from the pores of their bodies; while a species of locust found in Algeria will eject a noxious fluid for a distance of nearly two feet. Someof the "soldier" termites repel the attacks of hostile ants by squirting out a gelatinous liquid secreted by glands leading to a small opening at the end of their projecting

W. S. Pitt

GOLDEN CICHLID THAT BELIEVES IN SAFETY FIRST

The cichlid's eggs are laid on a rock and the parents keep the water moving over them by fanning with their fins for several days until hatching takes place. The little ones —perhaps four hundred of them—are then put into depressions in the sand, being moved about constantly until they are old enough to swim.

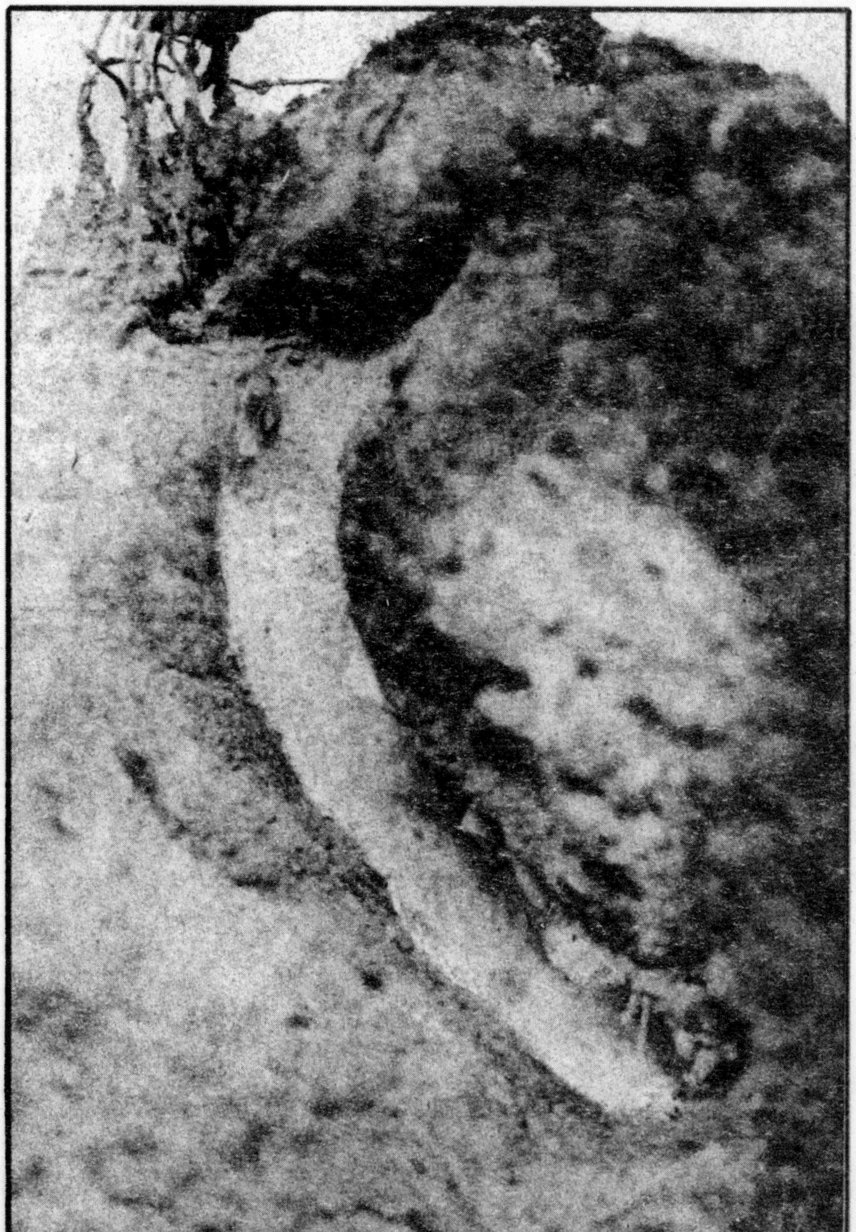

W. S. Berridge

SECTION OF A TRAP-DOOR SPIDER'S LAIR

This photograph shows a piece of earth, magnified, which contains the burrow of a tropical trap-door spider. The piece has been cut in half so as to show the whole burrow with the trap door at the top. This door moves on a hinge, and the spider lurks inside until something to eat comes within reach. Out darts the spider, drags its prey into the burrow, and the lid shuts.

Canon Atkinson gives an amusing account of the deception played upon him by a landrail that had been caught by his dog. The bird lay upon the ground upon its side as if it were dead, even allowing itself to be turned over without showing signs of life. The narrator then placed it in his pocket, but no sooner was it inside than it came to life again, and endeavoured to get out. The trickster was then replaced on the ground, and immediately it continued its efforts to deceive; but after remaining motionless for some time, it suddenly raised its head and flew quickly off.

But let us now consider the sea creatures and see what stratagems they adopt to evade their enemies.

Some of them seek companionship with jellyfish, sheltering beneath the stinging tentacles of their hosts; the young of the horse mackerel, or scad, and the fry of the whiting following this practice.

A species of fish inhabiting Australian seas selects as its partner the large jellyfish known as the Portuguese man-o'-war, an individual sometimes sheltering as many as ten finny guests at a time beneath its long, trailing arms, while a certain kind of herring will be found associating with a jellyfish found off the American coasts.

Other marine animals with curious defensive habits are to be noted in the spider crab, the octopus, the sepia, or cuttlefish, and the squid. The former, which receives its name from the triangular shape of its body, and the great slenderness and length of its legs,

beaks; while the oil beetles and ladybirds are other examples of insects that resort to this ruse when alarmed.

Among the birds there are quite a number that practise subterfuge, the feathered humbugs endeavouring to lure their foes from the vicinity of their nests by pretending to be wounded in the wing. The lapwing, the landrail, or corncrake, the water rail, the hoopoe, and the American spotted tinamou will all act in this manner, and it is somewhat astonishing to note that the ostrich has been known to play a similar game of bluff.

endeavours to keep out of sight of its enemies by making itself as inconspicuous as possible. It will attach pieces of seaweed or other marine growths to its carapace so as to make itself look like its surroundings. That the crab evidently realizes the benefit of its protective attire has been proved by an interesting experiment. Seaweed-covered individuals have been captured and placed in a tank bedded with small sponges, whereupon the shellfish discarded their original raiment, and, picking up some of the living sponges with their claws, attached these to the hooked hairs upon their shells as more effective disguises.

The octopus, cuttlefish, and squid are all provided with "ink bags" from which they are able to eject a dark-coloured fluid. This forms a "smoke screen," and discolours the surrounding water to such an extent that the creatures are able by this means to escape from their enemies. The "ink" of the cuttlefish is employed in the making of the sepia pigment used by artists; while the curious oval, broad, and flattened internal shell supporting the animal's body is known commercially as cuttle bone, and is often sold for hanging up in the cages of small birds. The internal shell of the squid, however, is very slender, one end terminating in an oval-shaped and flattened expansion vaned like a feather. This structure is commonly spoken of as the "pen," and as the squids are in the habit of emitting a dark coloured fluid as a means of evading their enemies, they have been given the name of "pen and ink fish."

A form of defence we have not yet mentioned is that of rolling up, an artifice indulged in by certain creatures that are only protected upon the upper part of their bodies, the under parts being soft and very vulnerable to attack.

A well-known example of such an animal is the three-banded armadillo, or mataco. "It has the power of rolling itself into a perfect sphere like one kind of English woodlouse," writes Darwin. "In this state it is safe from the attack of dogs; for the dog, not being able to take the whole in its mouth, tries to bite one side, and the ball slips away."

Other creatures that curl up when alarmed are the scaly pangolins of south-eastern Asia and South Africa. They roll up into a tight ball, the snout being thrust between the forelegs, and the tail pressed tightly against the body, between the hind legs. The bending of the body causes the sharp edges of the scales with which they are provided to stand on end, and for an enemy to attempt to bite such formidably armed creatures would most certainly be to court disaster

But an even more familiar instance of this habit is presented by the hedgehog It possesses numerous cutaneous muscles, one of which forms a broad band around the body When contracted this draws together towards the centre of the under part of the body the lower edges of the spine-covered skin, and as the head and legs are simultaneously tucked under the belly, the creature then assumes the shape

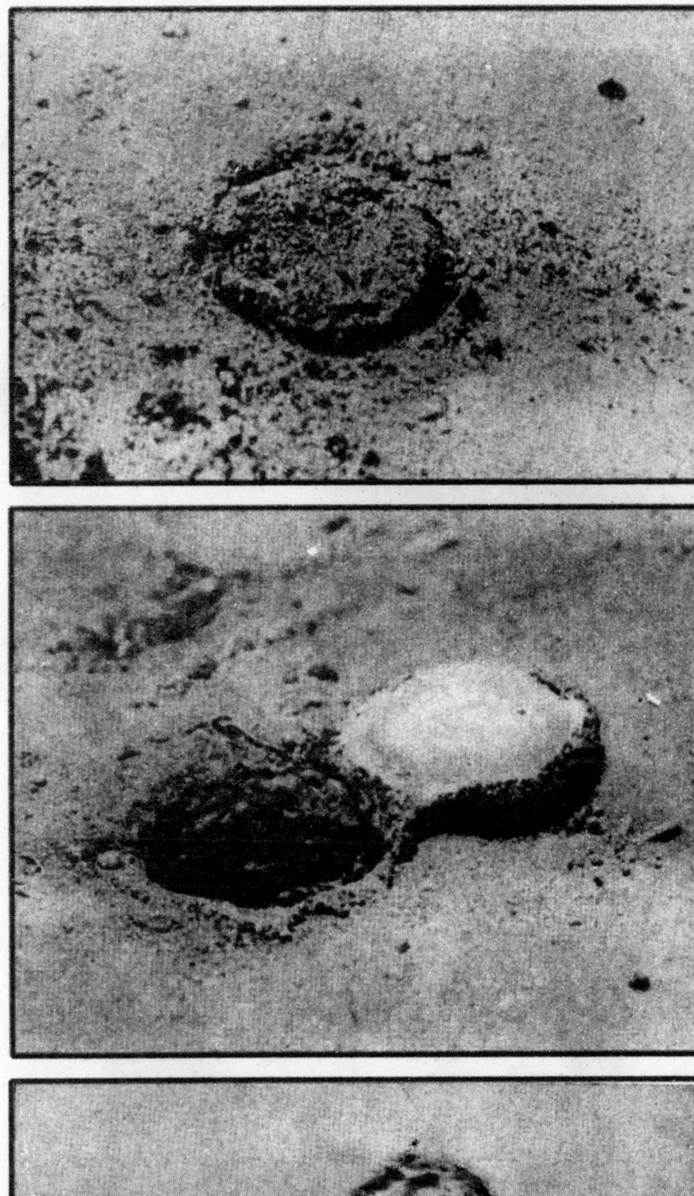

Otho Webb

OPERATION OF THE SPIDER'S "TRAP DOOR"

The trap-door spiders are found only in warm climates. The trap door of the "oubliette" they build is made to harmonise with the surrounding soil These photographs, natural size, show (top) the door just open, (centre) with the silk inner side visible, and (bottom) the owner emerging

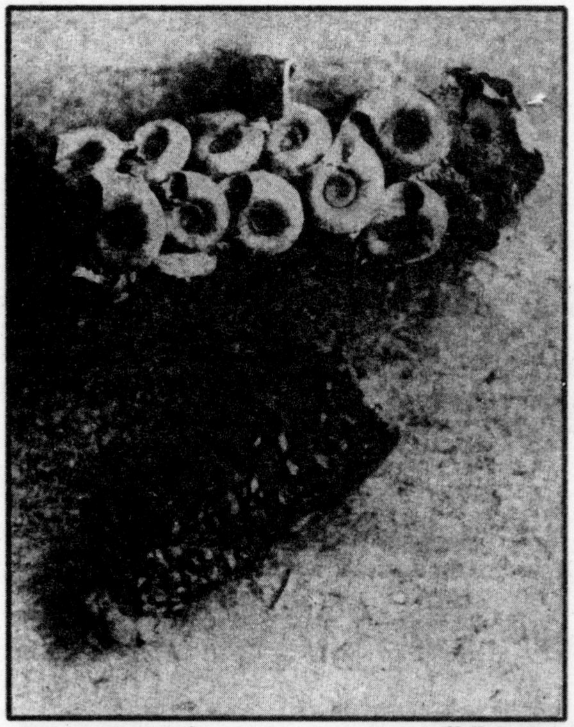

M. H. Crawford

J. J. Ward

CADDIS FLY CAMOUFLAGE

These photographs show the perfect caddis fly (bottom left) and its queer-looking larva when it has been removed from its wonderful case (bottom right); two cases (top left) very much magnified, one disguised with water snails and the other with gravel, and (top right) some miscellaneous examples of this clever camouflage.

of a ball, with its prickly armament standing on end. By this means it usually succeeds in defying its enemies, although a simple method of making it uncurl is to roll it into some water, or direct a jet of liquid into the small opening left where the head, legs, and the margins of the body-skin meet

The common porcupine will sometimes roll itself up into a ball when threatened by a foe, but more frequently than otherwise it will take the offensive by rushing backwards and endeavouring to thrust the point of its sharp quills into the flesh of its enemy. The ancient belief, however, that the creature shoots out its quills like arrows is quite erroneous, the mistake probably having arisen from the fact that the weapons are but loosely attached to the porcupine's skin, and may occasionally become detached and sent flying through the air for a short distance when the animal is delivering an attack on one of its enemies.

Even among the fish we have in the globe fishes some creatures that protect themselves by means of their spines. Under normal conditions these lie flat against the skin, but when alarmed the fish inflate their bodies with air, the skin thereby becoming taut, and the spines erect. When thus distended they rise to the surface of the water and float upside down. Although by this ruse they may manage to elude those fish that seek to prey upon them, they are then easily captured by human enemies, some of whom, it has been stated, will amuse themselves by the stupid and brutal practice of jumping upon the captives so as to have the pleasure of hearing them explode.

The adult frog-hopper

The frog-hopper magnified five diameters

First stages of cuckoo-spit

Fifteen minutes later

Half an hour from the start

After another quarter of an hour

Fifteen minutes later again

J. J. Ward

The frog-hopper leaving the froth

FROG-HOPPER OR CUCKOO-SPIT INSECT AND ITS NURSERY OF BUBBLES

Familiar to those who have gardens is the appearance, in spring, of a small mass of froth on the stems of various plants. This froth is exuded by the larva of the garden frog-hopper familiarly called the cuckoo-spit. The frog-hopper is equipped with a pair of strong hind legs which enable it to jump very strongly, and it lays its eggs in the stems of plants during the autumn, and in the spring the larvae hatch. In an hour, as we see here, one of these little grubs can surround itself with a mass of bubbles. It emerges quite dry.

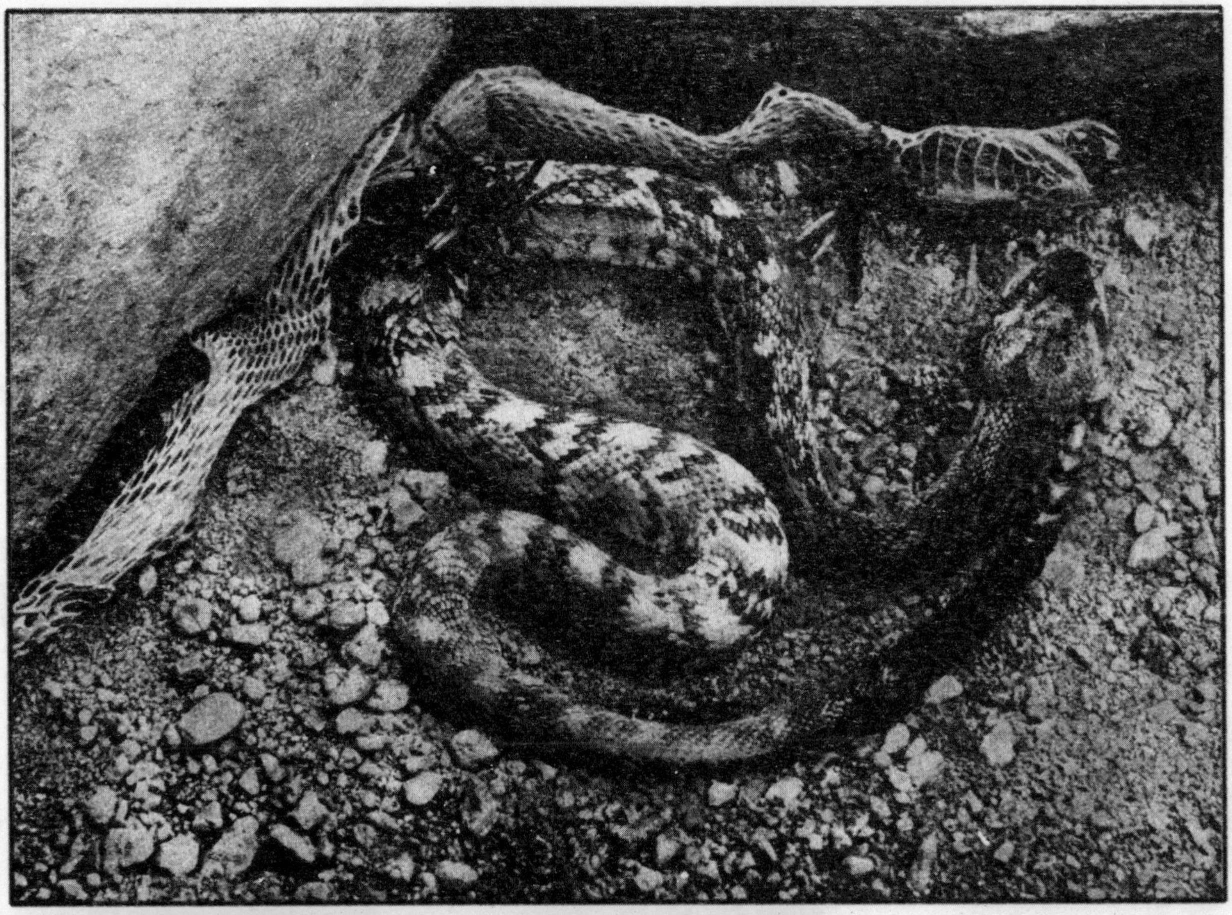

CARRIER SHELLS DISGUISED AND A RATTLESNAKE'S NEW SKIN

The carrier shells have sought disguise by collecting other shells and covering themselves with a collection of these so as to seem something else than what they really are. The top photograph shows a rattlesnake which has just cast its old skin and emerged with a new one. In other words, the snake has grown out of its old suit and fitted itself with a larger size.

frogs and toads will act in just the reverse manner, and when frightened will make themselves as small and inconspicuous as possible by expelling a quantity of water through the pores of their skin.

The soft-shelled tortoise is yet another creature that distends itself as a means of evading capture. Discovered in East Africa in the year 1920, this interesting reptile possesses a hard, dome-shaped shell when young, but, as it grows up, the carapace becomes quite flat, and so soft as to yield to the pressure of one's fingers. It hides between the crevices of rocks, wedging itself so tightly within its shelter by inflating its body with air, that it can only be dislodged with difficulty, and by the application of considerable force. But we have yet to mention a further method by which wild animals seek protection from their enemies, namely, that of placing sentinels to keep a look-out for danger. The baboons will act in this way, and in cultivated districts when a number of the animals are

The expansion of the body as a means of self-preservation is also practised by the South American barking frogs. They blow themselves out to an enormous size, at the same time often uttering deep-toned notes, and sometimes emitting sounds like the wailing of a baby. Curiously enough, however, other

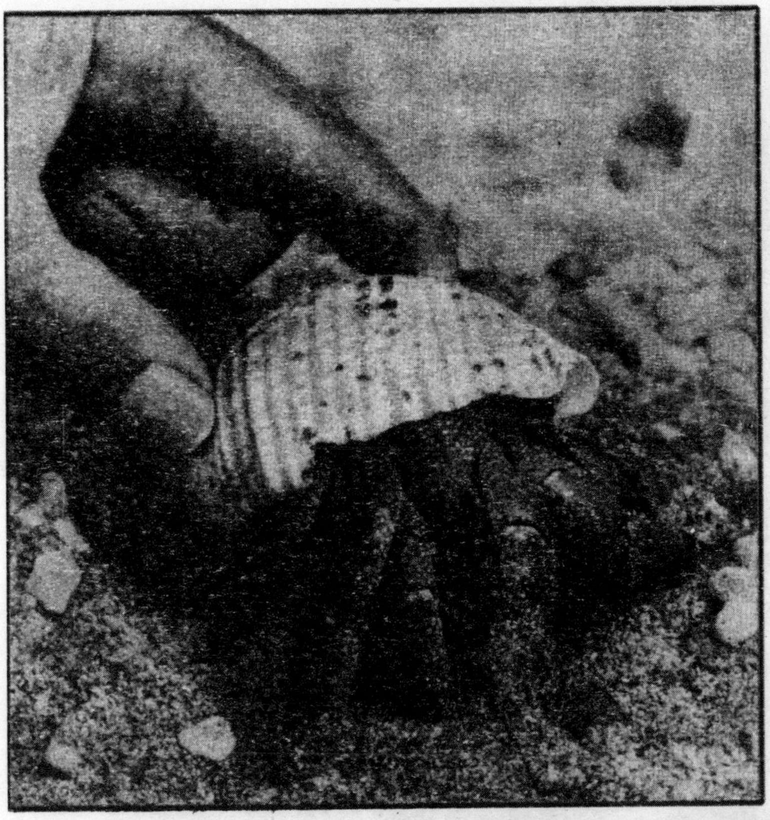

upon the ground with its hind legs when it scents danger, the warning signal being at once answered by all others within hearing, who quickly scamper off to the shelter of their burrows ; while a squirrel that has been disturbed when feeding upon the ground will immediately clamber up the bough of a tree, keeping the trunk between itself and its enemy until it is finally lost to view amidst the foliage of the upper branches.

The cunning of the fox is displayed in various ways, and many artful tricks it resorts to for the purpose of outwitting its foes. After having robbed a hen roost, it will return to its lair by a circuitous route, and it is canny enough not to visit the fowl houses in the immediate vicinity of its home. When chased by a pack of hounds, moreover, it has been known to intermingle with a flock of sheep ; while an individual has also been seen to perform the rather wonderful feat of running along the top of a newly clipped hedge in an endeavour to put the hounds off its scent and save its harassed life.

engaged in robbing an orchard, or stealing some other crop, they invariably depute several individuals to take up their stations at points of vantage, so that they may be ready to give warning to their companions should any danger threaten to disturb their proceedings.

A herd of kiang, or Tibetan wild asses will also be guarded by an individual who stands apart from the others while they are grazing ; while the little prairie marmots, or prairie dogs are other animals that do sentinel duty.

It has been stated in all seriousness that cranes will depute one of the flock to act as a guard at night while the remainder go to sleep, the guardian standing upon one leg, and clasping a large stone in the disengaged foot. Should the watcher get sleepy during its vigil, the foot relaxes its hold upon the stone which, falling to the ground, causes such a clatter as to immediately arouse the negligent bird. We regret to say, however, that this wonderful story cannot be accepted as being true.

The habits of the common fox, the squirrel, and the rabbit must not be overlooked under our heading, for they certainly display great ingenuity and watchfulness in evading their foes. As is well known, the latter will stamp

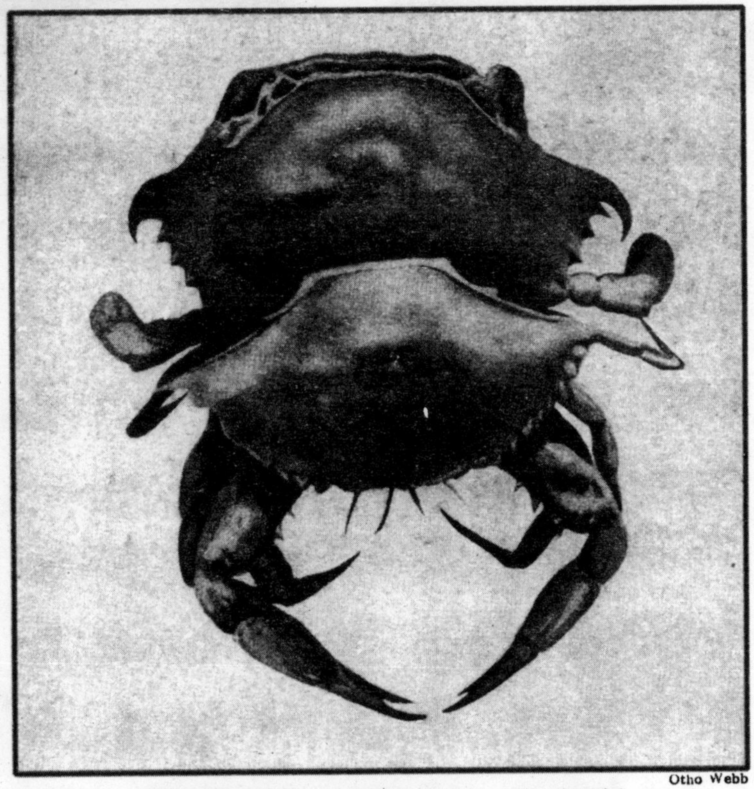

Otho Webb

THE WAY OF A CRAB WITH ITS SHELL

Every so often the growing crab becomes too large for its shell. At last the old shell splits and the crab emerges in a new one, which is quite soft, but hardens in time (bottom). Thus a so-called "soft-shelled" crab is one which has just gone through this process. Above is a hermit crab which, having no proper shell of its own, lives in the discarded shell of some other creature.

Autotype

SURVIVORS OF THE EARLIEST FORM OF MAMMALIAN LIFE: A GROUP OF KANGAROOS

Isolation from the rest of the world at an early period in the history of mammalian development is the secret of the marsupials' supremacy in Australia. At a time remote from the beginnings of human history, though comparatively recent so far as geology is concerned, the connection which seems to have existed between Australia and Asia was overwhelmed by the sea, leaving a chain of islands—now included under the term Malaysia—like the piers of a broken bridge. As a result, the early mammal forms which had already reached Australia were cut off from competition with the more advanced types that developed later, and survive to this day as living representatives of what are only fossil animals in other parts of the globe.

Chapter LXXXVIII

A Land of Living Fossils

By Frank Finn

Author of "The World's Birds"

"ADVANCE, Australia," is the man-made motto of the southern Commonwealth, and white-man-made at that; under Nature's dispensation Australia has been a scene of something very like stagnation—a sort of biological backwater and almshouse for antiquated animals.

The land of the world as a whole is concentrated in a practically continuous mass in the northern hemisphere, split by the mere crack of Bering Strait, the southern hemisphere containing only the great peninsulas of Africa and South America and a number of islands, chief of which is Australia, which ranks as a continent in itself.

The struggle for existence has been hardest north of the line, and many of the types of animals once inhabiting this hemisphere have gradually, by ice ages, desiccation and other causes, been forced southwards into the peninsulas and islands aforesaid.

The fauna of Europe in the Stone Age was, to a great extent, African; lions, hyenas, and even rhinoceroses, elephants and hippopotami existed—types all now pushed south. The lion lingered until Alexander's time at least.

The process is still going on in India, where chimpanzees, hippopotami, giraffes and ostriches once lived, and the lion, cheetah, and caracal still linger on, but in the case of the first two, are on the verge of extinction. Human animosity has had much to do with this in the case of the lion, but not in that of the African types found fossil in the Indian region.

Earlier still, monkeys and parrots existed in France, where marsupials of the type of the American opossums have been found fossil, these opossums being almost the only marsupials now found outside the Australian region, and one of them, the most widely-ranging and successful of all the pouch-bearing beasts, still living in the north temperate zone as well as in South America.

Before this again, marsupials, or marsupial-like beasts of the Australian type, occurred even in the British Isles, and some Australian-like marsupials have indeed been found living, though as great rarities, in South America.

AUSTRALIA, being the most out-of-the-way corner of all the southern lands, and cut off comparatively early in the history of the higher backboned animals, though late in the long ages of geology, has become the refuge of the destitute, which have long enjoyed there a measure of prosperity which is only now being menaced.

For when a country is cut off by sea, invasion by animal competitors becomes difficult, the active animal being in many ways at a disadvantage in overseas distribution as compared with the passive plant. Seeds may be carried by the wind, even when not adapted by wings or plumes for wind dispersal, as we see in the unfailing appearance of chickweed and the little wayside grass in flower-pots and window-boxes in towns; many, like the coconut, will bear flotation for long distances even on sea water; some adhere to the plumage of birds, others may be transported in mud clinging to their feet when leaving the margins of water; but few but minute and low forms of animal life can travel in this way.

The highest animals are the worst off in this respect; their volition hinders their dispersal, for none would willingly swim far out to sea, and even birds and bats have got to new homes overseas by being blown there rather than by voluntary exploring flights, a good case of this being an invasion of America by storm-driven flocks of lapwings. The insects are more on the level of the plants in this respect, being very liable to wind-carriage, while molluscs can adhere to the feet of birds.

Then, when an animal has landed in a new country, unlike the plant which lives on soil and air, it is faced with the problem of "making good," and this is the harder the higher its organization. Early visitors to the Falkland Islands which, if not oceanic, are at any rate rather far from the mainland, noted that the local fox-wolf, now exterminated by man, and the only large mammal ever found in a remote island, appeared to suffer much from famine during part of the year, and island forms of the Sambar deer in the East Indies are dwarfed to half the size of the mainland type. The lapwings, above mentioned also, having struck the New World too far north and in winter, appear to have perished there.

SO, once cut off in Australia, marsupials were protected from most rivals and had for their only invading competitors rodents. These are far more numerous in species there than would be gathered from what is stated even in the best scientific works. There are more species than in Europe, in fact; but these include none of the rodent aristocracy that Europe can show—porcupine, hare, beaver, squirrel, jerboa—but all belong to the same family as rats and mice, which have, now that man has come upon the scene as a new agent for distribution, shown themselves the best fitted of beasts to colonise new areas.

Rats and mice, with the storage instinct which leads them to lay up hoards of food in holes, and their omnivorous habits, might conceivably drift long distances on trees uprooted by cyclone or flood, and thus be less easily cut off by sea than their betters. But even among these rodents Australia has thrown off two distinctive types: the conilures or hopping rats, miniatures of some of their marsupial fellow-countrymen, and the beaver-rats, which would be better called otter-rats, for both in form and

MARSUPIAL METHOD OF CARRYING THE YOUNG

The order of animals called marsupials derive their name from a Latin word meaning a pouch. It is primarily this organ that differentiates the members of the order from the rest of the mammalia. The kangaroo is only about one inch long at birth—or from the mammalian point of view, is born prematurely—and continues its development in the marsupium or pouch.

in their feeding-habits they are more like otters than like their rodent relative the beaver.

THE dingo, or Australian dog, remains to be accounted for, and in his case human introduction is suspected ; at any rate, no doubt by virtue of superior activity and cunning, he appears to have driven out the two most powerful of the carnivorous marsupials, the thylacine, or marsupial wolf and the Tasmanian devil. Their Australian fossil representatives were larger, and perhaps the striped carnivore, big and fierce enough to kill a fighting staghound, which is reported from the thick bush of Northern Australia which the dingo cannot colonise, may turn out to be the old Australian thylacine.

It is among the carnivorous section of the pouched animals that the most interesting of Australian marsupials is to be found—the little squirrel-like banded anteater, which has teeth exactly like some of the small mammals—presumably marsupial—which existed in Europe when the reptile class was in power, and mammals had not got beyond the simple rat-shaped type, which remains the commonest among the mammalian class to-day; while any sort of mammal, if traced back far enough in the fossil fauna, becomes more and more rat-like.

This beast has no pouch, the family sporran being by no means a universal possession among marsupials, whose young, born as it were prematurely and exceedingly small, hang on to the teats of their mother by their specially modified mouths, and so are to a very great extent independent of it.

The other carnivorous marsupials represent the smaller carnivores, such as the weasel tribe, and the insectivores, in Australian animal life ; such are the " native cats," spotted animals which remind one of the martens of the north in form and habits, the tapoa tafa, generally rather absurdly called " brush-tailed pouched mouse " —" pouched stoat " would give a better idea of it—and a number of small " pouched mice," which are rather pouched shrews in their attributes. The curious pouched mole, a recent discovery, has a family to itself in this section. The bandicoots, which evidently got their name from the large bandicoot rat of India, approach the vegetarian marsupials in some ways, being largely vegetable feeders and having the peculiarity of the vegetarian marsupial's foot, the enclosure of the second and third toes in a common skin so that they seem to be one toe with a double claw, a peculiarity unique in mammals.

This family has thrown off one of the quaintest little oddities in the mammalian class—the pig-footed bandicoot, which has a shrew's nose, rabbit's ears, and the long slim legs of the hoofed animals, and mimics two leading groups of these by going on two toes in the fore feet and on one in the hind feet.

BENNETT'S WALLABY, AND THE GREAT KANGAROO POISED FOR A JUMP

Autotype

Found in the denser scrub of Australia and Tasmania and also in New Guinea, the wallabies, of which there are several specimens, are smaller than the typical kangaroos and are also more brightly tinged as to the fur. The specimen seen here (bottom) belongs to the species known as Bennett's wallaby. Above is the great kangaroo, which may weigh twelve stone and be five feet tall. The kangaroos represent the cloven-hoofed family of other parts of the world, being found in the open, feeding on herbage or else among the woods, according to species.

TREE KANGAROO UP AMONG THE BRANCHES

Tree kangaroos are found in the northern parts of Australia and in New Guinea. They are chiefly differentiated from the ground kangaroos by the structure of the fore limbs. These are very strong and nearly as large as the hind limbs, being used in climbing. These kangaroos spend the day in the tree tops coming down at dusk to feed upon ferns and other vegetation.

Less remarkable, but still a nightmare sort of beast, is the rabbit-bandicoot or "native rabbit," which is like a rabbit with a long nose and tail. This is said to hop on its hind legs, a habit so well known in the case of the kangaroos, the most familiar of marsupials to us, that it probably looms too large in the popular conception of a marsupial. The kangaroos are, indeed, the most numerous family not only of the vegetarian marsupials, but of the whole pouched group, but they do not all have long hind legs, and the shorter-legged kinds, like the tree kangaroos and potoroos, or kangaroo-rats, for example, go on all fours.

The larger kangaroos we know best take in Australia the place of the cloven-hoofed animals of other countries, and are very like them in habits, being polygamous, grazing, and browsing herders. They bring forth single young, and attain greater speed in the females than in the males. They also similarly occupy different stations, some being woodlanders like deer, others living in the open like antelopes, or on the mountains like goats; while at least one frequents low-lying land subject to floods, hopping quite happily through shallow water and crossing rivers of considerable width, freely.

Some of the smaller kinds are very like hares in their habits, and in this, too, they resemble the cloven-footed beasts, which also tend to be hare-like in their ways when of small size. The potoroos not only go on all fours, but actually burrow in the ground like rabbits.

The tree-kangaroos rather give one the impression of animals which have comparatively recently left the ground for the trees; but there is one kangaroo, the smallest of all, which is more adapted to a tree life, though it actually lives mostly on the ground. This is the rat-like musk-kangaroo, which, unlike all the others, possesses the first toe on the hind foot, and this so placed that it is capable of grasping, and also has one curious twisted grinder in the jaw which is characteristic of the great family of phalangers, or opossums as Australians call them. Like them, too, it lives on soft vegetable food, and takes animal nutriment also, eating palm-berries, roots, worms, and insects. The phalangers are all climbers, and, like climbing animals generally, usually eat some animal food, though belonging to the vegetarian section of the order. But the largest, and the only tailless one, the koala or "native bear," seems to be not only purely vegetarian, but very specialised in diet, living almost entirely on eucalyptus leaves. Specimens exhibited in the London Zoo walked, when on the ground, like true bears but with the fore-paws turned out instead of in.

The typical long-tailed phalangers are very like lemurs or squirrels in their ways, and most have developed on flying-squirrel lines, having a flounce of

AUSTRALIAN OPOSSUMS THAT SPEND THEIR LIVES IN THE TREES

In Australia phalangers are called opossums, and in this page we have two examples. The lower photograph is of a lesser flying opossum, one of the members of this family which has grown a special piece of expanding skin on its flanks. This is outspread when the animal is leaping from tree to tree and enables it to make long glides through the air. The upper photograph shows a short eared opossum sprawled out upon a tree trunk. Its outspread position is due to the fact that it is reaching as far as possible with both paws to get a good grip.

Autotype

Otho Webb

AUSTRALIA'S STRANGE ECHIDNA, OR SPINY ANT-EATER

In the lower photograph this strange-looking ant-eater has been rolled over on its back to show the long snout and the strong digging claws, which are all used for raiding ants' nests. The echidna is equipped with a special prehensile tongue for collecting ants. The hair of the body is mingled with short, strong spines and the spines are often so thickly set as to obscure the hair

skin along their sides by which they can glide for many yards. There is a very quaint little oddity in this family, too, the honey-sucking tarsipes, called noolbenger by the Black-fellows, which has a long nose and tongue, though, like the mice it resembles in size and general shape, its food also consists of insects.

The wombats form a very remarkable family with only a few species. They are tailless and have the size and burrowing habits of badgers but the gnawing ways and few incisors of rodents. They are not found outside Australia and Tasmania, and the kangaroos only extend into the Aru Islands and New Guinea; but the phalangers range west even to Celebes, where two species of the non-parachuting cuscus group hang on to territory where higher mammals such as pigs and apes are found invading the Australian region, which is separated from the Oriental by " Wallace's Line," the narrow sea running between Celebes and Borneo, and lower

Otho Webb

QUEER MAMMALS THAT LAY EGGS AND GO COVERED IN SPINES

As a rule the echidna does not roll itself up (bottom) if there is time for it to bury itself. It is seldom seen by day, but makes its appearance during the evening and is active through the night when it robs ants' nests. As it moves over the ground its gait is seen to be rather a shuffling one. The female lays eggs and these develop in the pouch with which, like the other marsupials, she is equipped. The young are suckled and carried about in the pouch for some time after birth. In the top picture the echidna's long snout can be seen.

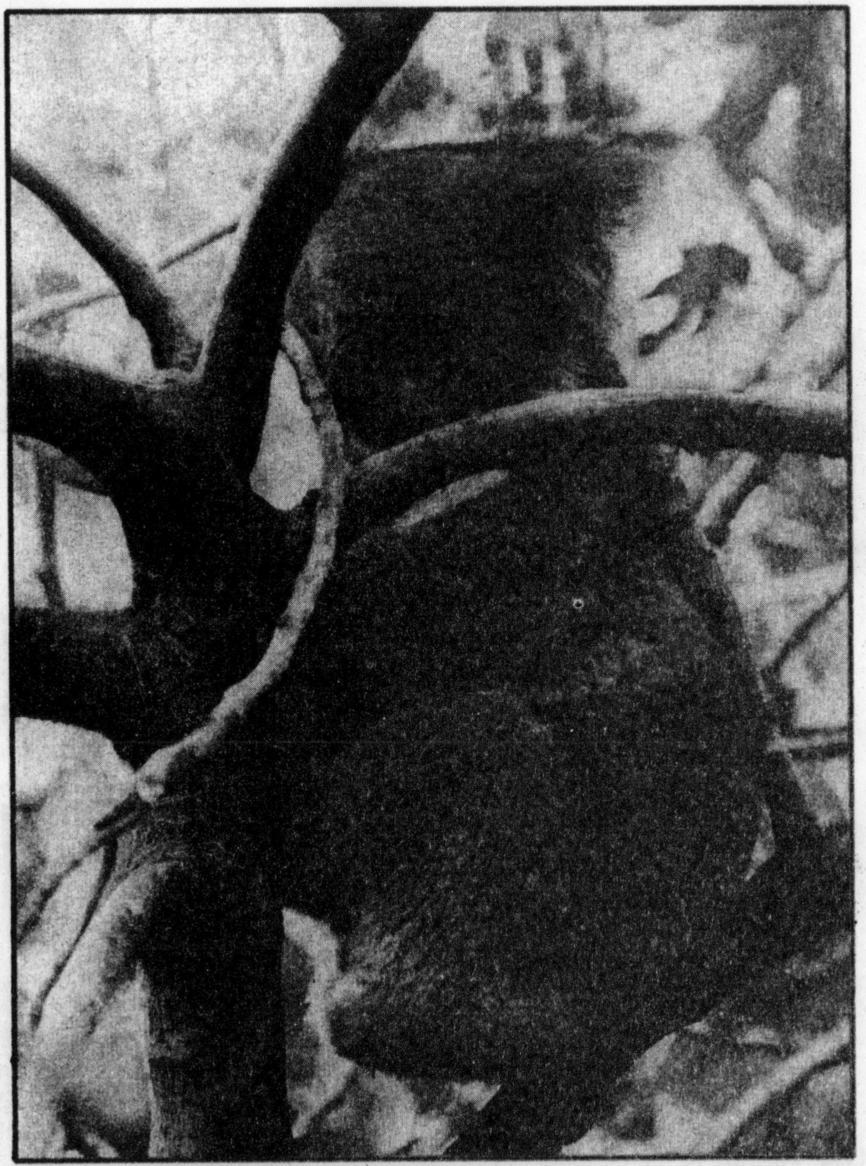

KOALA, A VEGETARIAN CLOTHED IN THICK GREY FUR

Almost the most attractive of Australia's unique fauna is the koala. It looks rather like a teddy-bear, is about the size of a poodle when full-grown and related to the wombat. The fur is very thick and woolly, grey on the back, yellow-white on the hind quarters and white on the belly. The cheeks are pouched for the storage of food.

down narrowing to a mere strait between the two little islands of Bali and Lombok.

The vegetarian marsupials have never been found outside this area, but two little animals, survivors of an anciently-extinct family, linger in South America and connect the vegetarian and carnivorous sections, having the single pair of large incisors in the lower jaw of the former, and the free second and third hind toes and large upper canines of the latter.

This, and the presence of marsupials of the Australian carnivorous type in South America, may show that there was once a land connexion between these two continents, or may merely be evidence of the former universal distribution of the pouch-bearers. Early and comparatively lowly-organized as these pouched beasts are, they do not represent a stage through which the higher mammals passed, but rather a strong side-limb, given off very low down, of the mammalian tree, which branch, having found a chance to develop unchecked in the Australian corner, has repeated in its growth, as we have seen, many features of the main tree. Like this, too, it has its dead branches, for in Australia, as elsewhere, there has been the usual outbreak of "gigantism," or the production of giant species, which the whales display at present. Such species have poor endurance as a rule, and so generally become extinct. The thylacine and "devil" of the Australian mainland were not sensationally larger than the living species, but the vegetarians have bred some monsters. A kangaroo with a skull a foot long and a wombat as big as a pony must have been imposing beasts, but were as nothing compared with the diprotodon, which was a great clumsy bear-shaped brute as big as a rhinoceros, with two great incisors in each jaw.

Stranger still was *Thylacoleo carnifex*—the "butchering pouched lion," to translate the name Owen gave it. Though small compared with diprotodon, it was a big beast, with the orbits of the eyes surrounded by bone as in ourselves and so many other highly-developed mammals, and with a most puzzling set of teeth—two pointed incisors in each jaw, no canines, and the other teeth not amounting to much except for a huge narrow, square-cut grinder on each side, quite unlike any tooth possessed by any other beast living or extinct; though it must be admitted that several marsupials, in being, or bygone, which have the single pair of incisors below, do have a large narrow grinder; but this, like the great "carnassial" grinder of the higher carnivores, is arched, not squared, at the top.

WHAT the thylacoleo did with this dire dentition we do not know; Owen thought it was a dreadful carnivore, and named it accordingly. But it was a phalanger, and should have been vegetarian, though the vegetarianism of the lower animals is seldom

KOALA THAT LEADS A COMFORTABLE, EASY LIFE IN THE TOPS OF HIGH TREES

Confined to Eastern Australia, the koala is an arboreal beast only occasionally descending to the ground. It feeds almost exclusively on eucalyptus shoots, moving about the tree-tops in a very leisurely manner. Most of the day is spent in sleep in some hollow of a tree, though the animal is not averse to sunning itself when it can find a really comfortable arrangement of branches, as here. Note the position of the hind limbs which are so hunched up as to touch the fore-limbs. If interfered with the koala screams loudly.

consistent, as we see with rats and pigs, and it is said that bones have been found bearing marks that would be produced by the thylacoleo's teeth. This might not prove it to be a carnivore, since the vegetarian porcupine is fond of gnawing bones, and deer fairly eat them up; but it may be suggested that the beast was partly a scavenger, and cracked and swallowed bones like the hyena, leaving its stomach to settle matters with the bits. At any rate, it must have been a fearsome-looking beast, in the face, much like the jabberwock in "Alice" and may yet turn up in New Guinea, since tales come thence of a creature which leaves footprints as big as a bullock's and has "a face like the devil."

The reason for these casualties in bygone Australian animal life is no doubt the climate which, unlike competitors, cannot be escaped by isolation. Australia was doubtless once less droughty than it is now, but droughts are always likely to occur, and large, heavy animals will make their own droughts by eating off herbage wholesale and then exposing the soil, which, trampled into dust, blows into water and silts it up. Our introduced stock are doing this at the present day, and thus repeating what the old large animals probably did. The carnivores must disappear with their prey, and ultimately the small animals, so much more frugal and prolific, win through, just as the rabbit scores off the sheep.

Circumstantial evidence of the extinction process was furnished by the discovery of a large number of diprotodon skeletons in a salt marsh which is even now dangerous to cattle.

The danger of crossing soft ground, always present for most large animals, is intensified by drought, when the borders of water become stretches of mud, and bogged and drowned animals poison the remaining supply. Moreover, marsupials, like so many other animals, have their epidemics; the charming koala, from being a common animal, has become rare through this cause, and epidemics are more dangerous to the existence of large species, owing to their smaller number of individuals as compared with small ones. Interesting scientifically as the marsupials are, they

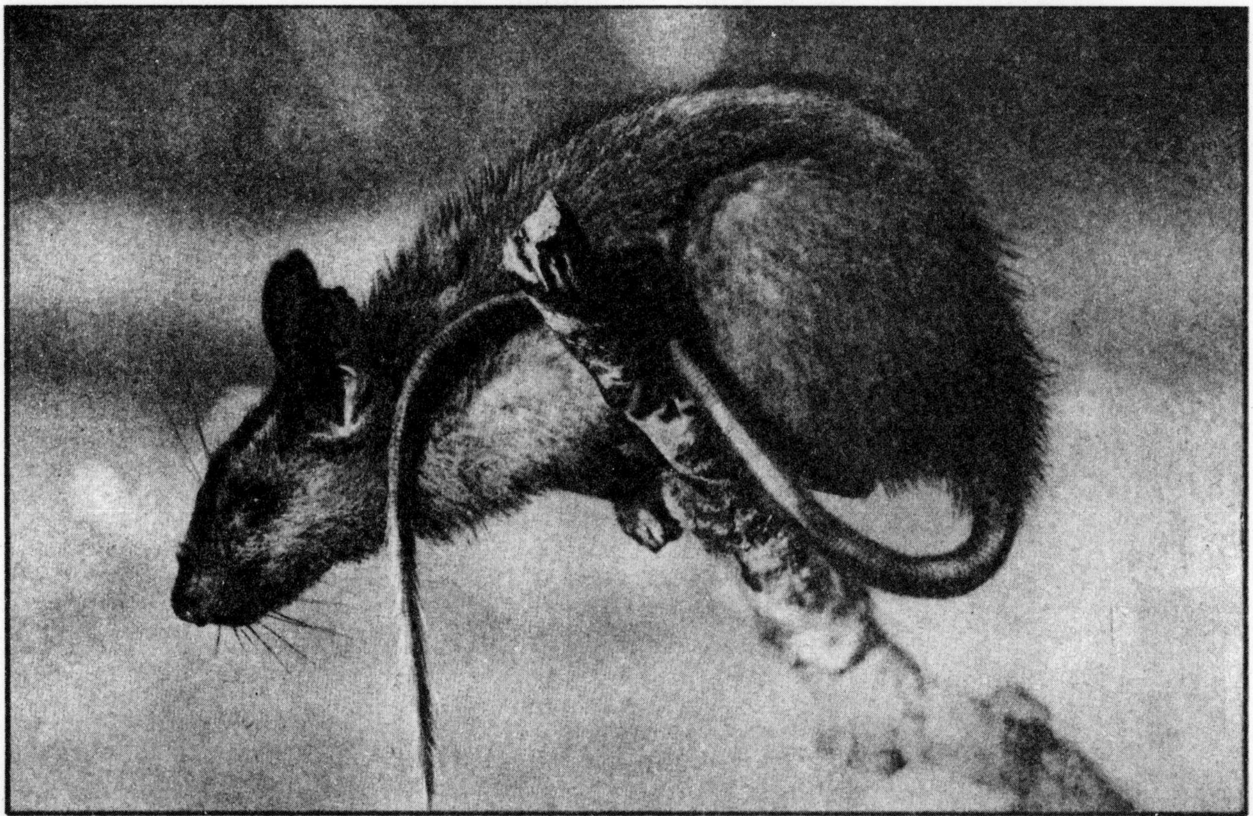

Mondiale

SPOTTED NATIVE CAT AND AN OPOSSUM OF UNCLASSIFIED SPECIES

The large, carnivorous marsupials have disappeared from the mainland of Australia though they still maintain a precarious living in Tasmania. The native cats, or dasyures, however, still keep a footing on the mainland. They are arboreal and seem to take the place of the martens of Europe, whose general habits those of the dasyures much resemble. The lower photograph is of one of these animals, while above is an unclassified species of opossum, very ratlike, found in the wild country of the Northern Territory.

CREATURES OF THE NIGHT: TASMANIAN DEVIL AND DINGO

A bane to the sheep farmer, the Tasmanian devil (bottom) has been remorselessly hunted. It is a marsupial and nocturnal, living in a burrow like a badger. Indeed, it seems quite blinded if exposed to the full glare of the sun and only comes out at night. It usually grows to a little over two feet, the tail adding another foot to its length. The upper photograph is of a dingo, the handsome wild dog of Australia. It is usually found solitary and is nocturnal like the Tasmanian devil. The colour varies between black and grey-red.

DUCKBILL AT ITS NEST AND THE TASMANIAN WOLF

Probably the weirdest of all living animals is the duckbill. It is about eighteen inches long, covered in fur, suckles its young, and goes on four short legs whose feet are webbed. It has a duck-like beak and lays eggs. The duckbill seems to be a survival from the time when there was an animal, half reptile, half mammal, which had got as far in evolution as to have hair instead of scales or feathers and to suckle its young, but had not yet given up laying eggs in favour of bearing its progeny alive. Above is a Tasmanian wolf.

PAIR OF BURROWING WOMBATS AND A RING-TAILED OPOSSUM

While kangaroos are found in New Guinea wombats (bottom) are entirely confined to Australia and Tasmania. There are only four species, and the animals are about two feet in length and rather bear-like in appearance. They burrow like badgers and live on roots and grass, but have the gnawing teeth of rats and rabbits. The fur is thick and coarse and may be yellowish-brown, dark brown or black. Above is a ring-tailed opossum in a characteristically acrobatic pose on a branch. It is holding on by all four legs at once.

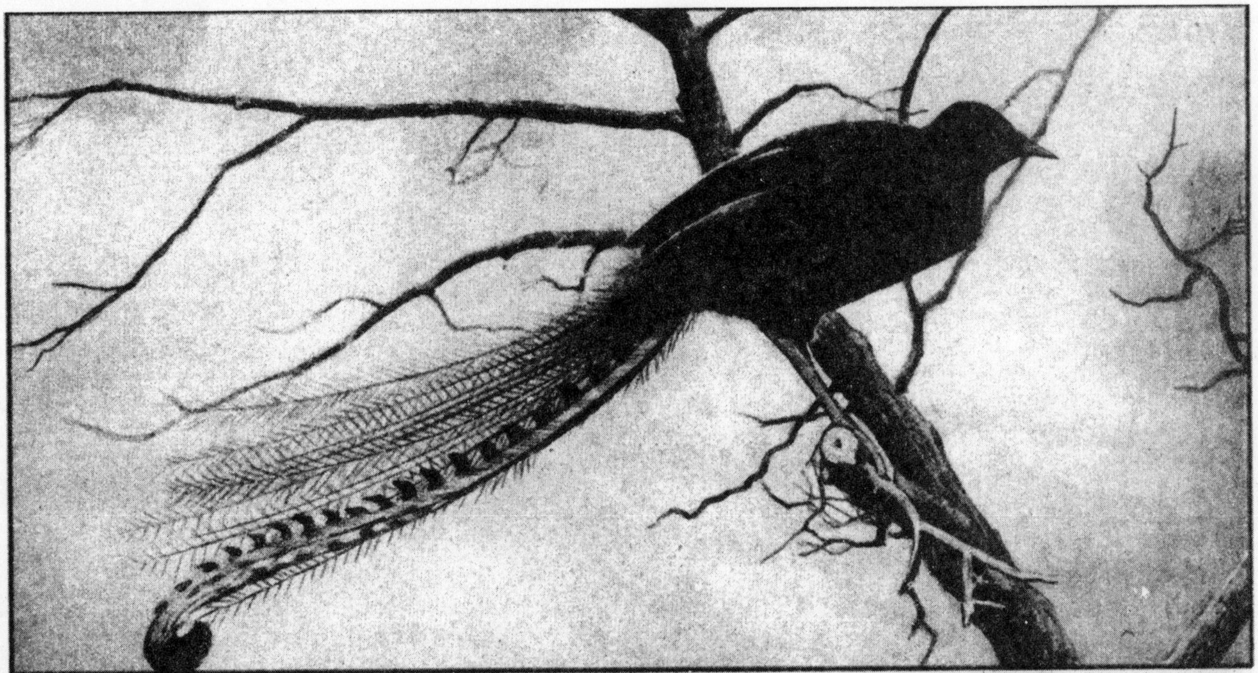

Smithsonian Report

AUSTRALIA'S UNIQUE BLACK SWAN AND LYRE BIRD

Nowhere else in the world has there arisen a black swan. This bird of sombre plumage is native only to Australia, although specimens have been often exported to grace ornamental waters in Europe. The beak is red and the under sides of the wings white. The upper photograph shows one of the beautiful lyre birds found in the denser parts of the forests of Australia. These birds seldom fly, and pick up their food, insects and worms, on the ground, but are very quick runners.

are commonplace compared with the monotremes, or single-vented mammals, the most celebrated of which is the well-known duckbill, or platypus. This is confined to Australia and Tasmania; but New Guinea as well as these countries can show examples of the other monotreme type, that of the echidna, or spiny ant-eater. Both duckbill and echidna reproduce by laying eggs.

The interest of these animals lies in the fact that, though strongly specialised on lines of their own, they are in some ways really representative of a half-reptilian mammalian ancestor, which had got as far as growing hair and giving milk, but still laid eggs. They have no teats, but sweat out the milk from specialised patches of skin. The duckbill, which feeds on small water-animals in the manner of a duck, has true teeth when young, afterwards shed and replaced by horny ones. These first teeth are like those of some of the earliest mammals, though others of these have teeth more like marsupials. Possibly the teeth became differentiated before egg-laying was dropped in favour of live-bearing, but as the remains of early mammals are generally only jaws or at most skulls, they do not really tell us whether the beasts in question were marsupials or monotremes.

FROGMOUTH THAT SLEEPS SOUNDLY ALL DAY

The Australian representatives of the night-jar family are known as "moreporks" because the sounds they utter are supposed to resemble the words "more pork." During the day the morepork, of which there are a number of species, sleeps so soundly (often in a hollow tree), that it may sometimes be taken off its perch by hand.

Considering their powers of locomotion through air, it is astonishing that the distribution of birds, and of bats among mammals, has run so closely parallel to that of ordinary beasts; Australia has bats, of course, but of quite ordinary type, like her seals and sea-lions. Among birds, in the emu and cassowary she has members of a group comparable to the marsupial mammals—lowly organized, but specialised as a side branch, and once quite generally distributed, but now nearly limited to the southern hemisphere. It is curious that the ostrich, the only species which is still found north of the line, belongs to the most primitive family, just as the only northern marsupial, the common American opossum, is one of the more primitive pouched mammals. The ostrich is more primitive than the emu and cassowary because it has the hip bones joined below as in reptiles and as in no other bird, and also it possesses much better developed wings, for these giant runners are simply birds that have made biped beasts of themselves by losing the power of flight.

Australian birds generally seem to be rather comparable to Australian rodents—invaders of a very ancient period, often specialised, but often quite of ordinary type; and sometimes they are even much the same as European species.

THEY do, however, often show old peculiarities. Australia holds a bird which is evidently ancient, and shows us what the ancestor of the wild fowl family was like in some respects. This is the so-called magpie-goose, a bird so slim and leggy, and with the feet so

Neville Kingston

Chas. Barrett

LIZARDS OF FRIGHTFUL ASPECT BUT PEACEFUL HABIT

Australia is rich in lizards and among them are two whose appearance might make the boldest creature chary of approaching. The stump-tailed lizard (bottom) sleeps all day and comes out at night to feed on insects. If molested it gives a severe bite but is never aggressive. The moloch (top) is equally inoffensive though quite as ugly. The larger spines are hollow.

slightly webbed and so well adapted, with their long hind toes, for perching, that if its head were cut off no one who saw it for the first time would class it as one of the duck tribe, but as one of the heavier perching waders, probably an ibis. Yet it has never attracted attention, even from Darwin, who missed so little, while its compatriot, the black swan, which is no more remarkable scientifically than the white bear, is known to everyone.

PRIMITIVE also in their well-developed hind toes are the characteristic Australian game-birds, the megapodes, or mound-builders, of which the brush turkey can always be seen at the Zoo. These bury their eggs like reptiles, and their young, which are hatched with fledged wings, look after themselves at once just as young reptiles do. The range of these birds is nearly the same as that of the vegetarian marsupials.

The cold-blooded tribes, backboned or otherwise, have been so much longer upon the earth than beasts and birds that they have seen far greater changes, and their distribution rarely coincides with that of the two higher classes. Thus there is nothing remarkable about Australian reptiles, though in New Zealand we get the tuatera, a reptile of very ancient descent with some relationship to amphibians. Among Australian amphibians the interesting point is not the presence but the absence of primitive types, for the newts and salamanders, which represent the most primitive type not only of amphibians but of land vertebrates, nearly all live north of the line and never anywhere near Australia. As they are bad travellers on land, and need damp and coolness, they have never been able to retreat southwards. Frogs and toads are common enough in Australia, but these represent a comparatively modern group.

Fresh-water fish, however, are very much on the same footing as birds and beasts and the three great southern regions each have their own species of the primitive lung-fish which were abundant in the coal period. The Australian variety is in some ways the most primitive of any, with its flipper-like fins, the fins of the others being reduced like the wings of most of the great flightless birds.

We may regard the great southern continent as a region of refuge and toleration.

Chapter LXXXIX

How We Study Life Beneath the Sea

By G. A. Steven

Of the Marine Biological Laboratory, Plymouth

THE sea covers over two-thirds of the earth's surface. According to recent estimates, its area is somewhere in the region of 140 million square miles, and it is believed to occupy a volume of between 300 million and 320 million cubic miles. This vast ocean world simply teems with living things of the most diverse forms and sizes, ranging from the largest known living animals, the whales, and the tallest plants, down to minute organisms

> Thick and numberless
> As the gay motes that people
> the sunbeams.

The scientific study of this wealth of marine life is of very recent origin, dating roughly from about the middle of last century when a few tentative voyages of exploration began to be made. Until this time it was believed even by the highest authorities that marine organisms were confined to depths of three hundred fathoms and less, and that all the vast sea world below that level was a sepulchral realm of absolute and everlasting calm and silence, permanent darkness, and intense cold in which no living thing could possibly exist. But in the year 1868 H.M.S. Lightning proved beyond all doubt the fallacy of this belief by dredging up from 650 fathoms a rich collection of marine animals, many of them wonderfully constructed organisms which had never before been seen. It was not, however, until the return of the famous Challenger expedition (1872–76), under the leadership of Sir Wyville Thomson, that the great "world below the brine" was clearly revealed. During her three and a half years' voyage of exploration the Challenger cruised over 68,900 nautical miles and dredged new and rare forms of life from 354 stations situated all over the ocean world, many hauls bringing up bizarre creatures from depths of over five miles.

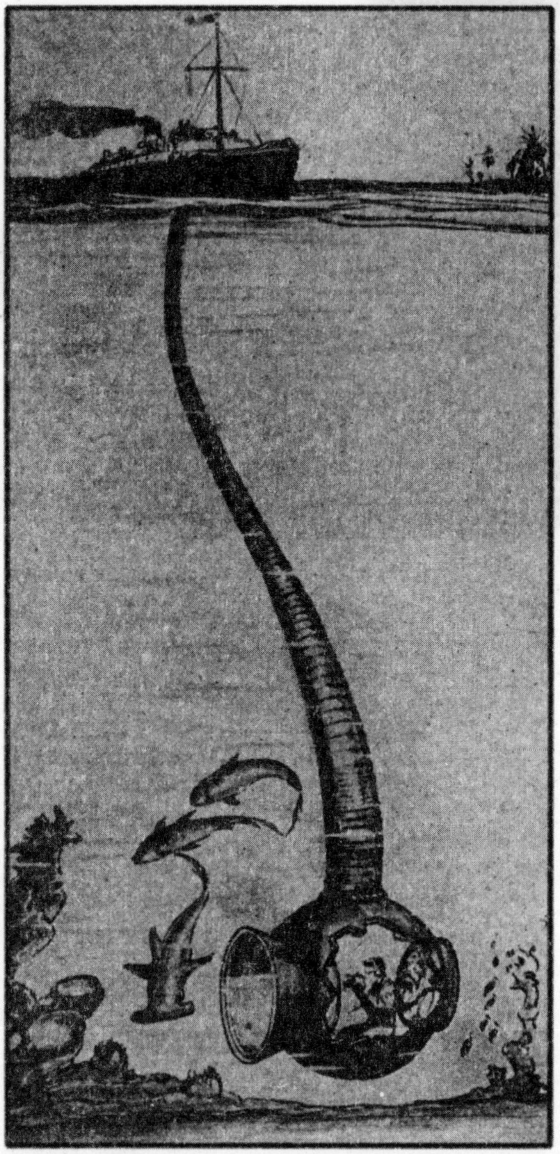

HOW SUBMARINE PHOTOGRAPHS ARE TAKEN

In this sketch we see how photographs have been taken under the sea in the tropics by Mr. J. E. Williamson. The tube is made of flexible steel rings and the photographer sits in the observation-room at the lower end.

Since the days of the Challenger great strides have been made in oceanographical research—advances rendered possible by the ever-increasing number and greater efficiency of the mechanical appliances available in more recent years. One of the first contrivances designed for capturing marine organisms for purposes of scientific study seems to have been the dredge. This instrument is still in regular use and is likely to remain so. It is of simple construction, consisting of a stout rectangular frame of wrought iron, to which is attached a strongly-made bag or net. The dimensions of the frame depend upon the size of the vessel from which it is to be worked, and the mesh of the bag is varied according to the size of the animals it is desired to catch. The dredge is particularly suitable for use on rocky bottoms. Its sharpened edges effectively dislodge fixed forms, and are sufficiently strong to break off pieces of softer rock thus bringing to light those animals—such as brittle-stars and sea-cucumbers—which insinuate themselves into crevices. The dredge is also used on soft bottoms, where its digging action unearths worms, burrowing molluscs and certain crustaceans which live buried in mud or sand.

For capturing the animals which live on, or swim just above, the surface of smooth ground, trawling is the most effective method. Two types of trawl are commonly used, the beam trawl

ON EITHER SIDE OF THE GLASS: DIVER PICKS A BOUQUET BY REQUEST

The native diver has swum into the range of vision of the window and has made out by signs in this silent world under the sea that he is to pick a plant from this marine flower bed. One of the excitements of this submarine observation post is that one never knows what may suddenly swim into view or what comedy or tragedy may be played within the distance of a few feet. Tropic fish will live in an aquarium, but down here there are not only fish but the thrill of the unexpected.

and the otter trawl, the former being more suitable for use with sailing ships, and the latter with larger motor or steam vessels. The beam trawl consists of an elongated triangular flattened bag of strong net, the mouth of which may vary in breadth from 20 to 50 feet, and the length from 45 to 120 feet, according to the size of the vessel.

THE upper edge of the mouth is straight and is fastened to a stout horizontal wooden beam, equipped at each end with a stirrup-shaped runner which keeps the beam raised about three feet above the sea bottom. The lower margin of the mouth is attached to a heavy "footrope" which is fastened at each end to the lower corner of the runner. This footrope is not tightly stretched, but curves backwards in a wide bight behind the level of the beam. As the trawl is towed along the sea floor the footrope drags heavily upon the ground, stirring up the animals thereon. These, prevented from escaping upwards by the forwardly projecting upper side of the net, are swept backwards into the apex or "cod-end." Everything on the sea floor is gathered up in the trawl—loose stones and other debris, seaweeds, invertebrate animals of all kinds, as well as fishes swimming just above the bottom.

In the more modern otter trawl the general shape and arrangement of net and footrope are the same as in the beam trawl, but the beam is replaced by a strong rope, the "headline," and the runners by heavy wooden "otter" boards like massive doors. Each board is shackled to the trawl-warp in such a manner that it moves forwards on one of its longest edges, with its surface set outwards at an angle of about twenty degrees to the direction in which the trawl is being towed. In this way the mouth of the net is kept open to its full extent—to which there is no limit other than that imposed by the size and displacement of the ship—simply by the kite-like action of the boards.

In another type of otter trawl which can be used by large and small vessels alike, the otter

SKETCHING NATURE FROM A WINDOW UNDER THE WAVES

A new world has been opened up for the artist by this ingenious invention which allows a man to sit comfortably, fathoms below the surface, and watch as from a window the glinting fish as they swim by and catch the tropical rays from the blue skies above. We see the artist, Mrs. J. E. Williamson, pausing, pencil in hand and sketch on knee, to mark the forms and the lines of the strange creatures that move, delicately poised in the wonderful transparent element on the other side of the plate-glass.

boards are replaced by patented dirigible otter boxes, which are open at each end and act after the manner of box kites. They can be adjusted to work at the surface, on the bottom, and at all intermediate depths—an important advantage which renders possible the capture, by trawling, of fishes and other animals which do not live on or near the sea bottom.

For work in very deep water the Agassiz trawl is used. This contrivance—devised by Professor Agassiz—is provided with two foot ropes and an iron frame so designed that it will fish effectively whichever side is uppermost. This is a very necessary quality for, in descending to great depths, the instrument is liable to turn over and over several times and will land quite as frequently on one side as on the other.

By the methods described above, the denizens of the deep can be caught for examination and description, but a quantitative estimate of their abundance cannot be obtained. To supply this information Dr. Petersen, a Danish zoologist, has designed an instrument now known as the "Petersen grab" which, working after the same manner as the well-known coal-grab, "bites" from the sea bottom a known area of sand or mud with its contained fauna. From the data furnished by a representative number of grab hauls the invertebrate population of a definite area of the sea bottom can be calculated. To estimate the fish population, however, is a more difficult matter which, up to the present, at any rate, can be attempted only by indirect methods.

Those plants and animals, many of them exceedingly small, which float or drift about in the sea and are known collectively as "plankton," require other methods of capture. The instrument almost universally used for this purpose is the tow-net, which is simply a cone-shaped bag made of Swiss silk or bolting cloth, the mouth of which is attached to a wooden ring. For taking very small animals (microplankton) the tow-nets are of exceedingly fine silk with a mouth diameter of eighteen inches, and a length of five

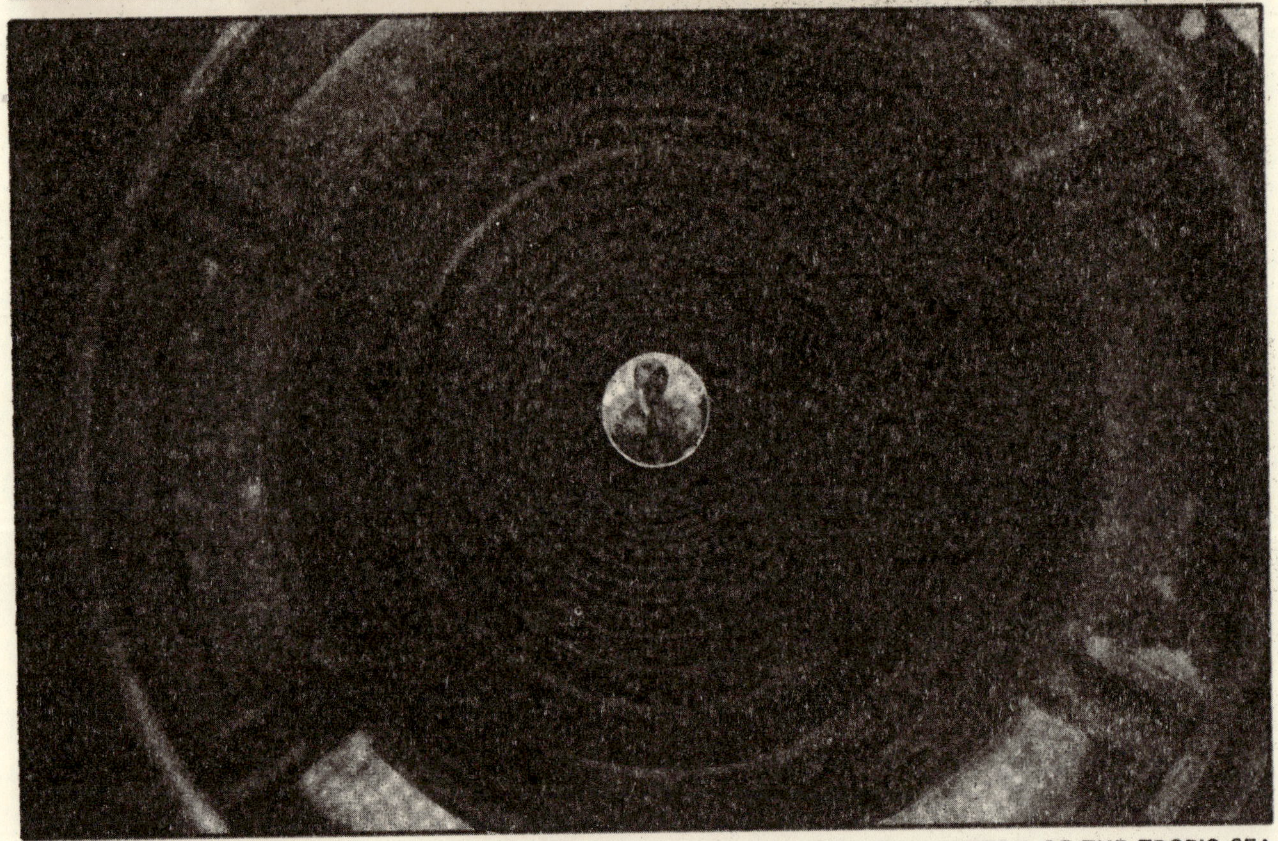

MULTITUDINOUS LIFE, VIVIDLY COLOURED, AND THE PHOTOGRAPHER AT THE BOTTOM OF THE TROPIC SEA

Lite luxuriates in the sea to an extent unequalled on land. In this photograph, and the others of the Williamson Expedition, we have a case of inhabitants of the land looking out, by means of special apparatus, upon the unwonted realms below the sea. This observation post reveals a constant pageant of life, fish of all colours and sizes against a background of plant life more vivid and fantastic than anything on land. The lower photograph shows the organizer of the expedition looking up the tube from the bottom of the sea.

BIG SHARK CASTS ITS SINISTER SHADOW ON THE SUNLIT FLOOR OF THE SEA

In the shallow waters about the coasts of the Bahamas the brilliant sunlight illumines the sea so brightly and the water is so clear that under-sea photography presents no difficulty as far as lighting is concerned. Notice that the big shark, gliding by upon his intent and hungry way, casts a strong shadow on the clear sand of the sea floor. Various other fish are moving about among the tussocks of weirdly formed weed which, tinted with the most varied colours, give ambush or sanctuary to pursuer or pursued.

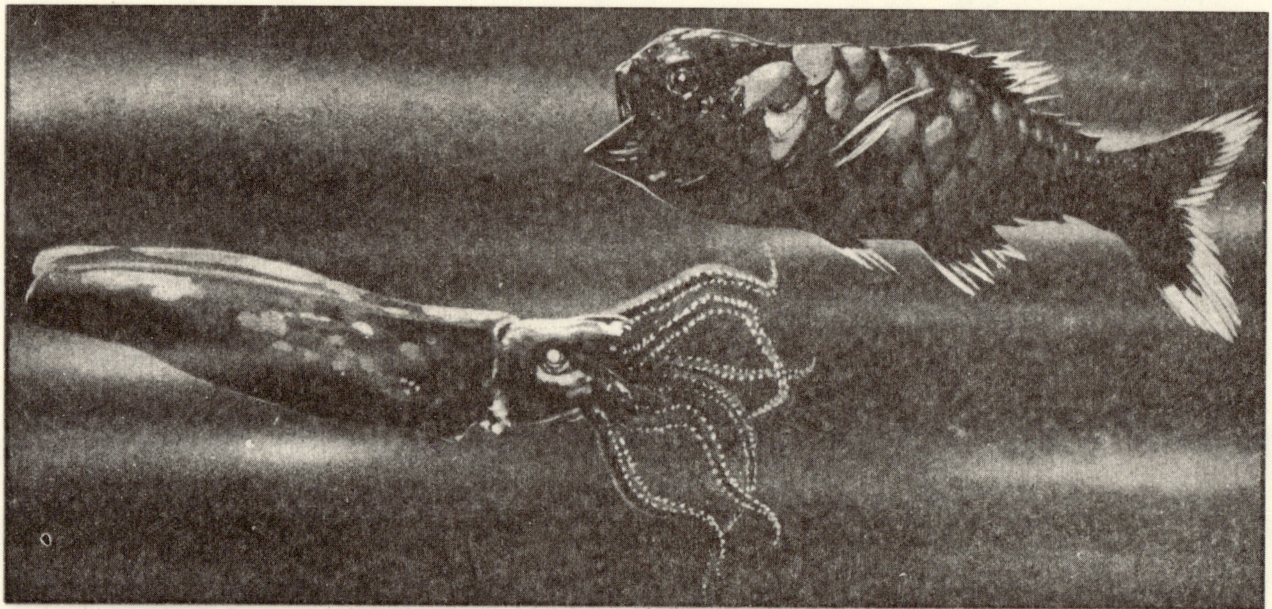

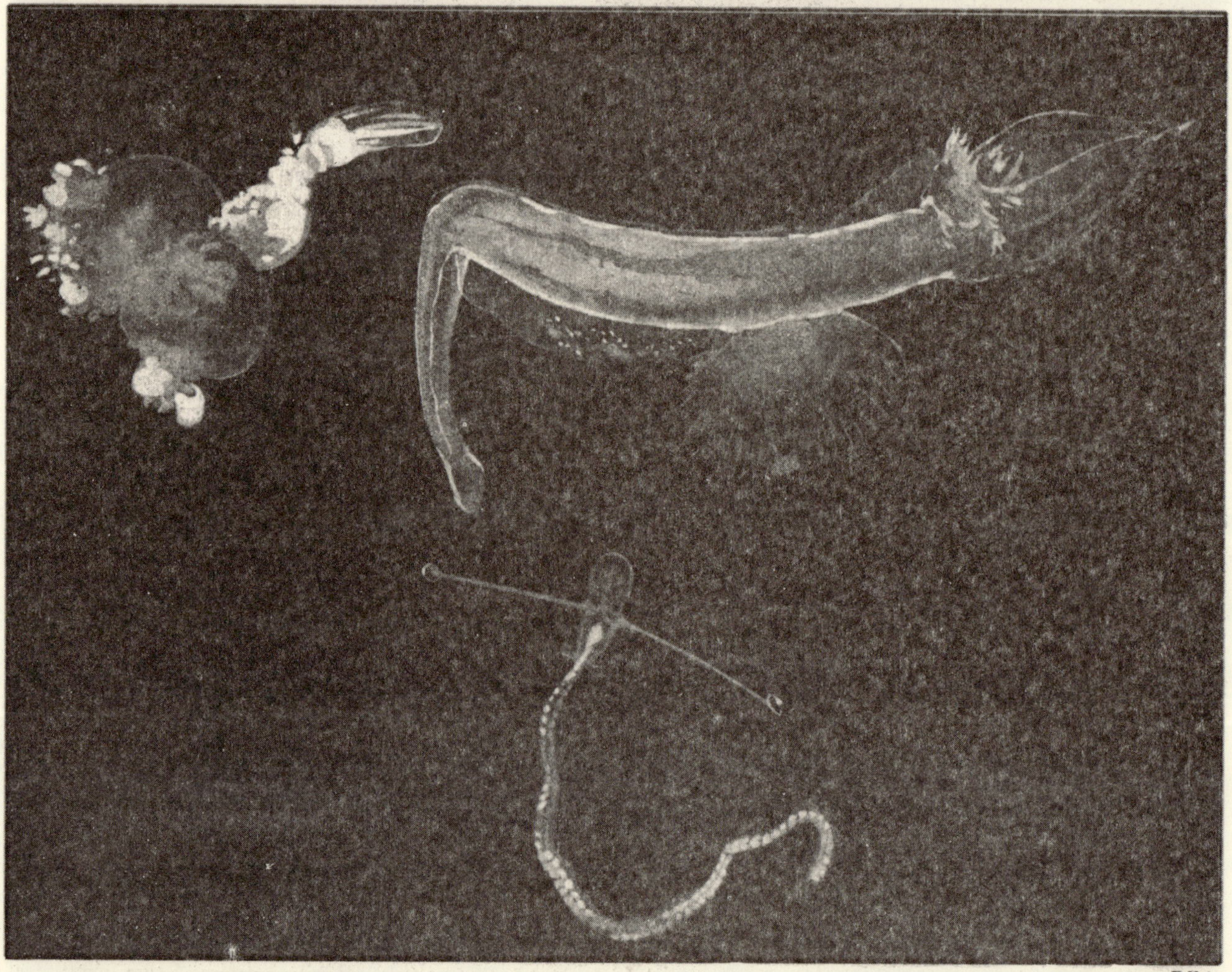

E.N.A.

SOME STRANGE REPRESENTATIVES OF THE LIFE BENEATH THE SEA

By means of dredges, trawls and grabs, the fauna of the deep seas is raised from its obscurity and brought up to the surface for examination by scientists. These enterprising methods have yielded some strange finds. The lower photograph shows three strange beings fished up from the bottom of the Hudson Gorge. The animal with eyes on the ends of stalks is particularly remarkable. The upper photograph shows a fish with turquoise tinted scales and a squid which has some thousands of luminous spots on its body. Until about the middle nineteenth century it was believed that no life existed in the sea below the three hundred fathom line.

FISH FAMILIAR TO THE ANGLER AND THE BREAKFAST-TABLE: BASS AND COD

These photographs were taken in an aquarium, and it is from such places that much of our knowledge of life beneath the sea must come. Apparatus such as the exploring ship and its flexible tube, illustrated in previous pages of this chapter, is, naturally, not very common and, in any case, with it life can only be studied in conditions that are entirely natural, at depths shallow enough to admit of natural lighting. Bass (bottom) are related to the perch. Above are some cod from two to four years old. These photographs, and those in pages 989 and 992, are by F. Schensky of the Heligoland Biological Station and are given by permission of Dr. Werner Klinkhardt.

One of the pioneers of undersea exploration is Mr. William Beebe, leader of several recent oceanographical expeditions, and author of two delightful books on his experiences—" The Arcturus Adventure" and " Beneath Tropic Seas "—books which all interested in marine and submarine exploration along the most modern lines should read. In the former book is described a diving helmet which was used with much success for submarine observation among the Galapagos Islands. This instrument, which is made of copper, fits over the head and rests upon the shoulders. To its lower edge four flattened lead weights, each weighing ten pounds, are attached to help to keep it in place. A hose is connected to the right side through which air is pumped to the diver, and two obliquely-placed glass windows in front give a fairly large field of view. The use of the helmet is simplicity itself. Garbed in a bathing suit, the diver steps over the side of the parent boat and descends the first few rungs of the ladder. The helmet is then slipped gently over his head by one of the boat's crew, pumping begins, and down the diver goes. The air inside the helmet prevents the water rising above the chin, unless of course, the wearer bends forwards, when the level of the water rises, relative to his face.

feet. When the larger plankton animals (macroplankton) are required, the ring-net or ring-trawl is used. This has a mouth-opening six feet in diameter and is about eighteen feet long. In order to capture only the organisms living in any particular layer, say between 200–300 fathoms, a net has been constructed which can be let down closed, then opened, hauled vertically through the desired distance, closed again, and then hauled up. In this way, by lowering to different depths and comparing the catches, valuable information with regard to the vertical distribution of the plankton can be obtained.

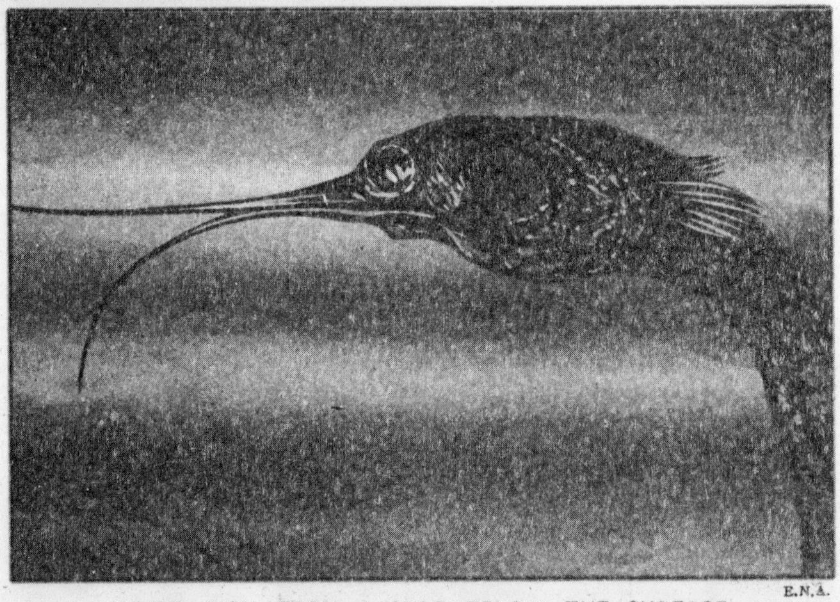

E.N.A.

WEIRD FISH FROM A MILE BELOW THE SURFACE

One of the most extraordinary things ever fished up from the depths is this so-called snipe-billed eel (bottom). Why it should have developed the extraordinarily bird-like protuberance on its head is a mystery, as is the way the two halves of the " beak " divide. Above we have an eel-like fish with a head like that of a snake in a nightmare. These teeth are really terrible.

But dredge and trawl, townet and grab, though they have enabled the marine biologist to build up a fairly accurate and consecutive knowledge of the nature and wealth of life in the sea, leave him almost totally ignorant of what may be termed the intimate daily life and habits of those ocean dwellers. Land animals have been closely studied in their native haunts by many observers, and the habits of most are fairly well known. But what goes on in two fathoms of water is to this day shrouded in mystery. The veil, however, is gradually being lifted by energetic and ingenious workers along new lines, particularly on the other side of the Atlantic.

In the last year or two this hitherto unseen world has been visited by man, observed, sketched, and even photographed in natural colours.

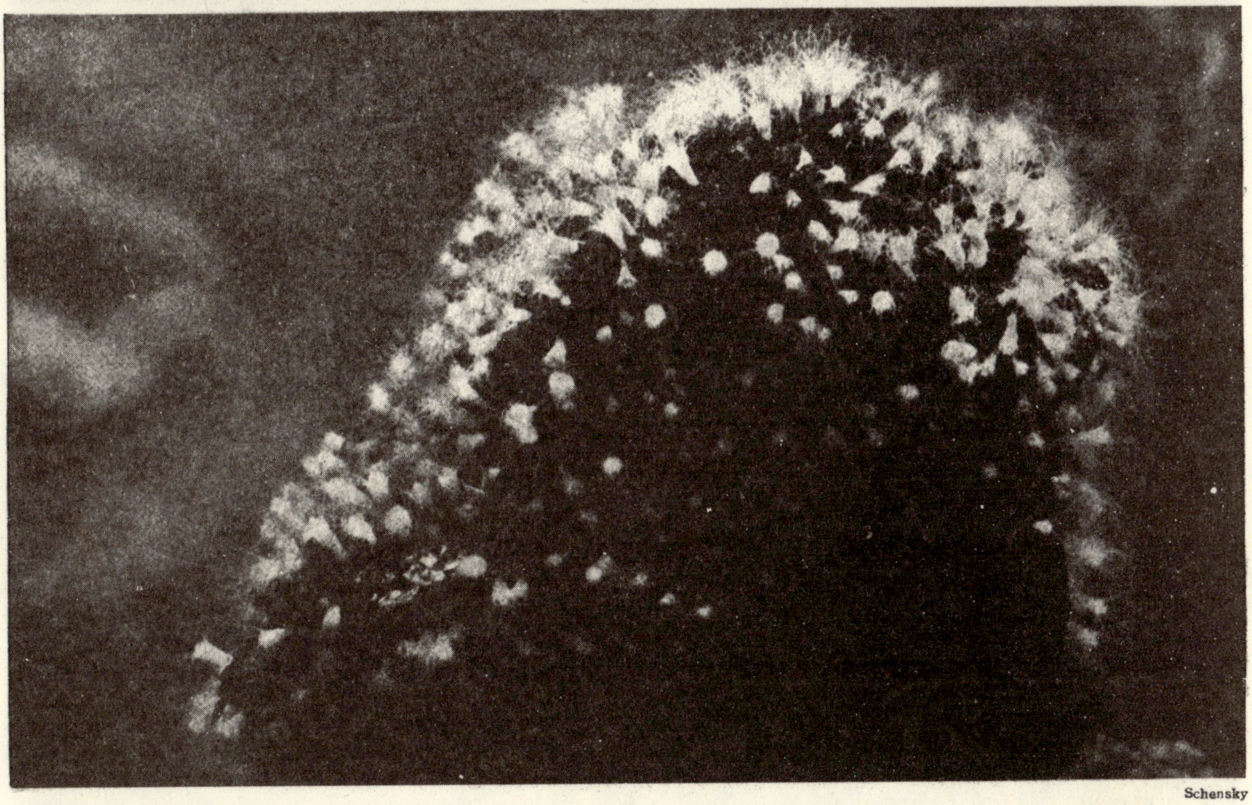

Schensky

SEA POLYPS LIKE A PYROTECHNIC DISPLAY, AND A REMARKABLE PRAWN GROUP

If one were to paint the momentary brilliance of a great burst of fireworks the result might well look, when photographed, like the lower illustration here, which shows some scyphistoma polyps, lovely creatures which grow beneath the salt sea. They are one of the two alternate generations of the disk jelly-fish. Sexual, egg-laying offspring alternate with asexual offspring (the form seen here) which produce jelly-fish by budding only. Above is a group of prawns. Some of these are in strange attitudes, as of supplication.

W. H. A. Fincham

FLOWER-LIKE FORMS OF OPELET AND DAISY ANEMONES

Underneath the surface of the sea there exist the most amazing forms of life, many of them reminding us of something on land and yet most of them with a touch of the bizarre—from the land point of view. But to study these forms of life, and especially the type seen here, it is necessary that the appropriate lighting should be in operation. A sea-anemone out of water is a sorry thing, but its true life can be watched through the glass panel of an aquarium. The lower group (opelet) is formed much like the tubular petals of some flowers.

The great advantage of the diving helmet over an ordinary diving suit—which is quite useless for this type of work—lies in the fact that it encloses only the head leaving the rest of the body free and unencumbered. As an example of what new facts of great interest may be gleaned by its use, one may mention only two of Beebe's experiences. When on the sea bottom he found that, by swaying gently with the movement of the water, all the inhabitants round about "from gobies to groupers, from shrimps to sharks," accepted him as something properly belonging to their domain and approached without fear.

But if he resisted this backward and forward aqueous surge and remained stiffly still, he was at once avoided as an object of suspicion. Here, at the outset, is revealed behaviour entirely opposite to that on

PHOTOGRAPHS FROM DAVY JONES'S LOCKER: VIVID LIFE IN THE DEEPS

When sailors wished to refer to the abyss over which their ships sailed they talked of Davy Jones's Locker. But none of these old salts had ever been down below to study the wonderful contents of that locker. Thanks to modern invention we can sit in an armchair and gaze at some of the wonderful creatures that occupy these once unguessed fields down below.

E. N. A.

land where the slightest movement startles wild life and only by absolute stillness can the observer attain his object of allaying fear.

The invention and use of the diving helmet has brought in its train a still more interesting and useful development of submarine investigation. With its aid under-water photography is now being undertaken with conspicuous success. In 1927 Mr. Floyd Crossby returned from an expedition to Haiti with over 1,200 feet of film illustrative of life on a coral reef below the surface of the sea. In January of the same year there were published in the National Geographical Magazine, Washington, D.C., eight natural colour photographs of marine life in its natural habitat—the first natural colour photographs that have ever been made beneath the sea Dr. W. H. Longley, a noted American ichthyologist, developed the technique by which this feat was achieved at a depth of two and a half fathoms.

A unique and very ingenious method of direct submarine observation, however, is that which was adopted by a Mr. J E. Williamson, who, with his bride, returned to New York City after spending the larger part of a seven and a half months' honeymoon under the waters surrounding the Bahama Islands.

They studied aquatic life beneath the surface from a specially built compartment attached to a long flexible metal tube with a boat as a base. The tube was invented by Capt. Charles Williamson, father of the photographer, for use in salvage operations, and it was while young Williamson was watching his father use it thus that he became inspired with the idea of adapting it for submarine photography. The tube is built of flexible sections firmly bolted together. To the bottom section is attached the more or less spherical observation chamber, slightly over five feet in diameter and provided with plate-glass windows. By adding sections at the top of the tube the chamber can be sunk to any desired depth. The diameter of the tube is two feet—large enough to allow a man to slip down through it into the observation chamber below. Here two or three people can be comfortably accommodated. Hundreds of under-sea photographs and thousands of feet of motion pictures have already been taken from this ingenious tube. In addition, many water-colour sketches, the first ever painted beneath the sea —sketches of living corals and the multi-coloured reef fishes which dart in and out among enchanted coral groves—have been executed.

Thus are the mysteries of the deep being explored.

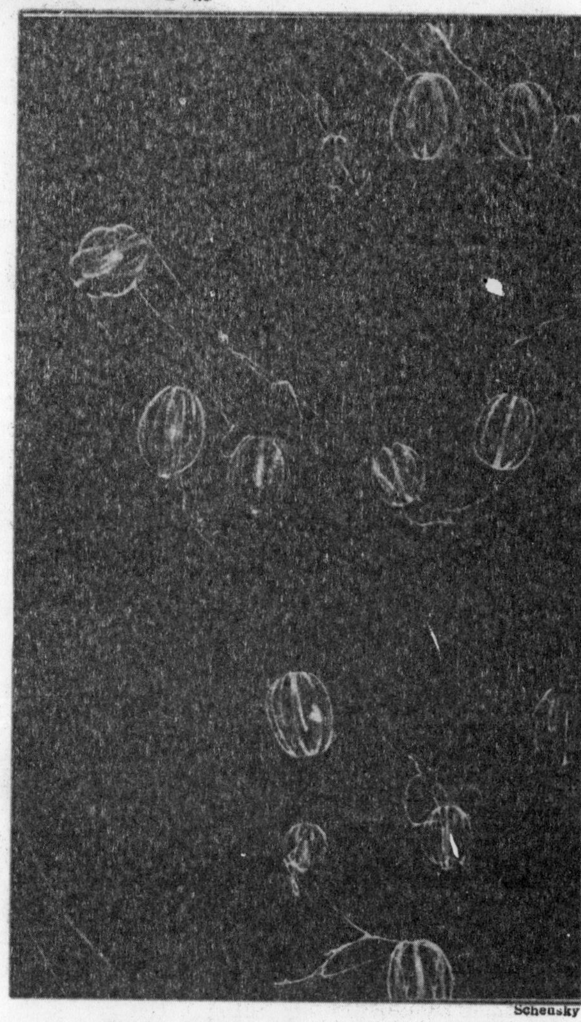

Scheusky

JELLY FISH AND HATCHET FISH

Below we see comb jelly fish or ctenophores, whose "bodies" may be more than 99 per cent. water, and above a hatchet fish from the deep seas. The curious shape of the last with its slim tail and enormous and suddenly swelling stomach is very remarkable.

Chapter XC

Some Mysteries of Animal Life

By E. G. Boulenger

Director of the Zoological Society's Aquarium

Every phenomenon of Nature is a mystery until elucidated. Thanks to painstaking investigators elucidation moves apace, and it is now generally recognized that few of the apparent enigmas are incapable of natural explanation. There is, however, still a wealth of unanswered riddles to excite the curiosity. Why, for instance, should certain animals be burdened with cumbrous appendages of no apparent use and presenting features that appear to be borrowed from others claiming no relationship? In this chapter we offer some explanation of a few of these enigmas, reminding the reader beforehand that such explanations are as yet put forward merely as plausible theories.

Quite a number of animals go through life loaded with adornments that cannot fail to cause them considerable inconvenience. Can fashion alone be the explanation? It is one not so absurd or illogical as it may at first appear if we consider man's self-inflicted agonies in the same cause. Animals, being less masters of their fate than man, persist in adornments that cannot be thrown aside at will. Certain chameleons, for instance, wear huge structures of skin and bone which protrude from the forehead like bowsprits and may exceed the bulk of the entire head; whilst the giant fish-eating crocodile, or gharial, has a box-like structure surmounting its snout which can be of no utilitarian value and may possibly prove an actual hindrance. The heads of the horned lizards of North and Central America are surmounted with enormous spines which in some cases exceed the creature's head in length. No use is made of these formidable-looking weapons for either offensive or defensive purposes, the reptile when molested relying on frustrating its enemy by shooting a fine jet of blood at its aggressor from the corner of the eyes.

F. W. Bond

MAHOLI GALAGO AND YOUNG

South Africa is the home of the maholi galago, an animal about the size of a rat and possessing extraordinarily beautiful eyes. It ventures out only at night and has a curious habit, mentioned in this chapter, when preparing itself for climbing trees

The use of the rattlesnake's rattle has been freely discussed. The utility of the apparatus to the creature is very problematic, for whilst it may serve as a warning to approaching enemies, it on the other hand draws the attention of hostile creatures to its presence. It has been suggested that the rattling sounds serve to call the sexes together; also that, resembling running water, they act as a decoy, attracting the serpent's prey. In this connexion it is worth bearing in mind that other poisonous snakes not provided with a rattle have the same habit of vibrating the end of the tail when excited or alarmed, and thus when reposing amongst dry leaves and twigs produce sounds very similar to those of the rattlesnake.

In the animal world certain apparently useless adornments are confined to the male. The bull hooded seal wears upon its crown a monstrous crest of fat extending from snout to occiput and reaching a height of six inches. The saiga antelope has its nose developed into a large puffy mound suggestive of disease or at the best a severe wasp sting. It is suggested that this organ may be a special provision to prevent sand entering the nasal chamber, but the saiga is sufficiently rare to preclude verification of this ingenious suggestion.

Nature is continually producing hypertrophies which sooner or later become a hindrance. The giant reptiles of the past developed such a wealth of armature that the wearer was

worst foe. The antlers often become interlocked during the duels of the rutting months, and many collections have been formed of horns that have become so inextricably jammed that in every case the duel has concluded by death from starvation on the part of both combatants. Antlers frequently become entangled with tree branches, placing the stag at the mercy of the hunter—whether beast or man. In one recently reported instance a "twenty-pointer" met its death whilst in the simple act of driving away flies. One foreleg became so involved with the profusely branching horns that the deer in its efforts to free the limb broke its own neck. Stranger still is the case of two mountain rams who, chancing to duel beside a young oak, drove their horns into the trunk and so remained captives until fortunately they were discovered by a ranger.

The reptile world offers one very striking instance of over-developed armature. This is frequently too encumbered to make effective use of the very horns and shields developed for its protection. The massive Triceratops evolved a head that eventually occupied one-third of its entire length and it must have been far too cumbrous to permit of rapid enough movement when confronted by an equally enormous but lightly armed lizard which could leap like a kangaroo, and was furnished with a set of teeth averaging three inches in length. The famous sabre-toothed tiger, contemporary with early man, produced a pair of upper incisors projecting beyond the mouth. The great length of these tusks prevented their being used in the normal manner as they barred the mouth even when the latter was open to its full extent. As its brain apparently failed to move with the times its demise synchronised with the sudden rapid improvement of pick-axe, spear and arrow-head.

A WEAPON of any description is only effective when easily operated; size and weight are in themselves no assurance of victory—the knight disappeared with the advent of the cannon, whilst the big battleship and the tank only live on sufferance from the aircraft with its high explosive, incendiary and gas bombs. In the wild the stag's picturesque horns that look so invincible when carried by some haughty buck in his prime frequently prove their possessor's

F. W. Bond

CHAMELEONS WITH USELESS WEAPONS

Certain chameleons have huge horn-like projections on their heads which might be taken for weapons of defence. But they serve no such useful end, and their purpose is a mystery. Below is a rhinoceros chameleon and above a specimen of Vosseler's chameleon.

F. W. Bond

FORMIDABLE LOOKING HEAD OF THE HORNED LIZARD: WERNER'S CHAMELEON

It is one of the little puzzles of which Nature is so full that an animal equipped, like the horned lizard (bottom), with a number of spikes on its head should make no use of them whatever for defending itself. On the contrary, this creature adopts quite a different method. It squirts blood from its eyeballs, a manoeuvre sufficiently horrifying to daunt the most bold attacker. Werner's chameleon (top) is also armed with spikes but depends entirely on making itself inconspicuous for its safety.

W. S. Berridge

F. W. Bond

THE GAVIAL AND THE UNACCOUNTABLE DEVELOPMENT OF ITS HEAD

Why the gavial, the great fish-eating crocodile of India's rivers, should, apparently, minimise the utility of its mouth by having a box-like structure on its snout is more than anyone can say. This is an extremely old animal, remains of it having been found in deposits of the Tertiary period. Possibly some former need, brought about by conditions now long vanished, induced the development of this—so far as we can see—useless appendage. The detail of the head can be studied from the lower photographs while above we get a view of the whole animal.

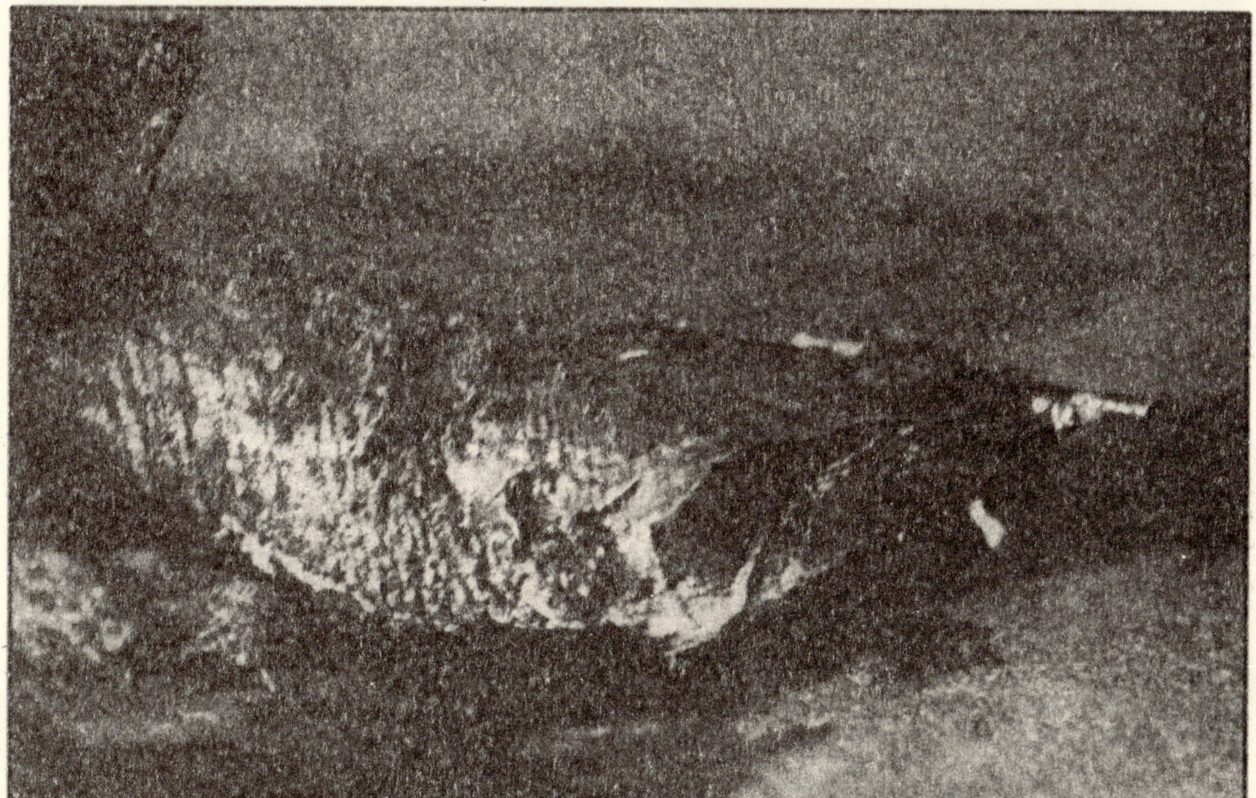

F. W. Bond

MATAMATA TORTOISE OF BRAZIL AND ITS STRANGELY-FORMED NECK

This weird-looking tortoise which lives in northern Brazil and in the Guianas has its shell corrugated in the most extraordinary way so that it looks like an aerial view of a knot of mountains. The neck is broad and elongated and bears a kind of fringe of fleshy projections whose use, if there is any definite use for them, is not clearly understood. They may serve either to disguise the owner from its food—tadpoles and fish—or from its enemies. As seen by itself (bottom) it is hard to guess that this object is an animal's head and neck.

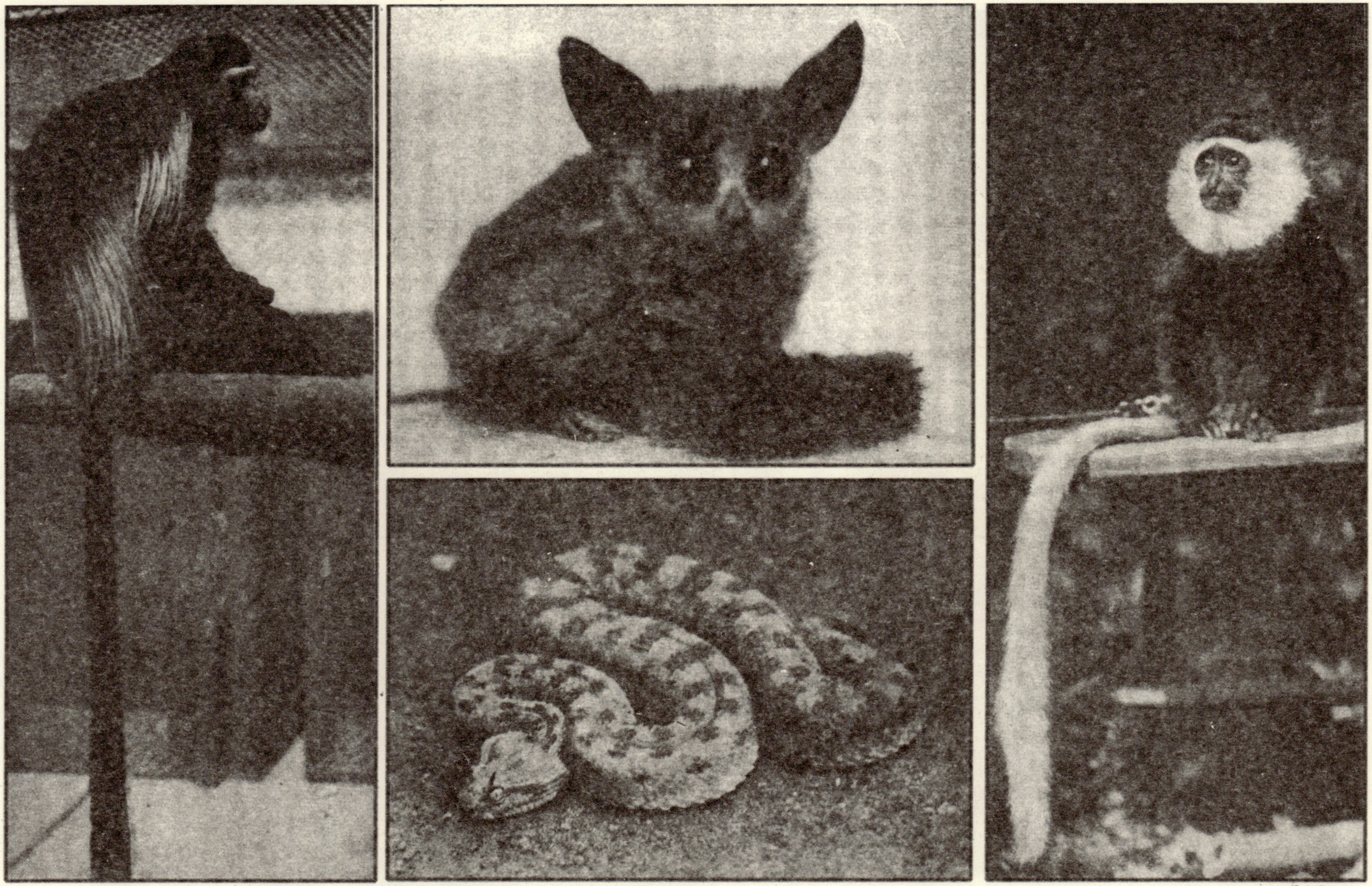

W. S. Berridge

ANIMALS PROVIDED WITH EQUIPMENT WHOSE REASON IS A PUZZLE TO NATURALISTS

Found in many parts of Central Africa, the guereza monkeys are remarkable in the development of their hair. Ruppel's guereza (left) also called the Abyssinian guereza, looks as though it had assumed a coat of goat-skin, the long locks hanging down like a garment. On the right we have the white-tailed guereza or colobus. We do not know the reason for these exaggerated coats of hair, especially as their wearers live in an intensely hot climate. The Cerastes (centre, bottom) is a viper possessing a horn above each eye. These horns are scaly and occur always in the males and sometimes in the females. Their purpose is still a matter for conjecture. The galago (top centre) is a nocturnal tree climber of mysterious behaviour.

Autotype

PAIR OF GNUS, ANIMALS WHICH STRANGELY COMBINE FEATURES OF ANTELOPE, HORSE AND OX

When we first see a gnu we are reminded of three animals at once, the antelope, horse and ox, so strongly that the gnu seems to be a kind of joke on Nature's part, rather than a piece of serious creation. The horns are strangely curved, though in early life the gnu's horns are straight and grow from the skull at some distance below its highest point. These weapons of youth are pushed outwards by succeeding growth so as to form the tips of the adult armament. The bases of the horns gradually grow towards each other until, in old bulls there is a kind of horn helmet as in the case of the Cape buffalo. It is still not quite certain to what animal the gnu is most nearly related, so puzzling is this inhabitant of the veldt.

F. W. Bond

STRANGE BEAK FOR CATCHING FISH

The Arabs call the whale-headed stork "father of a shoe," which is reminiscent of the alternative English name of shoe-bill. Seen in profile, the beak is concave (top) and a ridge runs the length of the upper mandible, ending in a strong hook. The bird is a fish eater, but this does not fully explain its strange beak development.

seen in the Atractaspis viper, a small snake with such disproportionate fangs that it is unable to use the two in unison. The fangs exceed the head in length and when "out for blood" the snake extends only one at a time at an obtuse angle to the roof of the mouth. The ringhals cobra of South Africa is a true enigma, since it spits poison, spraying the deadly fluid from its fangs to a distance of many yards. Why should it do this when few creatures care to challenge it, and when, as in the case of other non-spitting cobras, a single bite guarantees a meal or entirely discourages the aggressor?

The behaviour of animals is sometimes very hard to explain. Why does a dog often revolve, restlessly scratching, before composing itself to rest? One explanation is that the action is inherited from wild animals who were compelled to behave thus whenever scratching out a rest hole for themselves in dry earth, dead leaves or long grass. The suggestion is plausible and if correct proves how strong the hereditary instinct must be. The average pekingese, a breed intensively cultured for thousands of years, still shows the wild instinct when composing itself upon a scented cushion in a padded sleeping box or on an eiderdown quilt.

ONE OF NATURE'S MYSTERIES: THE GROTESQUE BEAK OF THE HORNBILL

This strange-looking bird is a black hornbill and comes from West Africa. The beak is enlarged by a hollow superstructure whose purpose is a mystery. It makes the beak into a formidable hammer, but the bird is not known to use it for any heavy work, such as the woodpecker does on tree trunks. The nesting hole in the trunk of a tree is found, not made, and the food consists of fruits and insects, the latter taken on the wing.

A real enigma is presented by the dainty little arboreal half-monkeys known as galagoes. The galago only ventures forth to feed on insects, fruits and birds' eggs after dark. Before climbing trees it always very deliberately covers the palms and soles of its delicately formed extremities with urine. As soon as the moisture has dried off the galago renews it before entrusting himself again to the topmost twigs and dangling creepers that form his home. The tree-tops in the tropics of both hemispheres swarm with arboreal animals—cat bears, spider monkeys, ant-eaters, and so on, yet in none of these is this curious habit developed.

To return to the features of structure which still remain unexplained. The gnu, a large, horsey-looking antelope of the African plains, presents at first sight a jumble of a number of normal animals. The gnu's legs and feet closely resemble those of antelopes; its tail is densely haired as a horse's; its muzzle is as broad and splayed as that of an ox; whilst its horns are like those of no other animal past or present. Much more remains to be known of the animal's general economy before attempting to explain the reasons for this extraordinary specialisation. The plain-dwelling rodent known as the

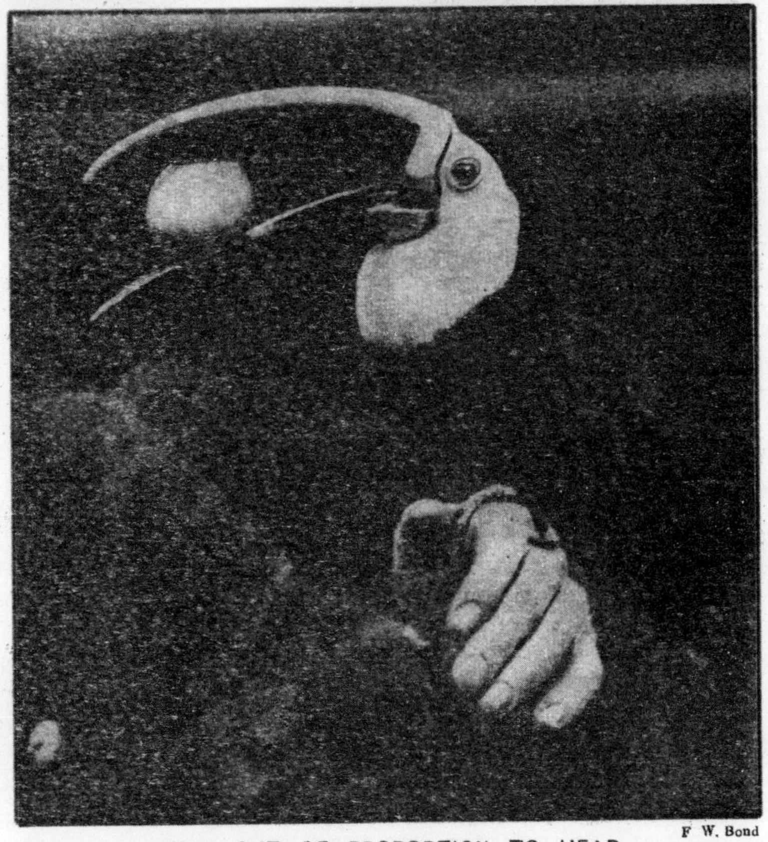

F. W. Bond

BEAK OUT OF PROPORTION TO HEAD

Compared with the rest of the bird the beak of the toucan is enormous and even disproportionate. Why it should need so huge a pair of mandibles is a mystery at present beyond our solving. Below is a red-billed toucan holding an egg in its beak while it perches on the keeper's arm and above is a specimen of Cuvier's toucan.

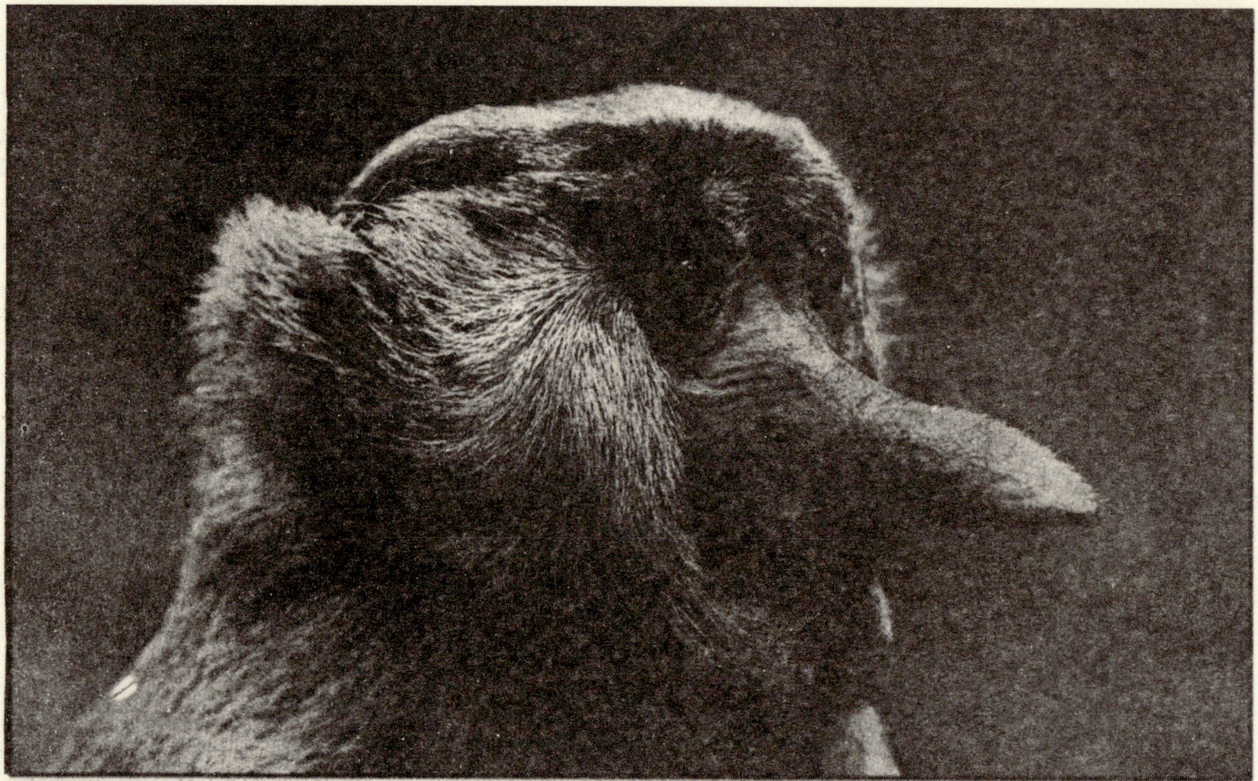

Autotype

F. W. Bond

DEPARTURES FROM THE NORMAL THAT EXCITE OUR WONDER

Why does the sloth hang upside-down ? The reasons for this inverted position are not easy to guess, since there seem to be no special advantages obtainable by hanging from a branch rather than lying along it. A life lived always topsy-turvy makes for indifferent progress along the ground, the sloths being all bad movers except in the trees. The upper photograph shows a proboscis monkey. What the purpose of the amazing nose may be and how it came to be grown are inexplicable problems.

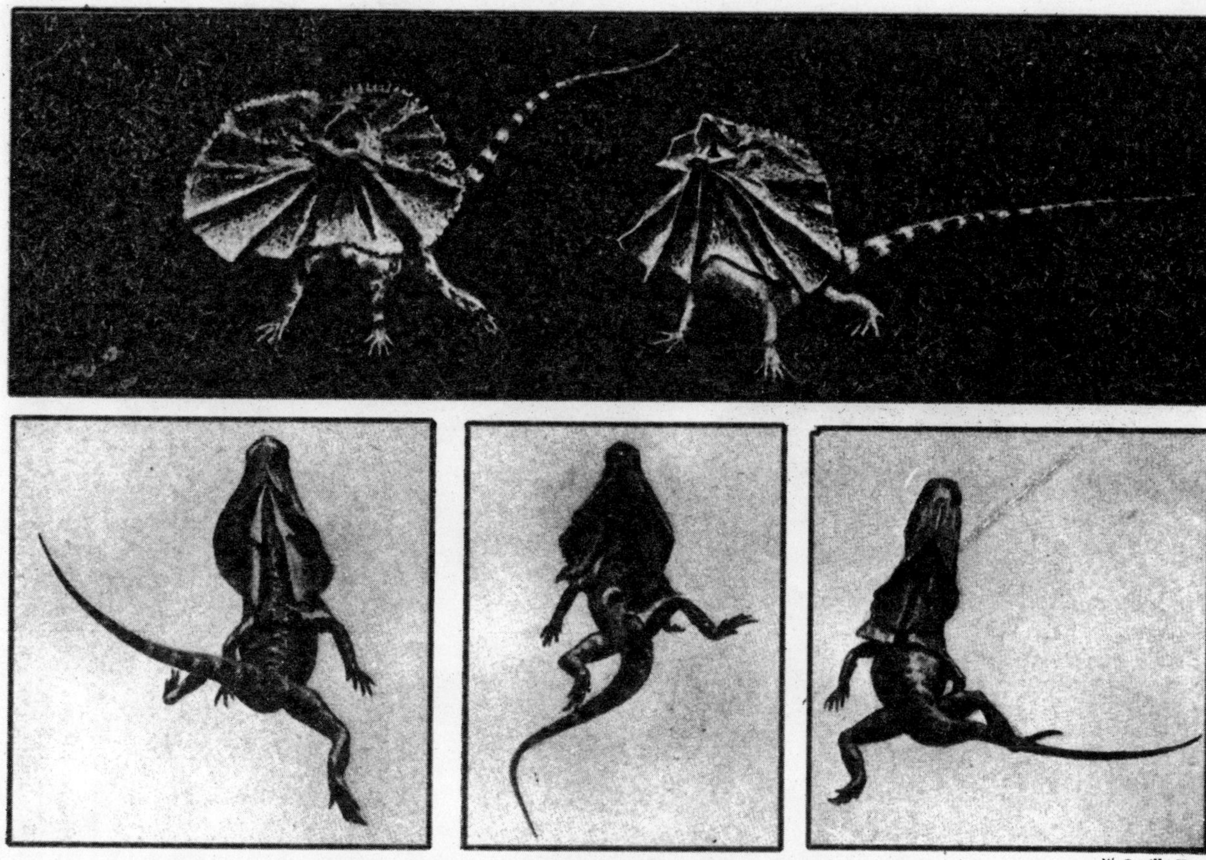

W. Saville Kent

AUSTRALIAN LIZARD THAT CAN BE A QUADRUPED OR A BIPED AT WILL

There is a strange lizard inhabiting Queensland that has developed, round its neck, a frill which it can expand like an umbrella. But more extraordinary than this is its ability to walk either on all fours or on its hind legs only. Its gait, when in the upright, or bi-pedal, position is very strange to watch (lower photographs). In all these the frill is down, while above we see it fully expanded. This is about the most remarkable of the Australian lizards, and it is uncertain whether it will tend to discard one gait for the other, and, if so, which.

uscaisha, of South America, is at first sight merely a super guinea-pig. Whilst conforming to type in general make-up it presents two features which have puzzled the most expert. Its immense upper incisors protrude not from beneath the lip but through a sort of key-hole opening in the middle of the lip itself. Further, the middle and inside toes of the hind feet are surmounted by large knobs of fat covered with thick skin, from which there sprouts a series of bristles so hard and inflexible as to amount to spines. These, it is suggested, serve to cleanse the fur of sand and grit; the key-hole lip, however, reminds us that much yet remains to be explained.

Hair and such similar developments of the cuticle as scales present the scientist with some of the most difficult problems. Some of the guerezas haunting the hottest parts of Nyassaland and Abyssinia go through life beneath a load of hair that might guarantee a musk ox or polar bear against catching a chill. Of what service can hair, or at best a development of the flesh or scales, which almost amounts to hair be to a frog or fish? At least one frog bears at its sides a heavy fringe of stout bristles, whilst the male of a South American cat fish has the head similarly adorned.

These mysteries will no doubt be solved. It is a question of time and very patient study.

H Bastin

A PUZZLE FOR THE NATURALISTS

This extraordinary-looking insect, whose name is hipocephalus, has long been a matter for debate and perplexity among the naturalists. It is related to the mole cricket, but the exact relationship has never been successfully determined. It is interesting to compare this specimen with the mole cricket seen in page 913.

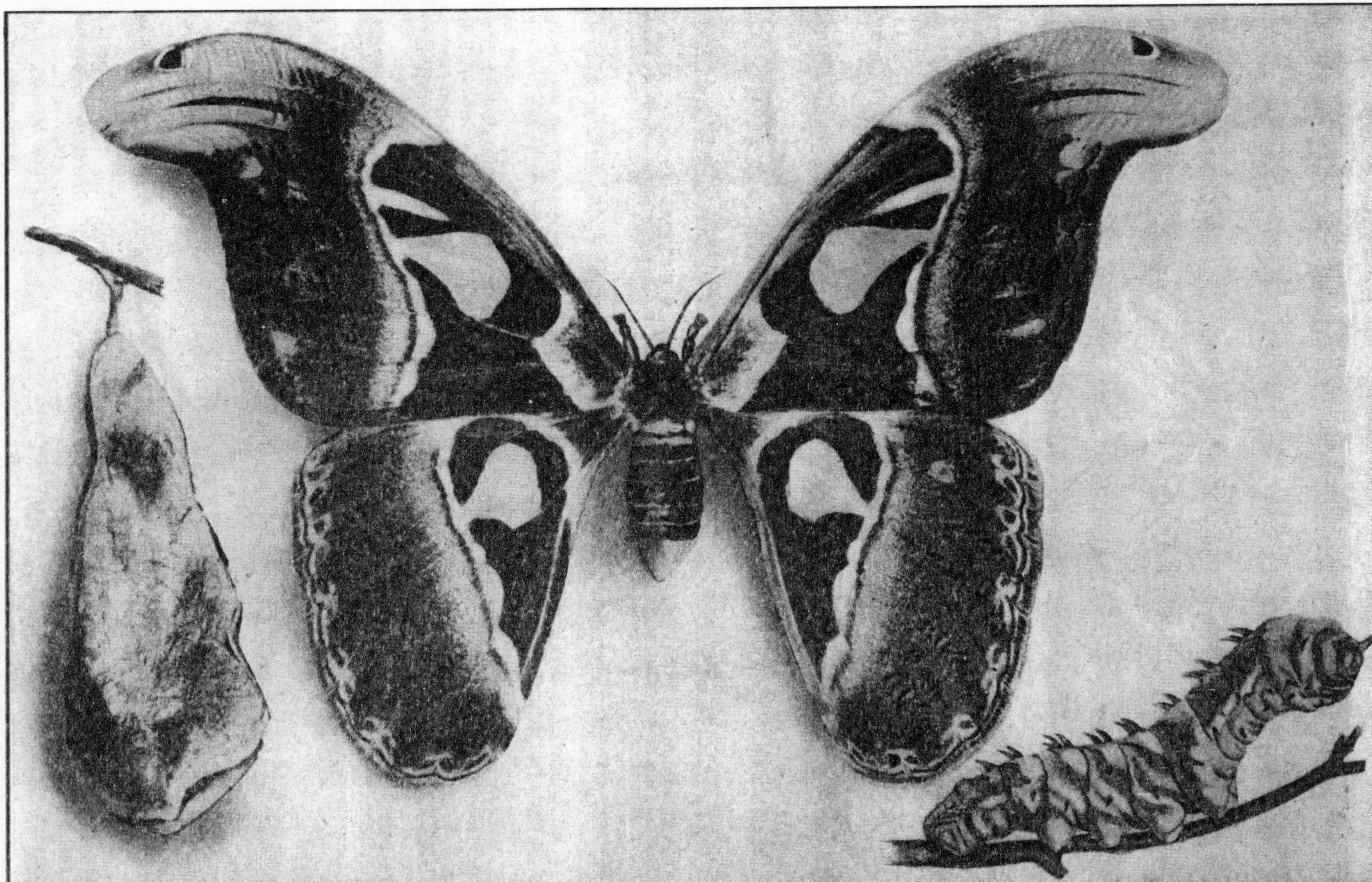

J. H. Watson

COCOON, ADULT LARVA, AND SPLENDIDLY-WINGED FEMALE OF THE ATLAS MOTH

The atlas moth of India, China, and Java is a giant indeed, with wings often a foot long and broad in proportion. It is a fine-looking insect, of a tawny colour and having a large triangular and transparent spot on each wing. The big cocoon spun by the larva is very valuable, since the atlas is a species of silk moth. This larva is a pale grey-green colour and is furnished on the back and sides with a number of spike-like projections. It consumes an enormous quantity of food, for the atlas moth into which it grows takes the place, among moths, that the hippopotamus and the elephant do among mammals, so far as size is concerned. This is brought about by a super-abundance of food and a more or less sedentary life.

Chapter XCI

Giants of the Insect World

By F. Martin Duncan

Librarian to the London Zoological Society

The phrase "giant insects" may seem to be rather a contradiction in terms, for insects (Pliny's "little vermine") are, for the most part, such diminutive creatures that, in spite of the vast numbers that surround us on every side, in the air, on and in the earth, amongst the foliage, and beneath the water, and the important part they play in the economy of the world, we are hardly even aware of their existence—save when in mass formation they contrive to make their presence known and felt, or individually assert themselves in ways that are mostly unpleasant. Unless they force themselves upon our notice by biting, stinging, destroying our crops or our property, we are usually content to ignore them; and to most people, I am afraid, "an insect" simply means an obnoxious little pest to be crushed on sight.

Yet the insect world, that is so inextricably bound up with our own, is full of interest and beauty. There is an infinite variety in the lives, the habits and forms of its tiny inhabitants, while in size there is relatively quite as great a disparity between the largest and smallest species as there is between a mouse and an elephant. The largest known insect is no bigger than a small rat, but this is a giant indeed in comparison with the majority of its kind.

Unusually large insects are not very common: some, indeed, are extremely rare. For among the frailer creatures of the earth, to be in any way conspicuous is a serious handicap in the struggle for life. The smaller, less obtrusive species have a far better chance of escaping destruction, and so, in the aggregate, have been more successful in holding their own and retaining their place in the scheme of Nature throughout the ages.

The larger and more brilliant insects are naturally denizens of those hot, sun-favoured lands where Nature revels in luxuriant growth and gorgeous colouring. Travellers in tropical countries bring back tales of wonderful butterflies rivalling exotic birds in size and splendour; gigantic armoured beetles equipped with fearsome jaws and horns, and other monstrous six-legged creatures.

One of the largest of the giant beetles is the great goliath (*Goliathus Druryii*), an inhabitant of tropical and southern Africa. It is an imposing creature from four to five inches long, and broad and bulky in proportion. Its colour scheme, though simple, is very effective; the horny wing cases folded over its capacious back have a soft, velvety surface, and are a rich chocolate-brown splashed and bordered with creamy white, while the shield protecting the thorax or shoulders is black marked with wide, longitudinal, cream-coloured stripes. The curious flat head, which is slightly convex, giving it a peculiar scooped-out appearance, is greyish-white and embellished with two small, black, odd-shaped horns. The legs are a reddish tinge, and the hind pair are fringed with long, silky, golden hairs.

S. Crook

DRAGON-FLY, LARGEST OF BRITISH INSECTS

Though rustic superstition has christened it "horse stinger" the dragon-fly of Britain has no sting wherewith to harm either horses or any other beings. It deals with prey by using its mouth, and the family includes the largest of British insects

In spite of their size and the powerful toothed claws with which they are armed, these ponderous beetles are harmless, inoffensive creatures. They haunt dense forests, moving slowly and clumsily over the ground, flying heavily round the tops of lofty trees, or feasting upon the sap of various tropical plants, especially a juicy kind of vine that festoons the forest trees of which they are particularly fond. The first stage in the life-history of the goliath beetle is passed hidden in the soil as a huge, fleshy grub. When full fed it fashions for itself a large, earthen cocoon in which to undergo its wonderful transformation into a perfect insect. The

S. Crook

MALE STAG BEETLE, A GIANT BRITISH SPECIES

Stag beetles, which we may see flying in an August evening with impressive hum and ponderous progress, vary greatly in size according to the nourishment obtained by them in their larval stage. This takes five years to run its course, and is spent in rotten oak. Common in the southern counties of England, an over-all length of more than three inches is not uncommon.

cocoon is oval in shape, about as big as a swan's egg, and, probably to strengthen the walls, which are remarkably thin, it is encircled by a solid raised band of the same material, though how a creature that builds its cocoon round itself contrives to form this outer band is a problem that has greatly puzzled many a "scientific gent."

The existence of these giant beetles was not discovered until towards the end of the eighteenth century, when the dead body of a fine goliath found floating down the Gaboon River by a naturalist caused great excitement among entomologists, and as much as £50 was given for a perfect specimen.

In point of size the goliath beetle is run very closely by several others of his tribe, that, in addition to their large dimensions, are the possessors of the most extraordinary horn-like projections which give them a weird and warlike appearance. Of what use these strange additions to their anatomy are to the insects is a subject that has given rise to much speculation and discussion. The old idea that they were employed as weapons of offence has been practically discarded, as these mammoth beetles are by no means pugnacious and have never been observed to engage in violent combat one with another. The long, sharp horns that rise sometimes from the head and sometimes from the thorax of the insect may, indeed, to some degree, be protective, and of service to their owners by causing would-be assailants to think twice before attacking so well armed a creature; but the generally accepted opinion is that their formidable-looking horns are primarily intended to serve as adornments wherewith the male insects may attract and fascinate the females of their kind, for the latter are hornless, and usually smaller, insects. The suggestion that in some cases the lordly males make use of their horns to seize and carry off a reluctant mate is difficult to authenticate as the female beetle is usually too slippery and active a lady to be coerced in so peremptory a manner.

One of the finest of these giant horned beetles is the hercules beetle (*Dynastes Hercules*), as it is popularly called. This species is a native of Guiana and the West Indies, and measures over six inches, the enormous horn into which the thorax is prolonged accounting for four of them. This horn curves slightly downwards, while a second one, rising from the head of the insect, curves upwards to meet it, thus forming what appears to be an enormous pair of jaws, or pincers. The upper surface of the lower horn is toothed and West Indian natives declare that the beetle can saw off the branch of a tree by seizing it in his "jaws" and whirling round and round it until it is completely cut through! The same "tall story" is told of another species, the golofa beetle of Colombia, which has a very similar pair of horns with saw-like edges.

The male hercules is a decidedly handsome fellow. His wing cases are a deep olive green colour, the head and thorax ebony black and the long upper horn is fringed with a short, dense growth of golden hairs. He is seldom seen abroad during the daytime, as these beetles are nocturnal in their habits, and hide away in dark corners until the evening, when they come forth to feed and fly about in search of mates.

THE elephant and rhinoceros beetles have gained their respective names from the peculiar shape of their horns. The elephant beetle (*Megasoma elephas*) is found in the wooded districts of Colombia. This insect, which is four inches

H. Bastin

GIANT TORPICAL WASPS, NATURAL SIZE

Luckily for the rest of Nature, the stinging insects do not reach such large dimensions as the innoxious kinds but, all the same, these tropical wasps are quite large enough to earn respect. The one in the lower photograph comes from South America, and is a hunter of spiders. In the top photograph is a giant wasp from the Eastern tropics. Both are given natural size.

H. Bastin

SOME HUGE STICK INSECTS OF THE TROPICAL FORESTS

Ours is not the age of really giant insects. Geology keeps records of dragon-flies with wings two feet across in a day when lizards were correspondingly large compared with present-day dimensions. Certain kinds, however, have still kept up some attempt at giganticism, among them the stick insects of the hot areas of the earth's surface. Here we have some specimens of stick insect from New Guinea, male (bottom left) and female (bottom right). The top illustration in this page is of another giant stick insect, reproduced one half its natural size.

H. Bastin

MOTH AND COCKROACH OF THE NEW WORLD COMPARED WITH SPECIMENS FROM THE OLD

Here, the lower photograph shows one of the largest of all the known moths. This is named Thysania and it comes from that rich storehouse of animal curiosities, South America. By way of contrast, and to emphasize the enormous dimensions of this flying wonder, a British moth, the death's head, which is the largest species found in Britain, is shown beneath it. Above is a giant cockroach from the West Indies compared with the common cockroach of England. The latter is nearly always referred to as the " black beetle."

H. Bastin

GIANT WATER BUG AND GIANT FOREST BEETLE OF TROPIC LANDS

Some of the giant water bugs, of which we have a fine example here (left), are four inches long and live in the tepid, sluggish waters of hot climates. With their powerful front legs they catch little fish and kill them with their sharp, stabbing beaks. They are strong fliers and, where they breed near large towns, are often seen in great numbers round street lamps. The right hand photograph is of a titan beetle, a native of Brazil and resembling an enormous stag bettle. The total length may be as much as six inches.

long and two in breadth, carries two horns on its head: a short, upper, lip-like projection and a long under one forked at the tip that curves upwards and has a distinct resemblance to an elephant's trunk. The actual colour of the beetle is black, but its entire upper surface, with the exception of the horns, is covered with a velvet-like pile of short olive-green hairs. This, however, is easily rubbed off, consequently almost every specimen that we examine has several bare patches on its back disclosing the shiny black armour beneath its "fur coat."

The great rhinoceros beetle (*Xylotrupes gideon*) is a native of Indo-Australasia. It is a grotesque and alarming-looking insect, not unlike the hercules, with an immense pair of pincer-like horns. It is not very much like a rhinoceros, however, so its popular name is not a particularly appropriate one, and is more descriptive of a smaller allied European species (*Oryctes nasicornis*) that is distinguished by having a short, stout horn, curving backwards from its forehead distinctly suggestive of the "nose-horn" of the great quadruped.

The fore-front of the great atlas beetle (*Chalcosoma atlas*), a gigantic insect of the Malayan regions, fairly bristles with fearsome-looking horns. A sharp, pointed spike in the centre of the thorax and a long, sabre-like affair on each side of it are directed forwards in a menacing fashion; while another, thicker horn beset with spikes, curves upwards from the top of the head. Yet, like the other giants of its tribe, the great atlas beetle is something of a fraud. It is actually a quiet, peacefully-disposed individual, not at all addicted to engaging in warlike conflicts

M. Duncan

ELEPHANT BEETLE FROM SOUTH AMERICA AND ATLAS BEETLE FROM MALAYA

In the dense forests of Colombia is found the huge elephant beetle (bottom), which is some two inches broad and four long. One of the two horns on its head closely resembles the trunk of an elephant. The black back is covered with a very delicate pile of olive-green hairs. This is easily rubbed off, showing the shining black of the wing cases underneath. The upper photograph shows a great atlas beetle from Celebes. Despite its fierce-looking horns it is quite harmless. Both these insects are seen here somewhat reduced in size.

J. J. Ward

MORPHO OF THE JEWEL WINGS AND A MIGHTY CATERPILLAR OF A MIGHTY MOTH

Many who have never seen a live morpho have seen parts of this creature's wings in jewellers' shops. These fragments are put under glass and made into brooches, never losing their brightness since the wonderful colours seen as the wing is turned this way or that are due, not to pigment, but to refraction of light. When seen flying in their tropical South American forests in the tremendous sunshine of those latitudes, the brilliance of colouring is dazzling. Above is a specimen of the huge caterpillar of Eacles Imperialis at the last stage of its growth.

M rtin Duncan

J. J. Ward

BUTTERFLY AND MOTH WITH SMALL BODIES BUT ENORMOUS WINGS

As large as the great morphos (see opposite page) are the big owl butterflies of South America which fly at dusk and display markings on the under surface of their hind wings which are uncannily reminiscent of an owl's face. The resemblance will be seen to be still more striking if the page be held upside down. As it is we are looking at the moth right way up and at the underside. The top photograph shows us a giant silk moth. Compared with the huge wings the bodies of these creatures are very small.

with other males of its own species or interfering with the smaller, less well protected creatures it comes in contact with. This beetle is somewhat long in the leg and is smartly, but unostentatiously, clad in a uniform of dark bronze.

All these giant beetles are closely allied and belong to an important group of Coleoptera known as lamellicorns, or leaf-horns, from the peculiar structure of their antennae—the end, or club of the antennae being composed of a varying number of thin, flat plates which can be expanded or closed like the leaves of a fan. These remarkable sense-organs are seen to perfection in the cockchafers, a well-known family of leaf-horns which has representatives in many parts of the world. Chief among them is the giant cockchafer of Assam, a noble insect, three inches long in the body, with an extraordinary pair of front legs over two and a half inches in length, and armed with two long sharp spurs, the second of these alarming-looking projections having a kind of secondary spike, or movable claw at the tip. These weapons and the saw-like edges of the thoracic shield make the giant cockchafer an uncomfortable creature to handle; and it must be anything but pleasant to have one of these enormous insects blundering against you after the clumsy manner of its kind, as it buzzes about in the evening, bumping into everything in its way. It is, of course, only the male cockchafer that has these curiously spurred legs; the female is smaller and unarmed; but both are handsome insects. The dark green wing cases have a sheen of gold bronze, while the head, thorax and legs are a brilliant metallic green, shot with copper.

In the dense tropical forests, where most of the gigantic leaf-horns live, these beetles do much useful work in attacking old and fallen trees, so hastening the natural process of decay by which the great trunks and boughs are converted into vegetable mould; for although the food of these great insects consists chiefly of the sap of plants and the nectar of exotic flowers, the larvae of all the species spend their days in consuming vast quantities of rotting wood and decaying vegetation. These great "white worms," as they have been called, grow to an immense length, and are most repulsive-looking things; but they are seldom seen, as they carry on their work in total darkness—hidden in the ground, among the roots of old trees, in decaying tree trunks and branches, or under piles of débris on the floor of the forests. They are dull, heavy creatures, moving only when they have destroyed everything in their immediate neighbourhood that can be attacked with their strong, horny jaws, and the rapidity with which they demolish everything eatable in their vicinity is astounding.

This, of course, is all to the good when the operations of the insects are confined to wild, overgrown, wooded regions, which (if it were not for the ceaseless industry of these vast armies of indefatigable workers) would in the course of time become impenetrable wildernesses of piled-up dead and dying vegetation; but when these big beetles invade cultivated areas the activities of their unattractive grubs are the reverse of beneficial, and considerable loss is sometimes caused by their ravages in timber plantations and coconut groves.

Another interesting tribe of wood-boring beetles is that of the long-horns (*Longicornes*), distinguished by having long, sometimes extraordinarily long, antennae. They number among their species several that are of heroic proportions. One of them, *Titanus giganteus*, a native of Brazil, equals the giant goliath in length and breadth, although the latter is, perhaps, the heavier of the two insects. The titan is entirely black, with a satiny sheen, and looks like a gigantic stag-beetle. A fine specimen may measure half a foot in length—if we include the enormous pair of toothed jaws with which it confronts all comers. When these jaws are closed the two sharp points cross each other and the formidable teeth fit closely together, so a spiteful nip from this terrifying insect is not to be encountered lightly.

Another tropical American species (*Masrodontia cervicornis*), popularly known as the sawyer beetle, is nearly, if not quite, as big as the titan, and is, moreover, a startling-looking creature attired in black and yellow. It is further distinguished by having one long tooth in the centre of each jaw and about sixteen smaller teeth on each side. In an ancient Natural History the following quaint description of the insect is given: "It hath a little broad head, great oxe-eyes, almost three fingers overthwart in length; it hath a forked mouth, gaping and terrible, with two very hard, crooked teeth; with these while he gnaws the wood (I speak by experience) it doth perfectly grunt aloud like a young pig."

That the sawyer beetle does make a grunting noise with its strong teeth while energetically engaged in sawing away at the branch of a tree is highly probable. It is said to "girdle" the branches, gnawing through the bark all round, in order to enjoy the sap. These branches, which are often already hollowed out by the larvae of the beetle, naturally snap off sooner or later and fall to the ground, and thus the "sawyer" has gained a reputation of actually cutting off the boughs of forest trees.

In contrast to these grotesque giant beetles we have the glorious tropical butterflies—world-renowned for their size and the beauty of their colouring. They are the treasures of many a collector's cabinet, but to realize the full glory of these brilliant, graceful insects we must see them in their natural haunts, gliding down the glades of South American forests or fluttering through wooded regions in far-Eastern lands where they rival the most gorgeous exotic flowers. It is the wonderful wings of these butterflies that entitle them to rank among the giants of the insect world; their bodies in proportion appear surprisingly small.

The bird-winged butterflies, fit associates of the bright-hued birds of paradise, are found chiefly in the Malay Archipelago. They are magnificent creatures measuring from eight to nine inches from

Martin Duncan

RHINOCEROS BEETLES OF INDO-AUSTRALASIA AND WEST AFRICA

Though not very much like a rhinoceros this beetle (bottom) of Indo-Australasia is an impressive creature with its bulk and its immense pair of pincers. Its appearance is at once grotesque and alarming although in its behaviour it is harmless enough. In fact beetles, large or small, though they give rise to much fear are innocuous creatures so far as human beings are concerned. The upper illustration is of another kind of so-called rhinoceros beetle, and it comes from the forests of West Africa.

tip to tip of their expanded wings, which are usually long and narrow—like the wings of a bird. Some species have most glorious blue-grey wings; others are velvety black, splashed with scintillating green and gold; some have wings that appear to be made of copper. These brilliant "bird-wings" are male butterflies. The females as a rule are not so brightly coloured, though they are even bigger than their mates, some species being quite twelve inches across the wings. In the Malayan forests and wooded mountain ranges, too, great "ghost butterflies" with pale semi-transparent wings dotted with black, flit silently and mysteriously about in the twilight. Most famous of South American butterflies are the great morphos, whose wonderful blue wings are so much used in jewellery. In the sunshine they are absolutely dazzling in their brilliancy and change in colour with every movement, turning, as the light falls upon them, from deepest blue to palest azure. At one moment the two wings on one side may be dark brown, while the opposite pair glitters like blue fire; again, all the wings are blue shot with yellow and brown, or brown rippled over with blue flames, then suddenly all light and colour disappear from the wings and they look almost white.

There are several species of these giant morphos, all peculiar to the great South American forests, where they may be seen gliding low with their wonderful wings outstretched down the open glades, or flying aloft, a hundred feet above the ground, with an

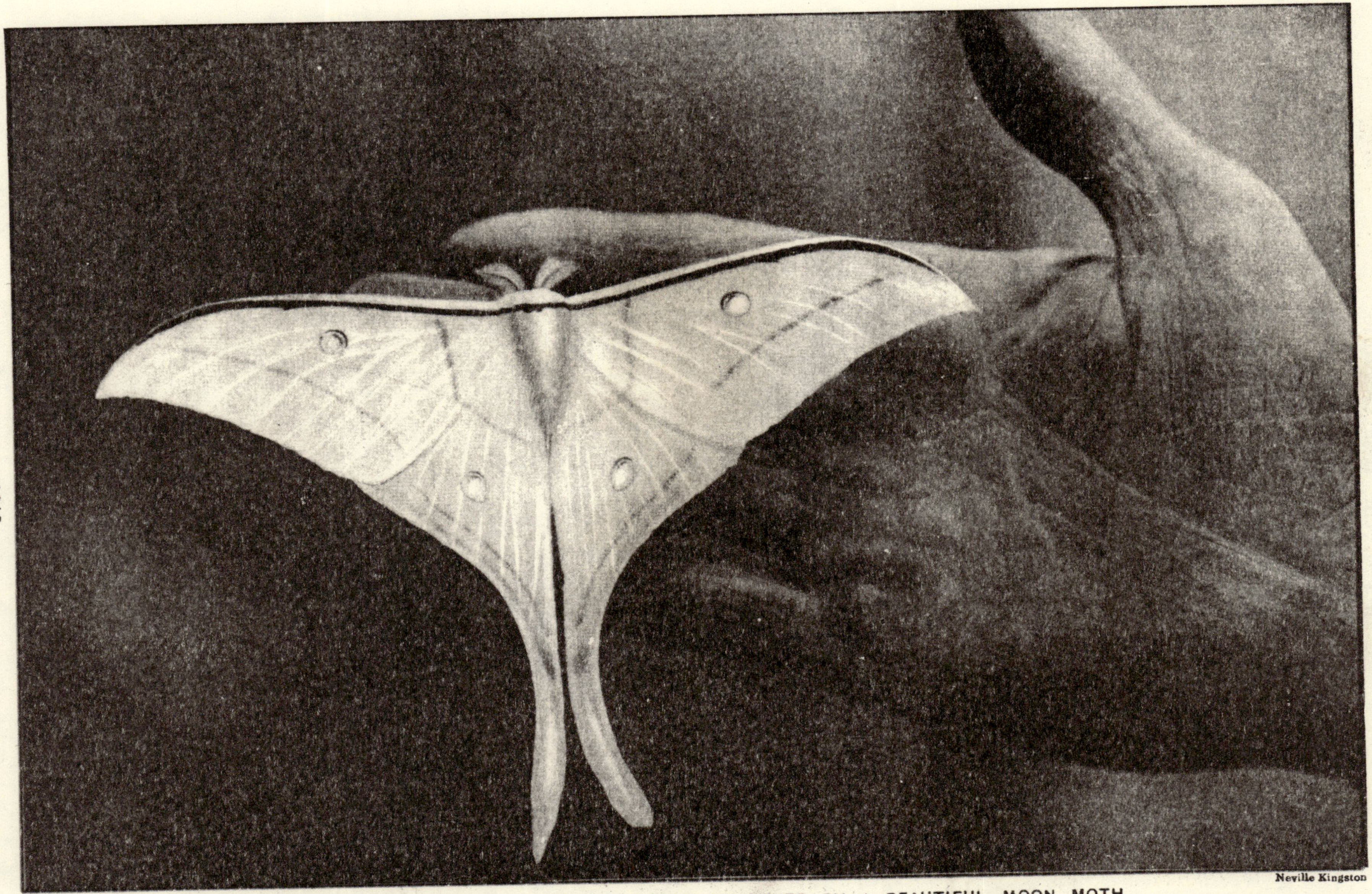

Neville Kingston

WIDE-SPREADING WINGS OF PALEST GREEN DISPLAYED BY A BEAUTIFUL MOON MOTH

Large in area but most daintily shaped and elegantly ornamented, the wings of the great moon moth are things of beauty. In this photograph, taken at the London Zoological Gardens, a specimen of the beautiful moth is seen just after emerging from its chrysalis. The delicate wings with their slender trailing tails are freshly unfolded to the sun and the insect is photographed on the hand of the keeper, who has just picked it up to watch the very last stages of preparation for the creature's winged life. Seen thus compared with human fingers we get a good idea of the large size of this moth. It is found in America and also in the Orient, the latter being probably its true home.

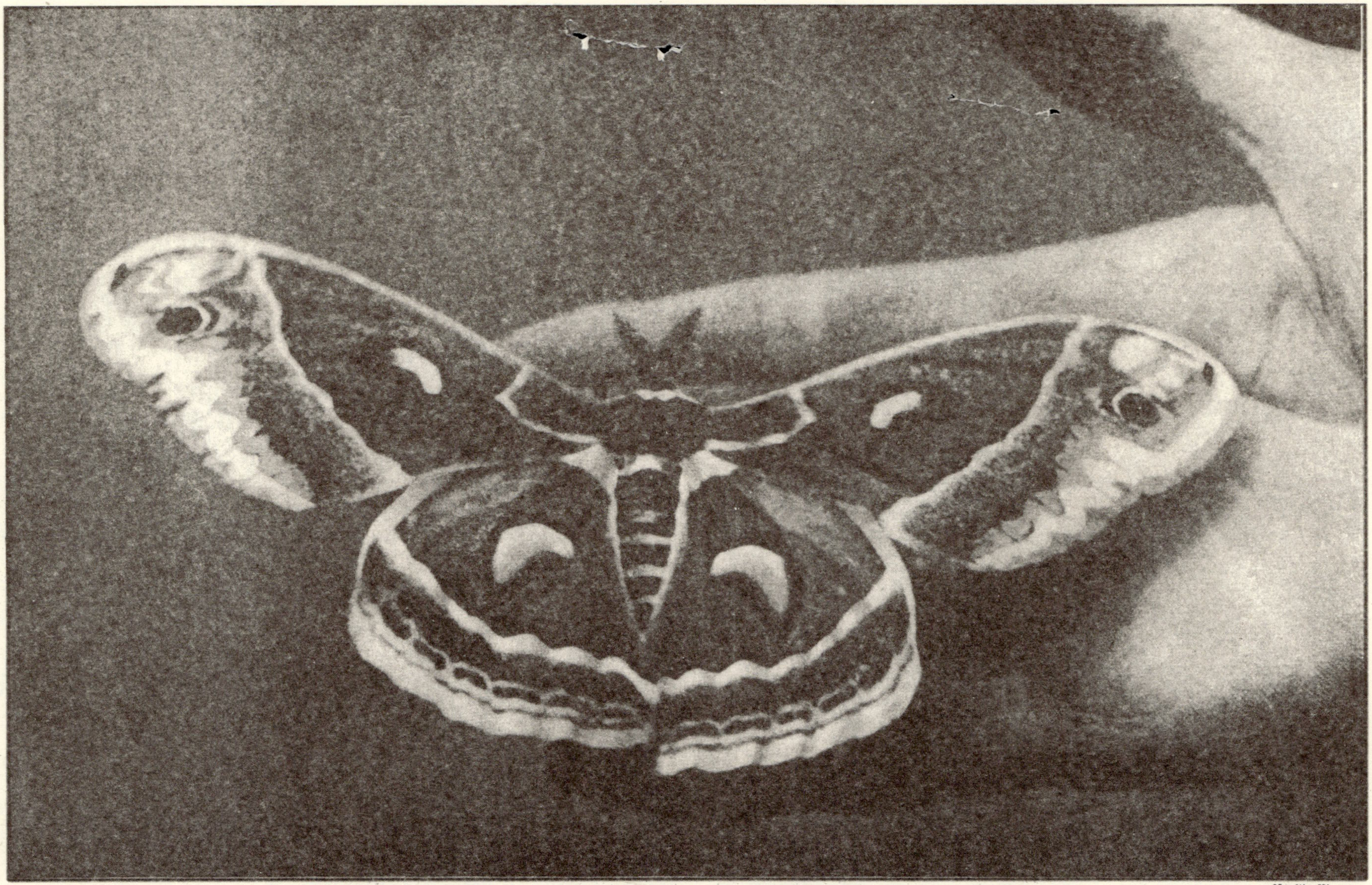

Neville Kingston

BIG CECROPIA MOTH OF NORTH AMERICA NEWLY EMERGED FROM ITS COCOON

It is not always realized that there is as great a disparity in the relative sizes of insects as there is between, say, the mouse and the elephant. Some insects are so small as to be mere specks to the human eye while, at the other end of the scale, the moths can produce titans. These are found in the warmer parts of the globe, where the heat of the sun and copious rain provide an abundance of food. The Cecropia moth, of which we have a specimen above, is from wing-tip to wing-tip as big as a man's hand, the wings being handsomely marked with grey, white and red. The big cocoon is about three inches long, and the caterpillar which spins it is a sturdy creature, and coloured green with blue and pink-red tubercles.

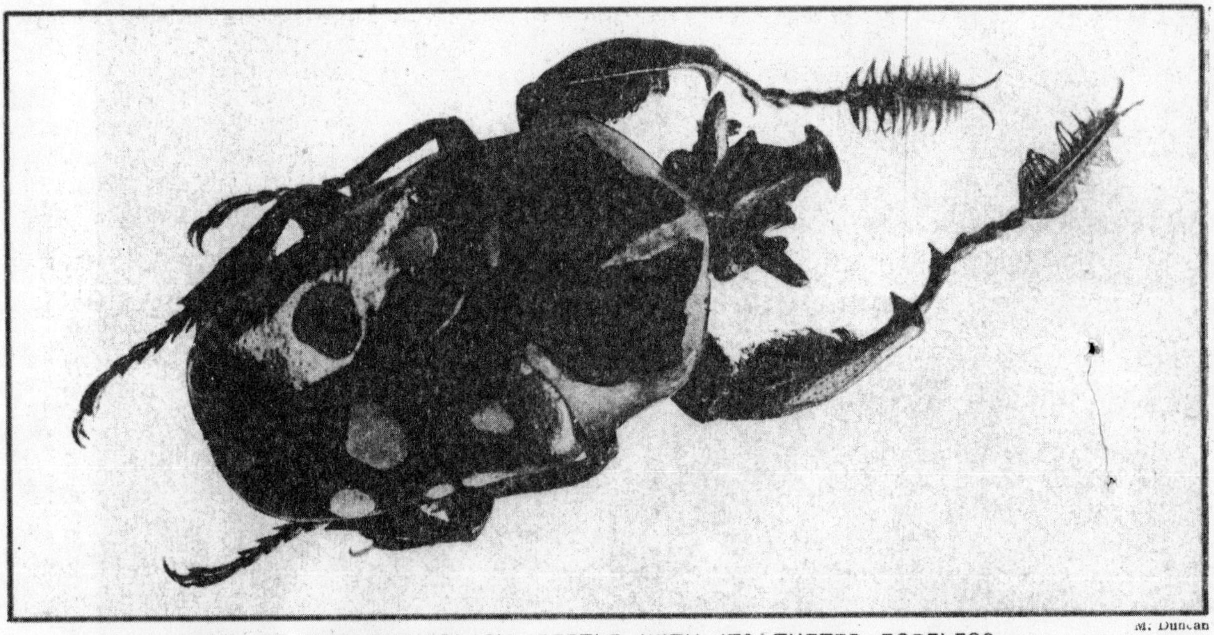

M. Duncan

MALE OF THE CHEIROLASIA BEETLE WITH ITS TUFTED FORELEGS

Although to speak of a giant insect may seem to be rather a contradiction in terms, yet, when we consider the insect world by itself we shall see that, relatively, some of its members are giants indeed. These giants do not attract anv general attention, because most of them live in tropical forests, and pass unnoticed in the luxurious vegetation amongst which they lurk. Our photograph shows the beetle Cheirolasia brukei which is brown and black with cream-coloured markings. This specimen is a male, as is shown by the hairy tufts on the forelegs.

undulating flight and occasional flapping movements of the wings. So conspicuous are these butterflies in the sunlight that it is said that the larger species can be seen flying a quarter of a mile away.

Another South American butterfly, equalling the largest of the morphos in size, is the great owl butterfly. Like the bird of ill-omen after which it is named, it flies at dusk, when the two great eye-spots on the under surface of the hind wings give the insect a strangely owl-like appearance in the dim light. When it comes to rest on a tree trunk, however, the resemblance is not so striking, as when the wings are folded over the back in an upright position only one " eye " can be seen at a time.

Even bigger than the owl butterfly is the huge owl moth of Brazil, whose soft grey-mottled wings, when expanded, measure nearly a foot across, but as they are not remarkable for their breadth, first place among the giants of their kind must be awarded to the atlas moths, whose wings are quite as long and proportionally broad. The atlas moth is an Eastern species of silk moth found throughout India, China and Java. It is a handsome, tawny-coloured insect with a large, triangular, transparent spot on each wing, and the immense silken cocoon it constructs is very valuable.

MANY of the larger locusts are big, heavy insects, often of grotesque form. The uncanny-looking weta-punga of New Zealand totals some fourteen or fifteen inches in length when its extraordinarily long hind-legs and antennae are stretched out—though the actual body of the insect is rather less than three. This creature, which is wingless, climbs tall trees with great agility and sits perched up upon the topmost branches surveying the surrounding country with its great, goggling eyes what time it contentedly munches the young, green leaves. If disturbed, the weta-punga makes a peculiar clicking noise by a slow movement of its hind-legs—apparently to warn off the intruder. When seized, it kicks out vigorously with its powerful hind-legs, inflicting painful wounds on its captor's hand with the sharp spur with which they are armed.

Among the stinging insects there is none that actually deserves the title of " giant." On the whole this is just as well, for imagine the effect of a sudden onslaught of a contingent of infuriated wasps each as big as a titan butterfly, or a swarm of bees as large as atlas moths! The hornets, that measure about one and a half inches from head to sting are, fortunately for us, the largest social wasps we are likely to encounter; while the violet carpenter bee of Southern Europe (a noble insect with a velvety black body and violet-tinted wings), though bigger than the largest bumble bee, does not reach terrifying proportions. This fine bee, moreover, is a solitary, peaceful individual that spends its working life industriously boring tunnels in old tree trunks, wherein to deposit eggs from which the offspring it will never see will eventually emerge to carry on the family traditions by becoming skilled carpenters in their turn.

In temperate climates insects seldom reach large dimensions. Most British species are small or of moderate size. Among the two or three exceptions the great green dragon-fly with its long, brightly-coloured body, iridescent gauze wings and great lamp-like eyes, must be given precedence. To see this superb insect hawking over a quiet, reedy pool is one of the delights of the countryside.

M. Duncan

GIANT COCKCHAFERS FROM ASSAM AND A COLOMBIAN BEETLE

Assam produces a giant cockchafer and we show here (bottom) two specimens, a male (right) distinguished by his immense front legs, which are spiked, rather like the antlers of a deer, and end in sharp claws, and a female (left) which is smaller and has a narrower and more compact head. The upper photograph is of the beetle Golofa porteri from Colombia. Two remarkable horns with saw edges rise from the head in a vertical and threatening manner. This insect is shown three-quarters natural size and the cockchafers one-half natural size.

W. S. Berridge

Neville Kingston

MYSTERIOUS ALBINISM AMONG THE BIRDS: ALBINO CAPE PENGUIN AND JACKDAW

Abnormalities of coloration are not uncommon in bird or beast, but albinism is something quite different. It is not a matter of colour variation, but of the absence of colour due to some deep-seated and inherited tendency. This expresses itself in the individual's lack of the pigment which always develops in normal specimens of the individual's race. A general whiteness is by no means true albinism, but may result from a force which inhibits colour in certain parts of the body. The penguin seen above (left) is possibly an example of this, while the jackdaw (right) is a true albino. Experiments have still to be made to complete our knowledge of this animal mystery.

Chapter XCII

The Mystery of Albinism

By Geoffrey Lapage

Head of the Zoology Department, University College, Exeter

THE lay reader of scientific books sometimes tells the man of science that his work would be more interesting and fascinating and easier to understand if it did not contain so many difficult scientific terms; and no doubt he is right in some degree. The mistake he makes is to suppose that the aim of science is to be interesting or charming or easy to understand, or that the man of science himself enjoys the strict use of terms that are precise and frequently ugly and not English. For certainly he does not. He often sighs to try his wings as a literary artist, but he knows that to yield to such a temptation would endanger that accurate statement of fact and law that is the very breath of a science. He must not, in other words, use the method of the artist or attempt the artist's aim. In this sense science and art can never meet, however desirable their cooperation may be in other ways.

The term Albinism is a good example of the kind of word to which exception may be taken. It is not a pleasing word; it is not even English, being derived from the Latin, *albus*, white. But if we discard it and speak of whiteness, or white colour in animals and plants, we at once find that we are unable to distinguish clearly enough between the different kinds of whiteness that exist. There is, for example, the white colour of cave-dwelling animals such as the cave-newt or olm (*Proteus anguinus*), which lives in the underground waters of Carniola and Dalmatia. This creature is white because it is never exposed to the stimulus of light. For the same reason the tapeworm or roundworm living in a bath of food in the dark intestine of a man or a horse is deficient in colour because light never reaches it. Other examples of this kind of whiteness will occur to the reader. But this is not true albinism.

Another kind of whiteness is a sort of protective coloration—a response by the animal to the colour of its environment precisely similar to that of the coloured chameleon or frog. If a plaice is put upon a ground in which white patches are prominent, it reproduces on its upper flattened surface a pattern of white patches so like those of the ground that it is very difficult for even that marvellous optical detective, the human eye, to see the fish. A similar reaction is the assumption of white winter coats by the Arctic fox (*Canis lagopus*), the mountain hare (*Lepus variabilis*), the stoat or ermine (*Mustela* (*Putorius*) *erminea*), the ptarmigan, the willow grouse and some other species.

IN the winter, when the white snow covers the world in which these animals live, they assume a snow-white coat which renders them less conspicuous and so enables them either to hide from their enemies or to stalk their prey more successfully. How this change is effected is not clearly understood. The mountain hare is said to moult its summer coat completely, including the under fur, and then to grow a new white one; but this has been denied. The whiteness of the American hare may be due, in part at least, to the appearance of gas in the substance of the longer hairs at their tips, so that the rays of light are scattered by the surfaces of gas bubbles. In addition new hairs, white from their first appearance, probably grow in the autumn. It is said that the ptarmigan's autumnal feathers actually become white, but whether moulting and replacement of coloured by white feathers also occurs, is not clear.

Such seasonal changes to whiteness do not, however, constitute true albinism. They never produce absolute whiteness, some colour always remaining, notably in the eyeballs where it must be vitally important to the retention of the keen sight which is essential to wild creatures. The glare of the white snow, moreover, must increase the intensity of the winter light, and especially of winter sunlight, so that pigmentation of the eye must be even more necessary then than in the summer. We shall see that in true albinism colour is absent

G. Hearn

A PARTLY WHITE BLACKBIRD

This bird has endeavoured unsuccessfully to make the old paradox about the white blackbird come true. Real albinism, of course, can show no signs of colour, for albinism means the lack of colour. But there has been some albinism in this bird's pedigree.

W. S. Berridge

contains a factor which prevents the development of colour in them, or lacks one or other or both of two factors whose co-operation is always necessary if colour is to appear. A true albino, therefore, does not possess the pigment which normally develops in the tissues. Not only is the pigment which is normally present in the skin and other superficial parts not developed, so that the skin, for example, is pink because the red blood in its blood-vessels is not masked by other colour, but even the pigment normally found in the deeper tissues is absent, also. The lack of external colour is particularly noticeable in the eyeball. The iris is colourless, and the eyeball itself also lacks pigment and is therefore pink for the same reason that the skin is pink, namely, because the red blood in its blood-vessels is not masked by other colour and is visible as the pink glow familiar to anyone who has kept pet albino mice.

Into such an eye more light must enter than into the normal eye protected by from the eyeball as from other parts of the animal's body.

It is obvious, therefore, that whatever our objections as writers or as readers to scientific terminology, there is real reason and necessity for it. We must distinguish between several kinds of whiteness and albinism is the name given to one particular kind of it, and to one only. When we write of it, therefore, any reader, whatever his nationality, knows that we are writing only of those animals or plants which, for some reason not yet fully understood, are white because their hereditary constitution either

ALBINO KANGAROOS COMPARED WITH NORMAL ANIMALS

Wild kangaroos are very difficult to approach and the lower illustration is a very remarkable photograph indeed. It shows two wild kangaroos in some long grass and one of them is an albino. Thus we get not only an example but an excellent comparison. The upper illustration shows us a captive kangaroo which is a true albino of the great kangaroo.

pigment. Albinoes are, therefore, abnormally sensitive to light. The human albino, for instance, shows what is called the albinotic facies, characterised by nearly closed eyelids, and peculiar blinking movements and puckering of the skin round the eyes. Most human albinoes also suffer from a kind of nystagmus which may depend, in some as yet unknown way, upon the absence of pigment from certain areas of the brain concerned with the control of eye movements. The pink eye, with its attendant disadvantages, is thus characteristic of the true albino and by it we can distinguish albinoes from such temporarily white animals as the ermine and others mentioned above which retain the coloured eyeball.

ANOTHER feature of the albino is that it breeds true to its albinism. If two albinoes are mated together, the offspring will all be albinoes also. This is due to the same cause as that which made the parents albinoes, namely, either the absence from their hereditary make-up of one or both of those factors without whose interaction colour cannot develop, or the presence in their inheritance of a factor which prevents the appearance of colour.

What these factors are we do not yet understand. But from the skins of coloured rats and rabbits and guinea-pigs, from the blood of insects and the ink-sac of cuttle-fishes, a ferment called tyrosinase has been extracted which converts chromogenic substances also present in the blood into melanin-like pigments. It is

W. S. Berridge

ALBINISM AMONG THE CARNIVOROUS MAMMALS

Here is a wolf (bottom) which is an albino, while above we have a remarkable photograph of an albino coyote on the edge of a precipice. This wonderful "snapshot" was taken by night with the aid of flashlight and the white fur shows stark against the blackness of the night in this wild place. So might the lightning have revealed one of the ghost animals of legend.

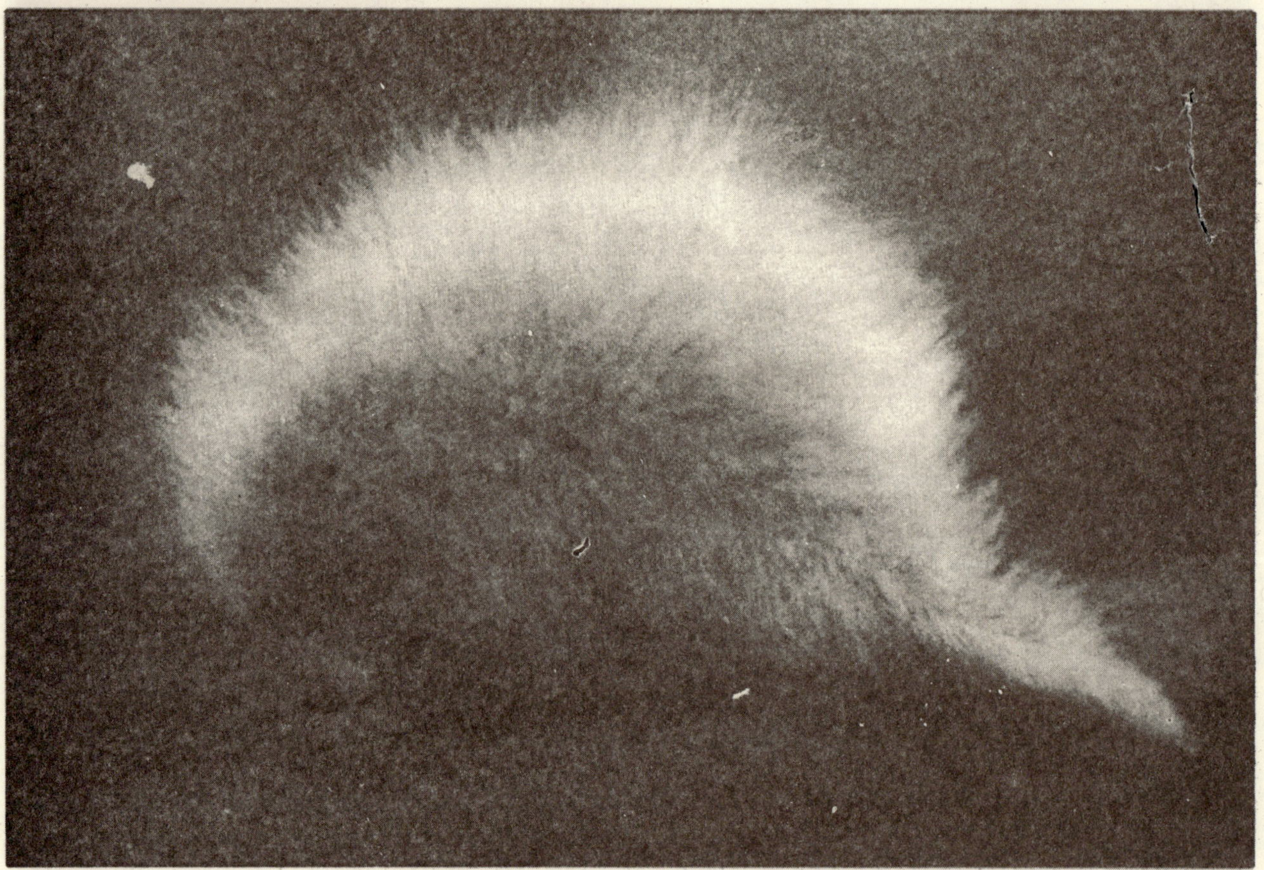

Neville Kingston

WHITE TREE PORCUPINE AND A WHITE MALAYAN PALM CIVET

Tree porcupines are not only covered with sharp quills but with long hairs and the latter almost entirely obscure the former. The absence of pigment affects, of course, quills and hairs alike as we can see by the specimen in the lower photograph, which does not show a particle of colour. Above is a palm civet from Malaya. This too shows itself a complete albino from the tip of its nose to the end of its extremely long and twitched-up tail. Ordinarily the markings of the palm civet show strong contrasts.

Neville Kingston

ALBINO OPOSSUM FROM AUSTRALIA AND AN ALBINO SQUIRREL FROM SUSSEX

The word albino is derived from the Latin word *albus*, meaning white. But all white animals are not albinoes. The true albino owes its peculiarity either to the absence in its heredity of one or both of the factors whose interaction causes colour to develop; or the presence in the inheritance of a factor which inhibits colour. What these mysterious factors are is not yet certain, but in the blood of certain coloured animals certain ferments have been found which are never present in the blood of albinoes.

W. S. Berridge

Nevil e Kin,ston

RARE WHITE COBRA AND WHITE ELEPHANT

Below is a white cobra in the possession of the London Zoological Society. It is rarely seen in collections of living wild animals and helps to show how universal is the working of the strange forces which prevent normal colour development. Above is a white elephant compared with a normal specimen. In Burma white elephants are the monopoly of the royal stables.

significant that these ferments are not obtainable from the skin of albinoes.

One theory is, therefore, that colour production depends upon the interaction of these ferments and chromogens and that albinoes lack the power of producing one or the other or both of them.

This theory accords remarkably well with the results of experiments on the inheritance of colour and albinism by animals and plants. Bateson's work with white sweet peas and stocks and many other experiments with animals, show that albinism, like colour, is inherited according to Mendelian principles and that it is reasonable to assume that in the chromosomes of animals definite factors or genes exist which represent the power of producing colour. It is further necessary in order to explain the results of breeding experiments, to assume that at least

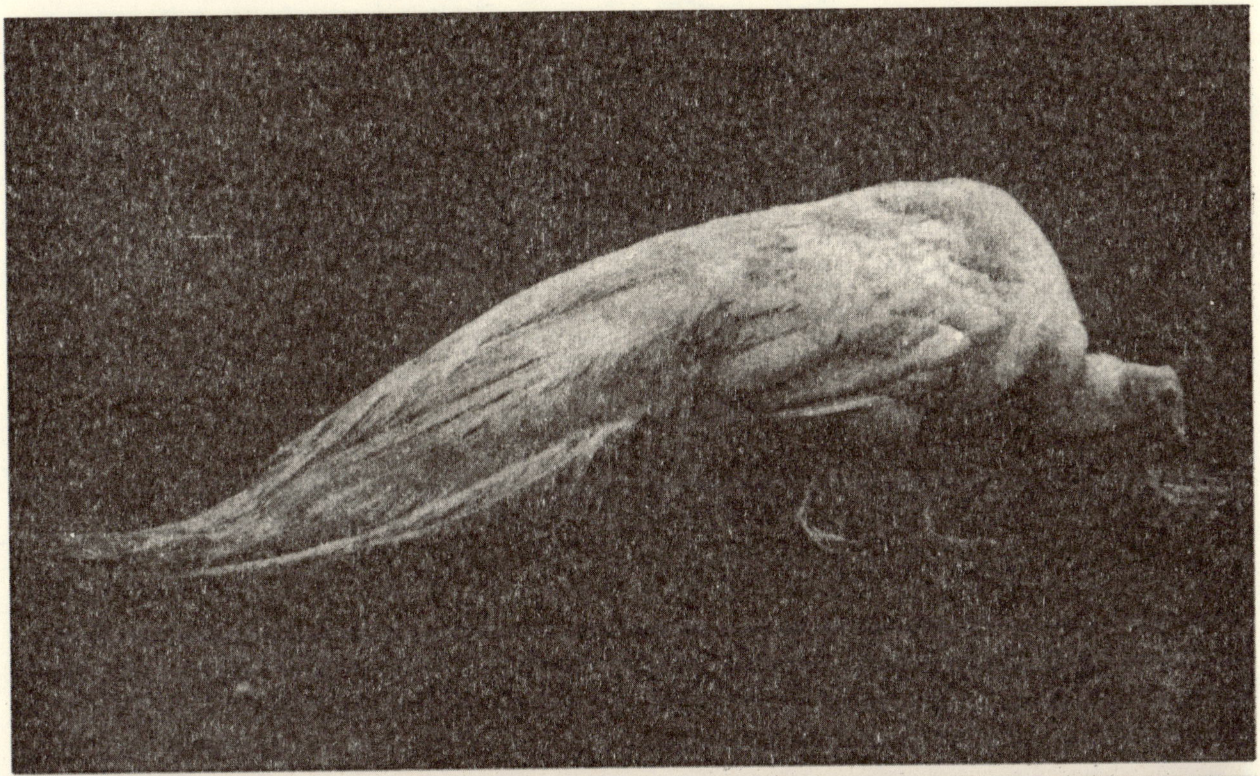

Neville Kingston

LOBSTER WITHOUT COLOUR AND A PEACOCK WITHOUT ITS GLORY

Lobsters are ordinarily a very dark colour and almost black—the well-known bright pink being, of course, the result of boiling for human consumption. Here is a lobster though, which has no colour. We see it photographed through the water. Above is a white peacock (see also p. 510) walking with its colourless tail down. Although such a bird is generally called an " albino " peacock, this can hardly be a case of true albinism as the peacock's brilliance of colour depends not on pigment but on the structure of the feathers.

W. S. Berridge

Neville Kingston

TWO ALBINO MANGABEYS FROM THE TROPICAL FORESTS OF WESTERN AFRICA

Lack of colour in albinoes is particularly noticeable in the eyeballs The iris is colourless and the "white of the eye" is pink, because the blood vessels are not masked by pigment as in normal animals. Pinkness is noticeable in the skin for the same reason. Our photographs show two mangabeys, both albino specimens, the one on the left being called Jamrach's mangabey. The one on the right is known as the sooty mangabey, and the complete absence of its normal colour characteristics is therefore the more marked. The name of mangabey, incidentally, alludes to a district of Madagascar whence this kind of monkey, when first classified, was erroneously supposed to come.

two such genes or factors exist without whose cooperation and interaction colour will not appear. These two genes are quite distinct and are inherited independently of each other. If only one of them be present in an animal's hereditary constitution, that animal will not develop colour. It is natural, therefore, to make the suggestion that these two genes represent the power of producing the above-mentioned ferments and chromogens respectively.

A true albino, on this Mendelian view, results from a sorting of its genes in such a way that it is left without either one or both of the genes whose cooperation is necessary to produce colour. It is thus that albinoes are produced in nature and by artificial selection controlled by man; and it is clear that, if this view be correct, albinoes cannot possibly produce colour so long as they are bred together. The only exception to this rule that albinoes breed true to their albinism, is the occasional occurrence among their offspring of reversions to the colour of remote ancestors which are similar to the reversions in respect to other characters which are familiar to those who are students of heredity.

W. S. Berridge

BARKING DEER THAT LACKS THE COLOURING OF ITS KIND

As the general colour of the muntjacs, or barking deer, is a rich golden bay an albino specimen is all the more striking. This little creature is only about two feet high and would be at a considerable disadvantage compared with its fellows since, being an albino, its eyes would be abnormally sensitive to the brilliant sunlight of India and Burma where it lives.

We should expect, of course, that such a special sorting of genes or factors as this theory requires would be rare and we know that albinism is, in fact, a comparatively rare phenomenon. It is known in practically every group of animals and in many plants, but it has not become established in wild nature, both because of its rarity and because, as will be explained below, it gives place to colour when an albino mates with a coloured partner. The disadvantages attending total lack of pigment must also decrease the chances of the albino's survival.

THE importance of clearly distinguishing between true albinism and other kinds of whiteness becomes evident when we study the inheritance of albinism closely. We must remember then that local areas of white such as the white plumage of some breeds of poultry, the white patches on piebald negroes and on piebald and skewbald horses, are not examples of true albinism, because colour coexists with them. Further, some animals, such as the Himalayan rabbit, the cinnamon canary and the "Siamese" cat, are born colourless and subsequently acquire pigment slowly during their early life. But if we study only clear instances of true albinism we find that colour always predominates over it if it gets a chance to develop. Mendelian theorists express it by saying that albinism is always recessive to colour. This means that if we pair, say, an albino mouse with a coloured one, the first generation of offspring will contain no albinoes at all. The missing colour factor or factors have been introduced by the coloured parent and they have enabled colour to develop. But if we now pair with each other the individuals of this coloured first generation, we shall get albinoes again in Mendelian proportions, that is to say, one quarter of them will be albinoes, lacking the colour-producing factors, and these will, of course, breed true to albinism so long as they are mated together. They are what is called homozygous for the albinism character, which is a shorter and more precise way of saying that their chromosomes are without one or both of the colour-producing factors.

While we agree, however, that true albinism is normally recessive to colour, a fact which we should expect, as Bateson pointed out, from the frequency

W. S. Berridge

RECUMBENT RHEA WHOSE FEATHERS SHOW THE RESULTS OF ALBINISM

Experiments with animals and plants, especially with white sweet peas and stocks, go to show that both albinism and colour are inherited according to Mendelian principles. A real albino is the result of a lack of the colour-producing faculty and albinos can never produce coloured offspring if bred with albinos save in the case of an occasional " throw-back " to some remote ancestor, an accident that may occur in other departments of heredity than colour. But albinism is rare in wild life because its disadvantages prejudice the chance of survival.

of its occurrence among the offspring of nearly-related parents—human albinoes, for instance, being commoner among the descendants of cousins who have married—yet we must not neglect experiments made with animals that are not true albinoes. The white plumage of the white leghorn fowl, for instance, is dominant to coloured plumage, and experiments show that this dominance is due, not to lack of colour-producing factors in the hereditary make-up of the birds, but to the presence of another and separate factor or gene which somehow prevents the appearance of colour. Breeding experiments alone will distinguish between such a dominant white bird and a recessive white such as the white Wyandotte whose whiteness depends upon the lack of the colour-producing factors. We know very little as yet about such inhibiting factors, but, as Punnett suggests, they may be commoner than we suspect, and may inhibit the appearance of other characters as well as colour. The beardless wheat may be due to such a factor preventing the appearance of the beard.

To sum up this part of the matter, we can say that whiteness may result from at least two classes of genes in hereditary constitution. In the first class are animals which are partially white because their chromosomes contain a gene which inhibits the development of colour in certain parts of their bodies. This white may be dominant to colour and the white leghorn fowl is an example of it.

In the second class are animals which are white because their chromosomes lack one or both of the genes or factors on whose interaction the production of colour depends. These genes may represent the power to develop a ferment and a chromogen whose interaction produces pigment. The white due to their failure to cooperate is always recessive to colour, because, when a coloured mate is introduced, it brings with it whichever colour-producing gene is missing. Of this kind of white there may be three varieties: first, a variety lacking one of the two necessary genes, say the one representing the power to produce a ferment; second, a variety lacking the second of the two necessary genes, say the one representing the power to produce a chromogen; and third, a variety lacking both these genes. The actual existence of the third variety has not been proved by experiment.

Certain other facts remain to be mentioned. We must not forget that although true albinoes are

Neville Kingston

ACTION OF ALBINISM ON THE FEATHERS OF A BIRD: A WHITE RHEA

Photographed with the camera inside its paddock this white rhea makes a fine picture standing against the bars. A bird so prolific as the rhea would naturally produce some albinoes every now and then. At one time as many as four hundred thousand of these birds are said to have been butchered every year for the sake of their feathers. Consequently the rhea is in danger of extinction, but the figures show how prodigious the rhea population used to be. This and the photograph in the opposite page show the effect of albinism on feathers.

Neville Kingston

WHITE WEKA-RAIL FROM NEW ZEALAND BESIDE A POOL

All the rails are water-loving birds and we see here a weka-rail by the margin of a pool. Ordinarily the weka-rail is brown and black in plumage, but this specimen lacks the tints characteristic of its kind. Experiments with birds that are white yet not true albinoes, such as certain white breeds of chicken, show that whiteness is dominant to coloured plumage, whereas if a normal bird breeds with a true albino none of the offspring will be albino. But if individuals of this offspring are paired, then a quarter of the resulting young ones will be albino.

without colour, they still can show the pattern on which colour would have appeared if it had been produced. Certain albino rats, for example, have longer and thinner hairs revealing the pink skin beneath them and arranged according to the colour pattern shown by their coloured relatives. In the same way the white tail feathers of an albino peacock (see picture on page 510), may show the eye-like markings of the coloured bird. We must conclude, therefore, that a separate gene exists for colour pattern and that this is inherited quite independently of the colour-producing factors.

FURTHER than this, Bateson's experiments with white stocks showed that no hairs were produced on these plants unless the flowers were coloured, which suggests a correlation between the factors controlling hairiness and those controlling colour-production. It is not unreasonable, therefore, to suggest that albinism may also be linked with factors controlling other characters, and such a conception is suggested by such evidence as exists that, in man and domesticated animals some degrees of albinism may be associated with lack of resistance to certain poisons.

We are not justified in asserting that albinoes are constitutionally weak, for in some respects they may be stronger than coloured forms. It is said, for instance, that white peaches in parts of America suffer less from the disease called " the yellows," and albino negroes are often taller and broader than normal negroes, although this may not imply greater vitality. On the other hand, albinoes show definite weaknesses in certain directions. The white pigs of Virginia cited by Darwin, whose bones turn pink and whose hooves fall off when they eat the roots of the paint-root plant which does not affect their coloured relatives, are an instance of this. When piebald cattle eat certain plants that cause inflammatory reactions in the skin, only the unpigmented patches are affected. Albino negroes, and even fair Europeans, are more susceptible to insect bites. The biochemists, indeed, may yet make very important discoveries about the part played by pigment, not only in the reactions of animals and plants to light, but in other new directions. While we understand so little the inheritance of colour and albinism itself, it would be premature to speculate about the inheritance of any weakness or strength that may be associated with either ; but if albinism does prove to be linked with certain constitutional peculiarities, such linkages may prove to be analogous to the linkage of hairiness with colour mentioned above or to the peculiar mode of inheritance of such diseases of man as haemophilia and colour-blindness.

Chapter XCIII

The Minute Life in a Drop of Pond Water

By W. H. S. Cheavin

Corresponding Member of the Manchester Microscopical Society

An airman in his airplane flying at a low altitude over an unknown city for the first time and looking down upon the many forms of activity going on beneath him would be in the same position as an observer looking down the tube of a modern microscope at the many forms of life to be found in the various ponds, lakes and reservoirs.

The latter are fed by rain water which, passing through the ground and accumulating in quantities in the hollow depressions, dissolve out the many salts necessary for the conditions to give rise to the multitudinous forms of life which eventually appear during the course of time. Such water, examined under various modifications, drop by drop, will reveal a great variety of the many types of animal and plant life which consist of only one cell, minute in size, yet this simple cell can live, move, feed and reproduce in the water in which it lives.

The majority of these simple-celled animals belong to the large group known as Protozoa, which can be divided up into several sub-groups containing well-marked types, now to be considered.

The single cell in each case contains the fluid substance, found in all animals and plants, known as protoplasm, a very complex chemical body, the composition of which is still unknown. All animals, whether they consist of one cell or many cells, contain protoplasm in their cell contents, and the only difference to be found in this living substance is in its functions. It is very remarkable to find in the simple-celled animals so many characteristic properties and functions found in the individual specialised cells of the higher animals.

Let us now examine several animals belonging to the Rhizopodia (meaning thread-like rays), whose living matter enclosed in a single cell enables them to produce pseudopodia (false feet), blunt or finger-like in form.

A small, colourless, shapeless, transparent mass, which can assume almost every variety of shape by contraction and expansion, moving so slowly that we can hardly realize that it has changed its position, is the well-known Amoeba. This animal is the simplest form of life, a most important example because it stands at the base or foundation of all life and throws much light on the beginning of organic structure and vital activity, giving hints on the nature of the first forms of life of which we know nothing directly.

The amoeba is found in the mud of all ponds and consists of a unified corpuscle of living matter having a close relation to the blood stream of all mammals whose blood cells or corpuscles have the same movement, thus deriving the name of amoeboid cells. Further, many forms of life begin as an amoeboid cell; even man, who represents the highest form of life in the animal world, commences his career in this manner. The amoeba, consisting of a single-celled mass of protoplasm, shows a dark spherical body at its centre which is known as the nucleus and moves about with every movement of this simple animal.

The fluid cell substance, protoplasm, near the outer parts, is seen to be clearer and firmer than that found in the inner parts where it is more fluid and granular, consisting of protein and fat bodies.

The protoplasm can be seen to move by a streaming motion in which the endoplasm from the inner parts passes outwards to the rind, where it becomes changed into ectoplasm and results in producing projections known as pseudopodia which in a similar manner by a reverse process can be withdrawn. New pseudopodia are thrust out at will from any part of the body in any direction. This movement is necessary for the locomotion of the animal, also to enable it to capture its food by flowing over its victim, generally a minute form of plant life known as the diatom. The diatom is engulfed and, as one writer terms the action, the amoeba unbuttons its waistcoat, the food is placed in contact with the body, and the waistcoat is buttoned up again which results in the food being absorbed. The disappearance of the diatom follows, and the waste products are rejected through an open space which eventually appears, and is known to science as the contractile vacuole.

The changing of the protoplasm by this streaming movement is the result of surface tension phenomena enabling the amoeba, by

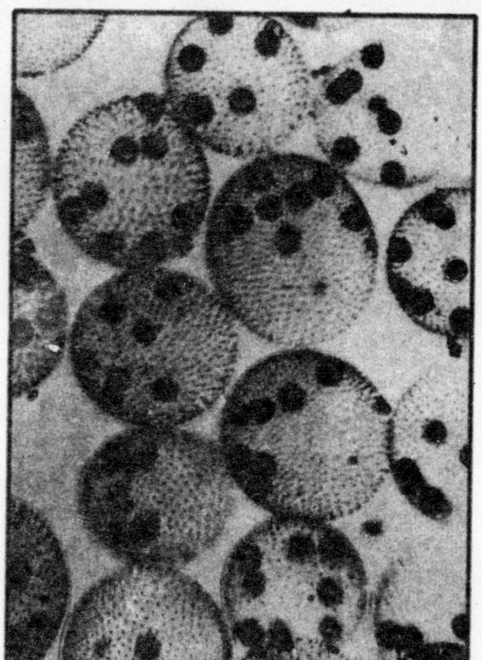

W. H. S. Hearn

GREEN GLOBES OF VOLVOX

Rolling through water go the green spheres of Volvox globator which comprise each a family of cells living together. The family moves by regular strokes of cilia which are like little lashes.

Minute Life in a Pond

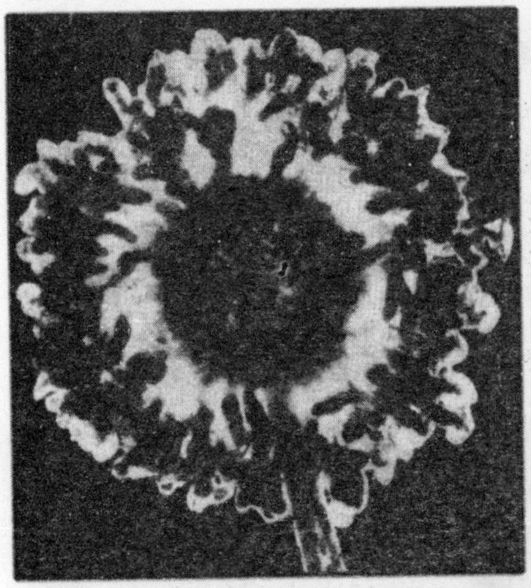

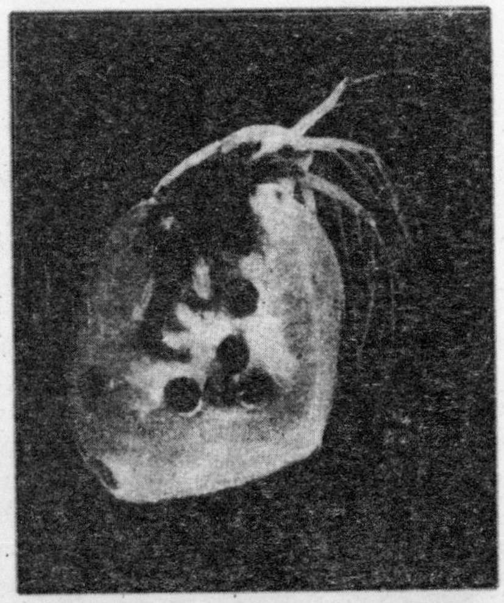

forming pseudopodia, to move in a wavy path quite orderly and not at random, as is often stated. This wavy path, in the form of a helical spiral, is related to the movements of all free swimming organisms, such as flagellates, ciliates, and so on, and is due to an automatic regulating mechanism present in all organisms inherent in the same way as the property of growth. Every animal moves in a regular smooth spiral of one kind or another when free from stimulation, and no organism moves in a straight or irregular path.

The amoeba and man are restricted to two dimensions in space, thus the amoeba in its habits and functions exhibits most of those found present in all animals to a greater or lesser degree.

The animal will soon perish when kept in water free from organisms which form its natural food, and even if these are replaced by chemical substances of a similar composition.

When under its natural conditions on attaining a certain size the amoeba will be seen to divide into two halves, each half containing part of the original nucleus ; this form of division is known as simple fission and is common to many forms of plant and animal life.

After a time this form of simple division comes to an end and two amoebae will be seen to approach each other, then fuse and surround themselves with a cyst or sheath ; after a time this cyst breaks down and minute spores are discharged into the water which gradually grow to the size of the original parents. If the pond dries up the amoeba at once encloses itself in a cyst and remains in this form in the dust produced from the mud when dried by the sun. The dust can be blown many miles, but wherever it goes, on becoming wet again in a new pool the encysted amoeba comes out of its protective layer and once more assumes its original life-history.

Owing to these facts, and experiments which showed that the animal can stand varying temperatures, it has been said that the amoeba is immortal. But this is not exactly the case, though by virtue of its simplicity it is in some measure exempt from natural death, which is the price paid for a body with its different kinds of cells performing different functions. There are many forms of amoeba which differ very much from each other ; a very low type known as Protamoeba shows no nucleus or contractile vacuole ; another type has a disc-shaped nucleus, and the animal can flow without change of form or pseudopodia ; whilst another type known as Pelomyxa contains many nuclei with refractile bodies.

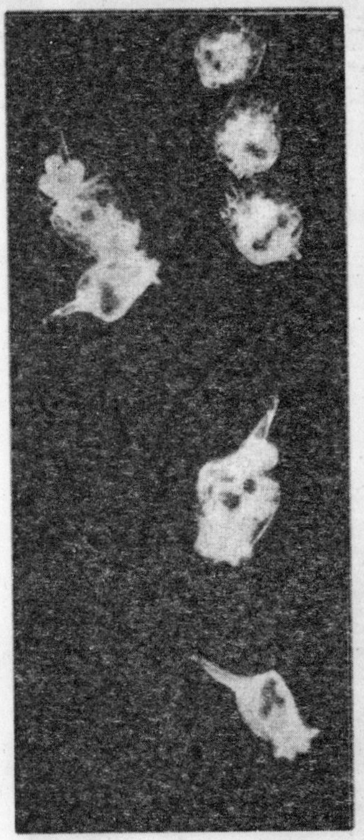

E. A. Botting

SOME OF THE MICROSCOPIC LIFE FOUND IN POND WATER

The rotifers, of which we have three examples in the two lower photographs, get their name from the wheel-like organs with which they are equipped. Here we have (left) specimens of Brachionus quadratus and a variety, rotundus, at a magnification of forty-five (x 45) and (right) Melicerta conifera which belongs to the order of rotifers called Rhizota, which means "the rooted." Above are a water flea (x 18, right) and a specimen of Lacinularia socialis (x 15).

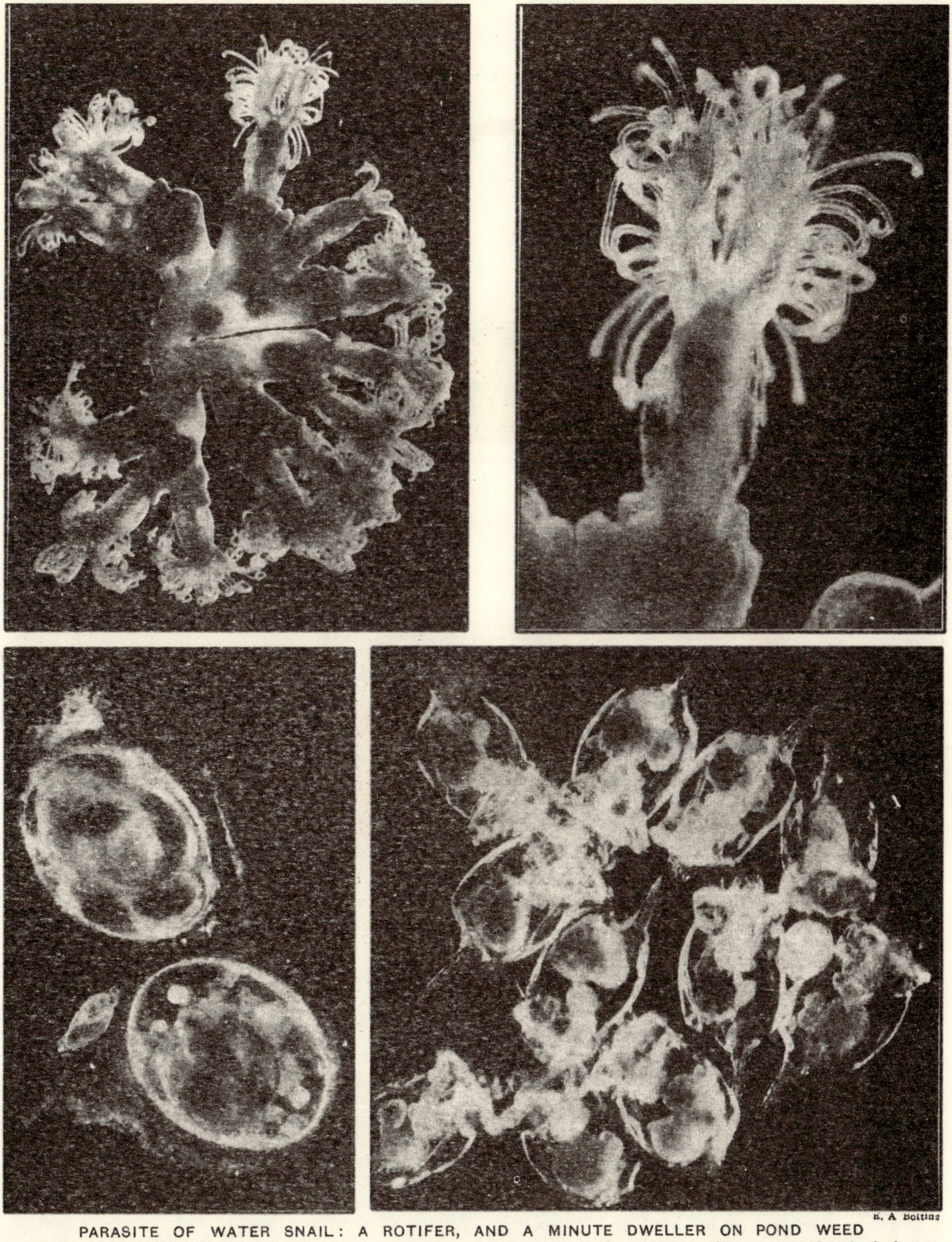

E. A. Botting

PARASITE OF WATER SNAIL: A ROTIFER, AND A MINUTE DWELLER ON POND WEED

One might wonder what preyed upon the water snail, seeing that " eat or be eaten " is the law of Nature. The answer is given in the bottom left-hand photograph, where we have an example of Proales gigantium, which is a parasite of the water snail, and lives inside its eggs. It is seen here at a magnification of forty (x 40). Here, also, are (bottom right) a specimen of a rotifer, Notops brachionus (x 120); (top left) Lophopus crystallinus (x 20), one of the polyzoa found on pond weed; and (top right) an individual polyp of the same creature (x 50).

E. A. Botting

HOW HYDRA VIRIDIS CHANGES ITS SHAPE AND POSITION

These photographs illustrate the power possessed by hydra viridis of changing both its shape and its position in a short time. The lower photograph was taken at a lesser power of magnification than the upper three. The hydra is seen attached to a fragment of reed and a young one is budding from the adult's side. Thirty seconds elapsed between the exposures.

Some Protozoa have a definite form and bear flagella or cilia and are known as Infusoria, the name given to all animals appearing in infusions of water containing organic matter and only visible with the aid of a microscope; this name was brought into use by the older microscopists of last century. A commoner type of infusoria bearing flagella, or whip-lashes, is seen in the Euglena, an animalcule of deep green colour making the water of the pond a dark green colour different from the lighter green of filamentous algae. The euglena swarm in large numbers and by lashing movements of their flagella propel themselves through the water at great speed. The flagellum is highly contractile and executes a number of rapid bending movements compared to a finger when beckoning.

The euglena, coloured green by the presence of chlorophyll, resembles plant life and by this means can perform the same photo-synthetic processes found in plants producing a form of starch from carbon dioxide. In addition, the euglena by the action of the flagella causes a vortex in the hollow depression from which it springs and herein minute particles of solid matter are ingested. It is stated as well that the animal can also absorb organic substances found in the water by the whole surface of its body.

The most highly-developed group of the Protozoa is found in a large number of one-celled organisms known as Ciliata, because on the body surface they bear many thread-like cilia; they have no power to form pseudopods and this is due to the fact that the body is enclosed in a pellicle, or cuticle.

A MEMBER of this group is seen in Paramoecium, which moves with great rapidity in a straight course with its blunt end foremost. It comes to a sudden stop, then turns and seems to hesitate, finally darting off in a new direction. The movements in this animal are caused by the fine hair-like processes which project from the body. These are seen to be pointed at one end, blunt at the other, and have a slipper-like form resulting in the name "slipper animalcule" being given to the creature. The body is enclosed in a pellicle having a groove leading to a mouth aperture; two nuclei are present, known as macro-

H. S. Cheavin

WONDERFUL COMMUNITIES OF MINUTE CREATURES LIVING IN FRESH WATER

The two lower photographs are of colonies of polyzoa; (left) one of cristatella (x 40) and (right) Lophopus crystallinus (x 40), showing each colony with terminal zooids. The top left-hand illustration is of cordylophora, and shows a typical polyp colony (x 40) with branches and scattered, filiform tentacles. Lastly, we have another and very remarkable example of a polyzoa community, that of plumatella (x 40) which can crawl about on plants as though it were a single individual instead of—as it really is—a large family.

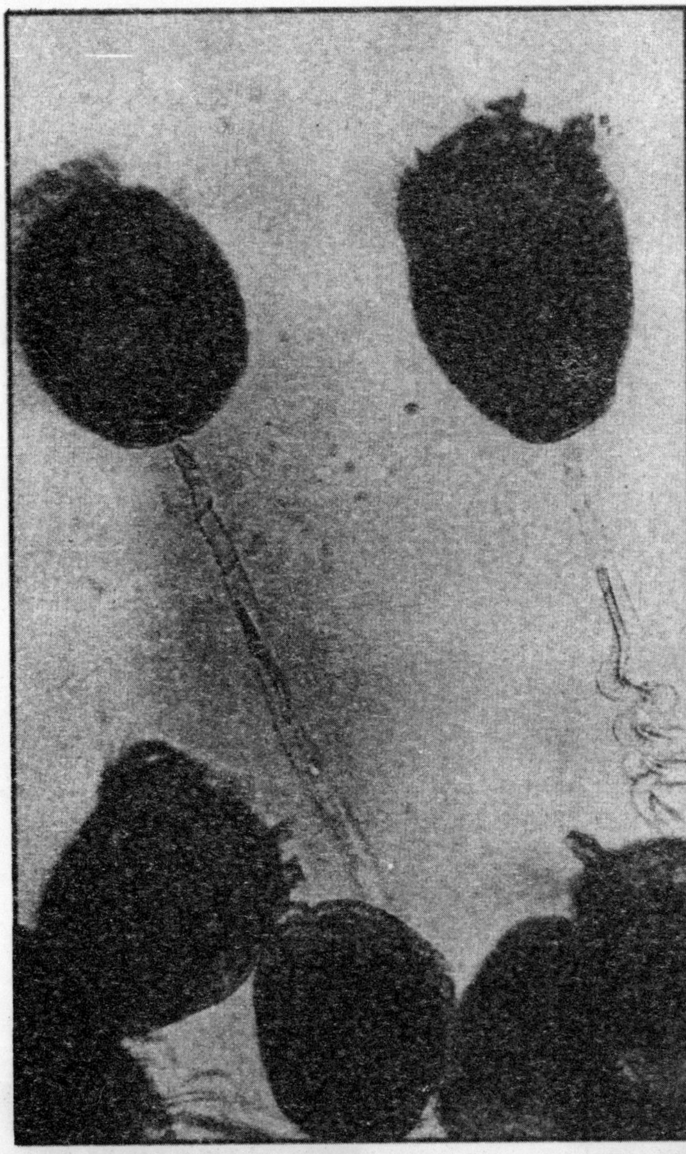

nuclei and micronuclei respectively, which perform the functions of nutrition and reproduction. Two contractile vacuoles are present in different parts of the body, and each one will be seen to contract alternately with great regularity.

When well supplied with food the paramoecium multiplies by binary fission, which takes place two or three times every twenty-four hours for four or five days. The offspring become smaller and smaller, finally showing signs of decay. The animals then conjugate in couples becoming attached mouth to mouth which by fusion transfer nuclear material ; the two fused animals, diminished in size, then separate, commence to feed and so recover the original dimensions of the parent.

Closely allied to Paramoecium is Stylonychia, the mussel animalcule, but a more advanced type in having stiff bristles on its oval flat body and a funnel-shaped mouth having a ciliated margin leading to the inner part of the cell. There is a nucleus and contractile vacuole which contracts rhythmically ; by means of its cilia or seta this animal can set up whirlpools bringing food to the mouth ; it can also stalk along the stems of pond weeds or swim freely in the water.

Another conspicuous member of this group is seen in Stentor, the trumpet animalcule, found free-swimming or attached to the under sides of pond weeds ; it is constantly changing its shape from a small knob, when contracted, to a trumpet form when extended. Long cilia, which are seen on the upper part of the trumpet, lash about in the water and sweep food into the open mouth leading to the digestive sac. Here the food is used up and the waste products are excreted.

Adhering to the stems of water weeds will be found the beautiful Vorticella, or bell animalcule, because each resembles in shape that of a wineglass on a long stem ; this animal is one of the many numerous forms of ciliated infusoria living in large colonies, each animal leading a separate independent existence. When disturbed the vorticella will be seen immediately to retract its stalks or stems and the cilia present on the rim of the funnel-shaped mouth cease their lashing ; after a short interval the animal resumes its normal position, lashing the water vigorously with its cilia, which produce vortex currents and so convey food material into the funnel-shaped mouth.

Vorticella reproduces itself by binary longitudinal fission dividing the body into halves, both of which become attached to

S. Cheavin

MICRO-ORGANISMS THAT LIVE BY MEANS OF WHIPS

Ceratium longicorne (bottom ; x 200) is one of the many organisms which propel themselves by means of flagella, or whip-like appendages. Above is a specimen of the vorticella (x 403) or bell animalcule which lives on water weeds and looks rather like a wineglass with a long stem.

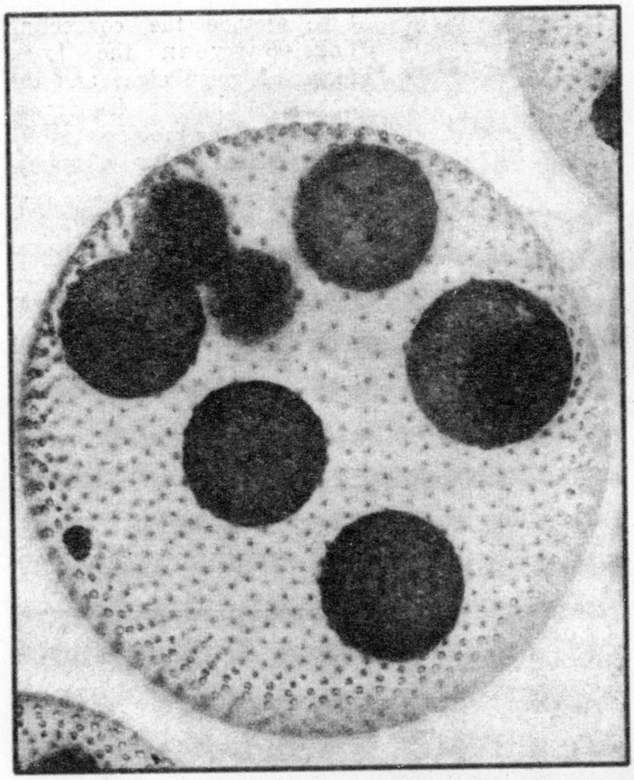

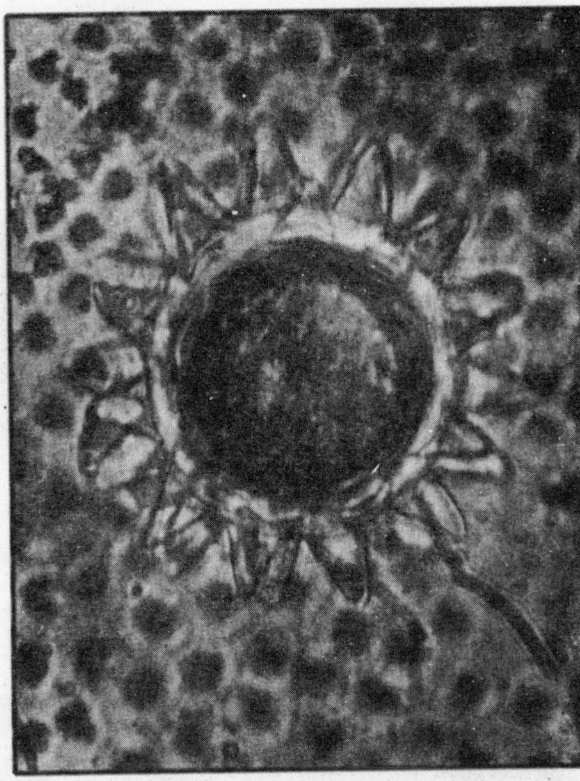

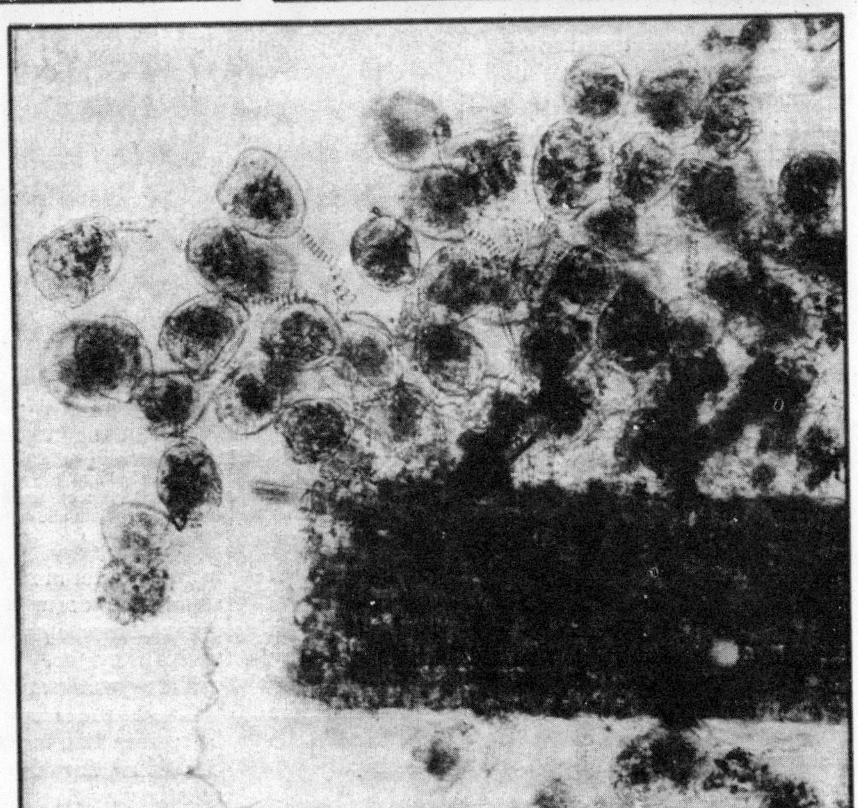

the same stalk. One half develops an additional ring of cilia at its point of attachment; then detaches itself from the stalk, swims away and in a short time attaches itself to a new position where it develops a new stalk and grows into a fully-formed vorticella. The other half of this division remains in its original position attached to the old stalk and this half may be looked upon as the parent and the half forming the new animal as the child.

Another form of reproduction in vorticella can take place by the bell dividing into unequal halves; the lesser half may divide up again into as many as eight parts, each of which can develop an additional ring of cilia to enable the part to swim away and seek an exhausted vorticella with which it fuses at the base, becoming absorbed; this union results in a new period of life for the new animal thus formed, which then resumes the normal division for reproduction.

The Epistylis, or nodding bell animalcule, is another type of

H. S. Chervin

COLONIES OF VORTICELLA AND VOLVOX AS THEY LIVE UNDER WATER

This (bottom) is how a colony of vorticella (x 186) looks on a fragment of pond weed when seen through a microscope. Above we see (left) a photograph of volvox globator (x 204) showing spherical daughter colonies in the mother envelope, which will eventually escape by breaking their way through; and (top right) a ripe oospore inside its mother (x 1116).

type provide the connecting links between the lower forms of green algae and the flagellates having flagella of equal size, the protozoan group exhibiting a mixture of animal and vegetable characters. The green colour of the sphere is due to chlorophyll, the same substance found in all green plants and used by them to produce food material from the carbon dioxide of the air and from sunlight.

Volvox belongs to the group of plants consisting of a colony of cells united together by protoplasmic processes having ciliated cells on the exterior which produce motion by lash-

LARVA OF THE WATER BOATMAN AND ITS ADULT FORM

One of the most easily noticed creatures of the pond is the water boatman. Its body is like an inverted boat, the back being keeled and the ventral surface flat. This little pond hunter swims under the surface on its back, not on the surface like the water-skaters. The lower photograph shows the larval stage while above is the adult bug, both much magnified

colony-living animals which unite in a form of bush recognized from vorticella because the individuals have no contractile filament. When disturbed their heads drop down their short stalks. These animals though associated together on the same stalks have no organic connexion with each other ; they are found parasitic on cyclops.

Another form of branching colony individuals is seen in Carchesium. A contractile filament in a stem is developed in each animal and they behave in the same manner as vorticella when disturbed. Carchesium differs in having a branched stem, each branch terminating in a bell-shaped body. When dividing not only the bell divides but also the stem, and the divided part remains attached to the parent stem. This form of division results in the course of time in the production of a large colony.

We now come to the Volvox globator, seen as a large number of rolling green globes propelled by regular strokes just as a boat is manned by a number of oarsmen. The motion is caused by cilia in pairs produced from the large numbers of individual cells which live together in the sphere as a family.

Volvox is usually placed by botanists amongst the lower forms of plant life, the Algae ; but it can also be regarded as a type of Protozoa ; whether we adopt one classification or the other, we are faced with the fact that living organisms of the volvox ing the water in regular strokes. Plants of this family sometimes occur in prodigious quantity in water, giving it a pale-green colour and an unpleasant odour, while they are generally the cause of foulness in drinking water and produce a distinct oily taste.

One of the simpler types of the volvox family is to be seen in Pandorina morum, a spherical green ovoid cell consisting of sixteen or thirty-two individual cells having flagella whose united action enables the sphere to swim about. Every cell in this sphere can form a daughter colony which swells up the mother cell and later this breaks down, setting the young colonies free. In Volvox globator we have a large number of cells in the sphere which

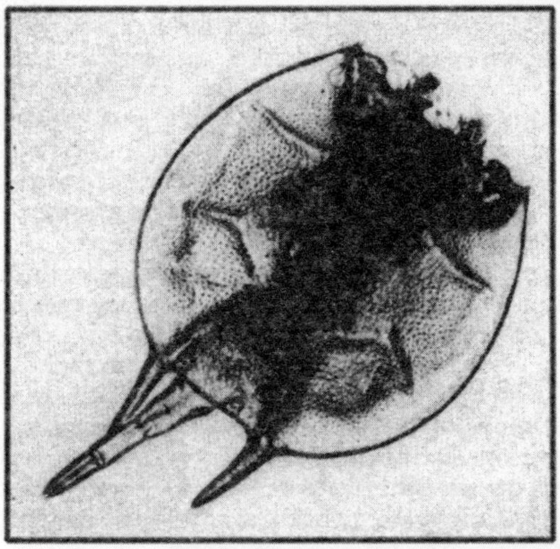

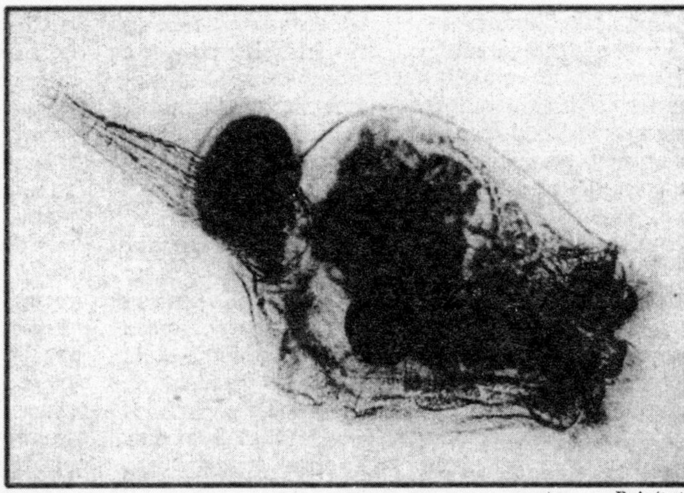

E A Botting

TWO MEMBERS OF THE REMARKABLY ADAPTIVE FAMILY OF THE ROTIFERS

Distributed very widely owing to their powers of adaptation, the rotifers, to which family the above specimens belong, are most remarkable creations. They are found in both salt and fresh water, though more numerous in the latter. They can live alike in lakes, reservoirs and ditches, or in slow streams; in water-butts, roof-gutters, and wet grass; in the intestines of earthworms and slugs; and as parasites of volvox globator (see page 1033). The above photographs show (left) Noteus quadricornis (x 200) and Brachionus rotundus (x 200).

consists of some two hundred to twelve thousand cells enclosed in a thick membraneous envelope. These cells form a single layer and each cell body does not fill the envelope, being separated by a considerable space; the enveloping part pressed up against other enveloping parts has a hexagonal outline. Each cell has a nucleus, contractile vacuole, chromatophor, amylum body and a pair of flagella which give the colony its power of locomotion. These cells can reproduce by division, and so increase the number of units in the colony.

Reproduction is limited to a smaller number of cells of larger size having no flagella, and by means of binary division result in new spherical colonies formed in the mother envelope, where they fall into the central cavity, first developing flagella; after a while the colony escapes by rupture of the maternal wall.

LATER a new type of colony begins to form, differing from the previous colonies in having a larger number of non-flagellate cells; these new colonies increase in size, become deep green in colour and fall into the central cavity of the mother cell; these cells are ova, becoming fertilised later by another type of flagellated cell formed in the same way as the ova cells. A fertilised ovum results which surrounds itself with a double cyst wall provided with spines and projections; this is a zygote, or spore, which can survive the winter and later, in spring, develops by repeated cell division into a volvox colony.

Volvox is the culminating point of mobile spherical forms, and though its individual cells are of a primitive type the entire organism, owing to the differentiation of its compound cells, shows that it is a summary of the evolution of sex, and suggests the successive steps through which unicellular organisms gave rise to the multicellular and—belonging to neither or either the animal or vegetable kingdom, but equally to both—brings us face to face with the unity of nature, a most important point in the wonderful theory of evolution.

In fresh water, especially from some reservoirs and lakes, tiny spherical masses are observed covered with a protective layer of spines, or spicules; these spherical masses are statoblasts, or gemmules of the common fresh-water sponge, two types of which are found in Britain, though the majority of the Porifera, or canal-bearing zoophytes, constituting the sponge family, are found in the sea. The gemmules of the fresh-water type are produced by the adult sponge in the autumn when food is scarce and the colder weather begins to set in. The parent then dies away, the gemmules, surrounded with a horny shell and strengthened with siliceous spicules, survive and in the spring float away from the dead parent, developing by bursting out from the interior into new sponges, thus having served two purposes, one of protection and the other of dispersion.

The adult sponges are green in colour and generally found attached to some object in the water, branches of trees, stones, etc. Fresh-water sponges are a source of trouble in waterworks and have been found to block up pipes owing to their dislike of mud, which clogs up their pores.

Let us now examine a few examples of the larger types of animals found in ponds, lakes, etc., which can be held in larger drops of water than those described in the former types.

These are radially symmetric, having one body cavity which serves alike for digestion and circulation and include in the large group Coelonterata, polyps, corals and sea-anemones. Reproduction is effected by budding from the body of the parent or by formation of a fertilised egg, both giving rise to an entirely new individual.

The green Hydra viridis, fixed by its base to aquatic plants, is a solitary animal consisting of a long, two-layered body surmounted by a crown of several hollow tentacles seen to be waving about in the water; the animal can also lift itself up by the tentacles, stand on its head or creep by looping movements. If disturbed the animal retracts the tentacles, contracts its body and forms a small mass which eventually, when its alarm is over, once more expands and resumes its activities.

THE hydra feeds on small animals such as daphnids, or water fleas, which on coming into contact with the tentacles become paralysed. The tentacles bend and convey the victim to the opening or mouth, where it passes into the body cavity to be digested, the unwanted portions being expelled through the same opening; the whole procedure being possible of observation through a microscope. The hydra can be cut into several pieces, each piece growing into an entire animal. These fragments must be a fair sample of the body to produce this effect; further, the animal has been turned inside out, which gave the impression that all the cells, inner and outer, were of the same kind, but this, of course, is wrong, for it was found that the animal after a time reversed the process, or if prevented, the cells by growth restored the animal to its normal condition. The usual method of reproduction is by budding, which is first seen as a bulge in the body of the parent on the outside. This first forms two tentacles, and more are developed later when the bud has broken off and floated away in the water to carry on a free existence of its own.

A sexual method of reproduction takes place in the autumn season, when male organs are produced below the bases of the tentacles, and lower down still the female organs; the two kinds of reproductive cells may form on separate animals. The male organs become expelled into the water and, on reaching the female organs, bring about fertilisation, forming the eggs Later these eggs fall away from the parent and remain in the bottom of the pond in a quiescent condition till the spring, when they produce young animals which then carry on once more the life-history of their progenitors.

CLOSELY related to the hydra, which is a solitary animal form, are colonial forms belonging to the great group of polyps which produce a complicated type of bud setting free a medusa, and this develops generative cells distributing its products far and wide; the sexes are always separate, and when they meet unite to form the egg, developing the larval form, which swims to the bottom, attaches itself, and grows into a new polyp colony. The greater number of these polyp animals live in the sea, but in fresh water we find one example, Cordylophora, which becomes a nuisance in waterworks by growing rapidly, choking up the pipes at all times of the year.

Floating in the water of a pond will be found seed-like bodies, or the statoblasts of the polyzoa, small animals growing together united into colonies formed of polyp-like organisms, which present a superficial resemblance to colonies of hydroids.

The free-floating statoblasts are the summer forms, differing from the fixed forms produced in the autumn, which remain at the base of the colony when the parent colony has died down, and in the spring open out like a watch-case. The individual then emerges to start a new colony. The full-grown animal is found attached on the underside of water-plants as a jelly-like mass which, under observation, will be seen to expand into a number of erect tubes surmounted by crowns of tentacles which can be retracted or protruded by special muscles traversing the body cavity. The mouth is present in the midst of the circle of ciliated tentacles, and the disk bearing them is known as the lophophore, serving both for procuring food by whirlpools in the water and as a means of respiration. The digestive organs are in the body cavity, containing an alimentary canal and a simple form of nervous system.

Reproduction is effected by the two forms of statoblasts which are really a form of bud; in some forms, such as Cristatella and Lophopus, parts of the animal can separate off from the colony and divide spontaneously, also the former type can crawl over objects in the pond as if it was a single individual instead of being a colony.

THE polyzoa are mostly marine, and found between tide marks or on the floor of the ocean, but some types are found in fresh water, whilst others are phosphorescent and others excavate passages in shells of molluscs. The statoblasts facilitate the distribution of the species and can become attached to the legs, webbed feet, or other parts of water birds, and so are carried long distances over the earth's surface.

Pond water may also contain examples of higher forms of animal life known as Crustacea, which have their body with a hard external skeleton known as the carapace, or shield, the body segments carrying antennae, or feelers and jointed legs.

A common form of this class is found in the active, free-swimming cyclops, so called because of the single eye seen in the middle of the head; the animal, when swimming, is pear-shaped in outline, broad in front, tapering behind; the abdomen ends in a caudal fork consisting of two lateral processes bearing a large number of setae; in the female the eggs are carried in a couple of ova sacs attached to the last segment of the thorax; the females largely outnumber the males, and are so prolific that they can produce many millions of young. When hatched they appear in the form of an oval Nauplius, which, passing through several moults, acquires the adult form. Five pairs of feet are present, four pairs being used for swimming, and in this action the cyclops swims upside down.

Another common form of the Crustacea found in pond water is the common water flea Daphnia pulex, so called because of its jerky movements when propelling itself through the water. The body is enclosed in a transparent bivalve shell, through which we can see the whole of the organs.

Chapter XCIV

The Wonderful Wanderings of Animals

Dr. Marion Newbigin

Author of "Animal Geography"

As the seasons come and go the noontide sun swings up and down in the sky, its rhythm punctuating that of all living creatures. With us its upward climb in spring means that buds unfold, and the seedlings which have been lying dormant within their hard coats are stirred to a new life. Once Midsummer Day has passed and the downward movement begins, there is a notable check to the rush of growth, and the first frosts of autumn find the plant world already prepared for the long period of rest.

Even in the inter-tropical belt, where the noon rays never deviate far from the vertical, and average temperatures are always high, the sun tends to carry with him in his swing a cloud mantle. Thus the moisture, which is as necessary as warmth to living things, increases as the vertical sun draws near, and diminishes as it retreats. Again, therefore, there is a rhythmic change, though the beats are far less marked. Finally, in Polar regions the long summer days, during some at least of which the sun never sinks below the horizon, mean that green plants can carry on those vital processes which depend upon light with a continuity which goes far to make up for the slowing down due to the slant of the rays and the resultant low temperatures.

Here then the beats are accentuated, the alternation between the cold dark winter and the short bright summer being very sharply marked. Everywhere, that is to say if plant life is possible at all, it shows to a greater or less degree seasonal variation, this being least marked in low latitudes and most marked in higher. The plants of necessity can but wait till the earth's revolution brings the sun back to them. But many animals have great powers of locomotion, and can use these to "follow the sun." Migration in the strict sense is the name given to such movements, which are one form of response to the changing seasons.

Two main types of migration can be recognized, even if in practice the distinction is not always sharp. Most large grass-eating mammals live in flocks which require much food at all times, and soon exhaust the herbage of a particular spot. Such animals are necessarily wanderers, and to the daily and local movements, determined not only by the search for good feeding-grounds but by other causes, such as the need for water, for shelter from large beasts of prey or from insect pests, and so on, there must be added large-range movements made necessary by the passage of the seasons. These may be horizontal or vertical; for it is a commonplace that high mountain ranges display the climates and vegetation of different zones of latitude as one ascends from the base to the crests. The caribou of Northern Canada move northward in summer as growth begins in the Barren Grounds, and southwards, often in great bands, to the forest edge or even into the forest itself, in autumn as the Polar snow-cap extends gradually over the lands. As spring creeps slowly up the great mountain chains of the world, melting more and more of the snow, exposing more and more of the resting plants to the sun's beneficent rays, various kinds of herbivores follow in its train.

Such migrations of wild herbivores are always tending to be replaced by those of domesticated or semi-domesticated flocks and herds, where the movements are controlled and regulated by the herdsmen. Examples are thus now relatively few, though there is a good deal of evidence to show that they once occurred on a very large scale. The bison of North America, for instance, now virtually extinct as a wild animal, seems to have formerly migrated through a wide range of latitude. But though the phenomenon is often imposing, both on account of the distance traversed, and the great numbers involved its causation is relatively simple, and little of the nature of a special instinct need be assumed to account for it. In particular it should be noted that as a rule the area traversed is throughout suited to the animals, which feed on the march. The movements are a continuation of the ordinary short-range ones, the initial cause being the need for finding

W. S. Berridge

FIELDFARE, A WANDERER OVER EUROPE

Breeding in northern Europe, the fieldfare comes south in winter to find unfrozen ground whence it can obtain the snails and worms on which it feeds. England is a favourite resort, and the birds usually return to the same locality year after year.

HERD OF NEVADA WILD HORSES GALLOPING OVER A FLOODED PRAIRIE

Shepstone

Fast-moving animals like the horse can " follow the sun " as the influence of its distance or nearness comes to bear upon the supply of vegetable food. The scene captured by this photograph reminds us of the days when vast herds of wild horses used to inhabit the vast plains of Europe and Asia as a remnant still does in Mongolia. As the seasons change and the food supply moves from south to north and back again, such animals, living in large communities and needing great quantities of food, must change their feeding grounds accordingly. The mustangs seen here are not true wild horses, but the descendants of domestic individuals that took to the wild. They make a fine sight as they splash their way over a flooded prairie.

W. S. Berridge

ONE OF THE AMAZING WANDERERS WHOSE JOURNEYS END IN DEATH

Of all the animals which are famous for their wanderings the Norwegian lemming has most appealed to popular interest on account of the extraordinary tales told of its migratory habits. In Norway, where arms of the sea continually split the coastline, the onward march of the lemmings is sometimes only stayed by the ocean itself. These little rodents, which inhabit northern Asia and Europe, increase locally, every now and then, until the food supply is inadequate and migration must take place. Few of the wanderers ever return.

suitable food. Indications of an approaching change of weather, to which many animals are very susceptible, may start a movement on a greater scale than usual, and local variations in relief may make it necessary to pass rapidly from one feeding-ground to another some distance away. But in the general case the migration is probably leisurely, and not a sudden passage from one zone to another.

Again, in all such cases the animals breed at a time when pasture is most abundant and richest in foodstuffs, and the young, though fed at first on the mother's milk, the flow of which is stimulated by the lush grass, soon learn to nibble at her side. Thus conditions favourable to the mature forms favour the young also. This is generally true of mammals, particularly land mammals. Just because young mammals are fed for a longer or shorter period on the mother's milk they are, as it were, largely independent of their natural surroundings for some time after birth, as they are also during the often prolonged period of gestation. With birds, reptiles, fishes, insects and many other kinds of animals it is otherwise. The eggs which are laid may require certain special conditions before hatching can take place, conditions not necessarily the same as those which best suit the adult out of the breeding season. Further, the young forms on hatching may be quite unlike the parents; they may require to be fed by the adults, as occurs with almost all birds; they may need food of a kind not taken by the adults, when it is a necessity for survival that hatching should take place in a suitable medium. Thus a second great type of migration is one whose purpose it is to ensure the well-being of the young. This is often much more complex and difficult to explain. Once their parental duties are over the adults may return to the point from which they started, either to repeat the process in a new season, or, as happens with some kinds of salmon, eels and many insects, death may follow at the end of the single migratory movement, and it is the young only which ever return.

Both these types of migration are regular, to-and-fro movements, whether they affect the individuals, as with birds, or the generations, as with some fish, and appear as automatic as the motions of the earth, which seem to be their stimulus. The suggestion that it is the movements of the earth which induce some members of the salmon family to migrate from salt water to fresh to spawn; the eels to reverse the process and move from fresh water to salt; and

E.N.A.

STURDY VAGRANTS OF SEA AND LAND IN THE WILDS OF NORTH AMERICA

These fine seals (bottom) were photographed on St. Paul's Island, off the Alaskan coast. Seals make enormous journeys to their breeding grounds ashore. The upper photograph is of six moose, marching in single file along the frozen surface of a river in British Columbia. They are probably in search of a suitable site for what is called a "môose yard," a space trampled in the snow till the surface is firm, where the animals can feed on tree bark and defend themselves more effectively against the wolves.

CARIBOU SWIMMING AN ALASKAN RIVER ENCOUNTERED ON THE MARCH

During the course of migration north or south, animals usually follow more or less well-defined trails. Often the journey involves the encountering of formidable natural obstacles of which rivers are the most dangerous. Here we see some caribou swimming an Alaskan river during the process of migrating to new pastures. The caribou is condemned always to wander, its big journeys only being extensions of the daily excursions for food. These activities all help to weed out the weaker individuals and preserve the vigour of the race.

certain other fish like the herrings, with other marine animals, such as some cuttlefish and some jellyfish, to travel from deep water to shallow for the same purpose, may seem absurd. But the ocean no less than the surface of the lands shows seasonal variations, as in its minute floating plants, in its temperature distribution, in its salinity and so forth, and such changes do, with the associated currents, exert great influence on the movements of marine animals.

Before discussing examples of this complex second type of migration among birds, which show it in its most striking form, we have to note that apart from such regular, seasonally-controlled movements, others occur of quite different character. Their special features are first their irregularity in time, and second the absence of that return to the starting-point which is so characteristic of true migration. Swallows, swifts, cuckoos and other common migrants go each autumn but return every spring; fieldfares and redwings seek in winter the unfrozen ground on which alone they can feed, but as spring comes in their breeding-grounds they leave; the true birds of passage put in their fleeting appearance in spring and autumn, but each summer and each winter finds them elsewhere. As compared with such regular movements we have phenomena like the appearance in Britain from time to time, but often in great abundance, of unfamiliar butterflies or birds, or the occasional spread far beyond their normal habitat of rapidly-multiplying rodents like lemmings.

The case of the lemmings has always aroused great interest, though it is not really unique, other small mammals migrating in similar fashion. What happens is that at certain quite irregular periods of years the numbers of this small tundra animal increase far beyond the available food supplies in their mountain (as in Scandinavia) or Arctic habitat. Naturally social animals, when, under the stimulus of want, they begin to invade neighbouring areas they do so in swarms which may attain almost incredible numbers. While in the normal sedentary condition the animals avoid water, when on the march they swim, or attempt to swim, streams, rivers, lakes and other bodies of water on their way. It is often said that the march is continued to the sea, into which all plunge and are drowned. This is, of course, a picturesque overstatement, due to the fact that observations have been made mainly in Scandinavia, where movement to the lower and more productive grounds, if sufficiently long-continued, necessarily leads to the sea.

There is not a little analogy between these lemming migrations and those of locusts, which often multiply in similar fashion within a particular area till the food supplies fail, and then swarm outwards into adjacent areas. In both cases the swarms attract much

E.N.A.

Mondiale

NORWEGIAN AND ALASKAN REINDEER THAT MAKE GREAT SEASONAL MIGRATIONS

Large herbivores of northern or sub-Arctic regions tend to follow the movements of the snowline. The reindeer still make great marches from one season's feeding ground to another. In Scandinavia the herds are becoming domesticated and their movements controlled, to some extent, by herdsmen. The lower photograph shows a herd of Norwegian reindeer. They are fine swimmers and, when on the southward march in winter, often swim off from the mainland to the islands for food. Above are some Alaskan reindeer.

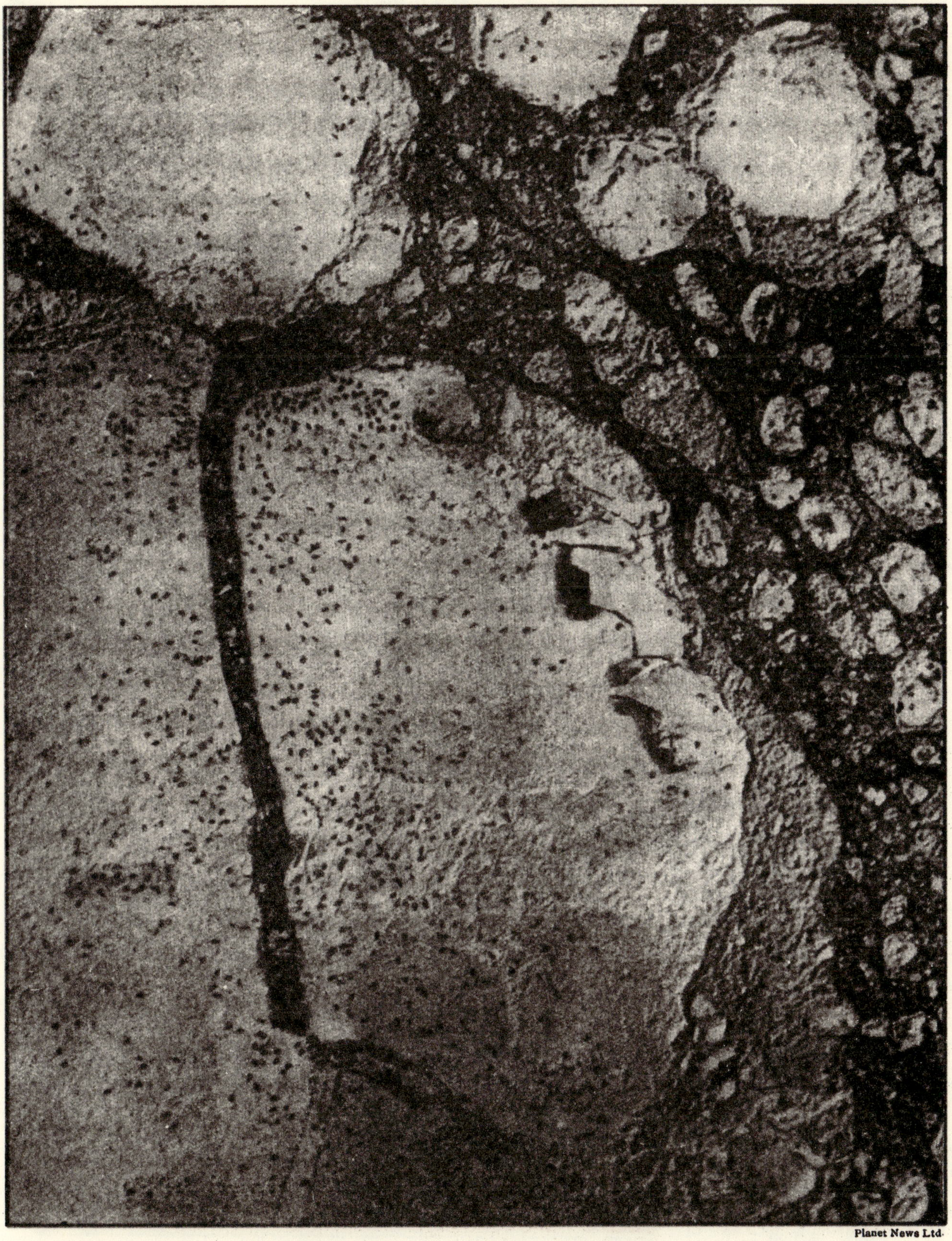

Planet News Ltd.

HOW A SEAL HERD LOOKS FROM AN AEROPLANE FLYING OVER THE FROZEN SEA

To realize the size of a seal herd it is necessary to be up in an aeroplane. This does not disturb the animals and allows, of course, a very wide view of the surrounding floes. The wonderful photograph which we have here was taken by an aeroplane employed by a sealing expedition. To save much time in locating the herd the aircraft was sent up and, covering an enormous distance in a short time, compared to a ship, sent the whereabouts of the seals to the sealers by wireless. Such methods seem to presage the seal's extinction.

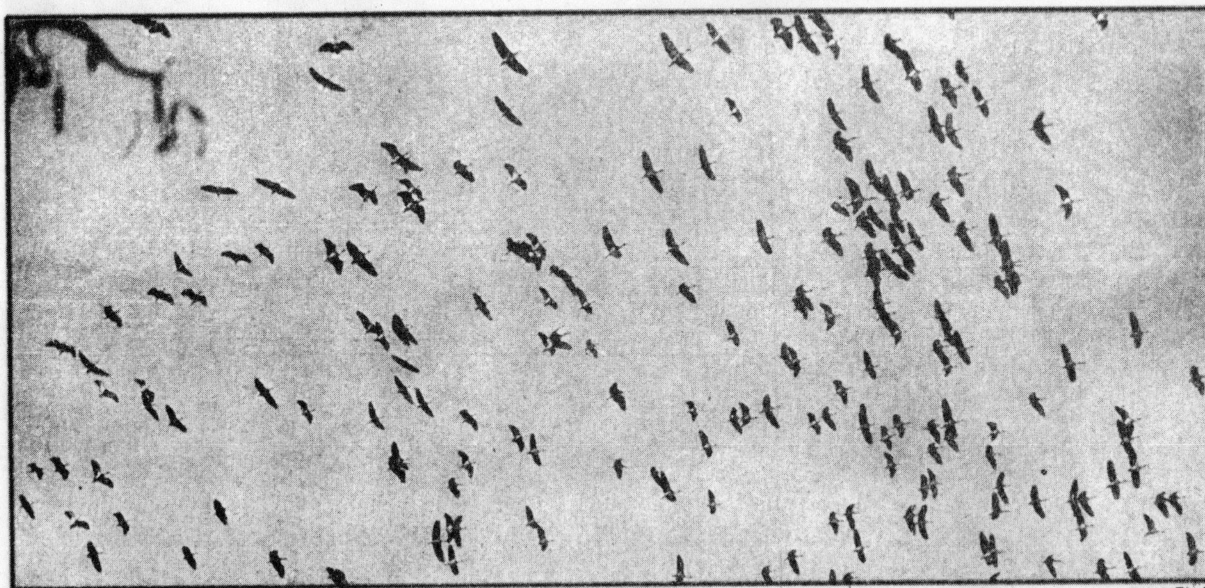

Frank Birtle

attention because of their destructiveness, and because the dead or dying stragglers may pollute water supplies and in other ways affect human life. Other cases of the same phenomenon are less noticed because these elements are absent. For example, the painted Lady butterfly is as a rule rare in England. But in certain years, particularly if favourable winds prevail at certain times, great swarms cross the Straits of Dover, and the butterfly becomes locally very common.

THE immediate cause of such sporadic increases in numbers of certain kinds of animals is probably those marked nonperiodic variations in climate which are known to occur in many parts of the earth. But the outward movement, from one standpoint, is but an illustration of the general tendency of organisms to spread over the earth, a tendency kept in check under normal circumstances by the struggle for existence. In the case of the lemmings it seems to be established that the swarming neither results in a permanent increase in numbers within the original habitat, nor in a colonisation of new territory. On the contrary, indeed, it would seem

Oliver G. Pike

GREY LAG GOOSE AND AUSTRALIAN WILD FOWL

Once the grey lag goose (bottom) used to breed regularly in Norfolk, but now it is chiefly as a winter visitor that this bird is seen in England. The impression of eagerness in its flight cannot be forgotten when it has once been seen, and is largely due to the long, stretched forward neck. The upper photograph shows migrant Australian wild fowl in flight.

ARROW HEAD OF WILD GEESE ON THE WING FOR THE LONELY NORTH

That the Irish gave to those of their compatriots who, in the eighteenth century, left their country to seek their fortunes abroad the name of "the wild geese" suggests that these birds are, in actuality, great wanderers and travellers. The wonderful flying wedge moving remotely across the sky but travelling very fast, which is a flock or gaggle of geese, is one of the most stirring sights in wild nature. So high can these wonderful birds fly that they cross the Himalayas, and it is thought that they then reach an elevation of over six miles.

that not only do most of the migrants die without leaving progeny, but that as a result of the migrating process the original habitat shows a diminished lemming population for many years afterwards. If, however, the period of abnormal weather conditions which we have assumed to be the cause of the sudden increase of numbers had not been a mere variation, but an indication of the approach of a secular climatic change, an extension of the range of the species might have taken place.

SUCH an extension, though not due to a climatic change, has taken place in the case of the brown rat. Originally, it would seem, a native of Western China, this animal is known to have penetrated into Europe from Asia in the early part of the 18th century. It swam across the Volga, and migrated along the line of rivers and canals. This was the beginning of an enormous and world-wide extension of range, accompanied by a great increase in numbers. Rats share with the lemming and many other kinds of rodents the habit of migrating in bands when the local food supply fails or conditions prove unfavourable. But the success of the brown rat, as compared with the failure of the lemming, is due not only to its omnivorous habit, its intelligence and ferocity, but to the way in which it attaches itself to man and finds food and shelter in his buildings, storehouses, corn ricks and so on, so that it is in part protected from the struggle for existence as it affects truly wild animals. Its success is aided by civilised man's habit of destroying, wantonly or of necessity, the predatory animals which find in such small rodents their natural prey.

Still another type of movement is illustrated by the wandering ants (*Eciton*) of Central and South America, animals again as remarkable for their numbers as for their destructiveness. They are true nomads, not forming permanent homes like most social insects, but moving from place to place in search of food, the temporary nests serving merely as nurseries for the young. The ants on occasion invade man's dwellings in great bands, and then disappear, giving the impression of an army on the march. But again the explanation is simple. The lands in which they dwell show little seasonal change, but the social habit of the insects means that the resources of a particular area are soon, though temporarily, exhausted. The ants have therefore acquired the nomadic habit, though if all the facts were known it would probably be found that the range of the raids of any particular

E.N.A.

BROWN PELICANS AND WILD DUCKS AND THE FORMATIONS IN WHICH THEY FLY

While the pelicans may seem about as clumsy as possible on land yet they are extremely powerful flyers, taking up formation in long lines and maintaining them with as much precision as a squadron of fighting aeroplanes. These lines in which they fly may comprise hundreds of birds and are a most impressive sight. Pelicans fly with the neck bent back over the body and the huge beak resting on the breast. They make considerable journeys to and from their feeding and breeding grounds, estuaries and lagoons being their favourite haunts. Skeletons of pelicans have been found in the fen districts of Cambridgeshire, but the birds never visit England now. The right-hand photograph shows wild ducks. They can attain a speed of a mile a minute.

W. S. Berridge

FOUR STRONG-WINGED VISITORS TO THE BRITISH ISLES FROM FAR COUNTRIES

Found over the greater part of Europe and Asia, the woodcock (bottom left) breeds over a very wide area—northwards as far as the Arctic Circle and southwards as far as the Alps and the Himalayas. Those individuals which breed in the south are probably residents, but those from the north are migrant. Many of the latter visit the British Isles in the autumn. The wheatear (bottom right) comes north in the early spring to breed, arriving in March and being one of the earliest migrants in Britain. The cuckoo (top left) having seen its young safely launched into the world in the care of foster parents, leaves for the south some time before its offspring are ready. The waxwing (top right) is another visitor to Britain from afar.

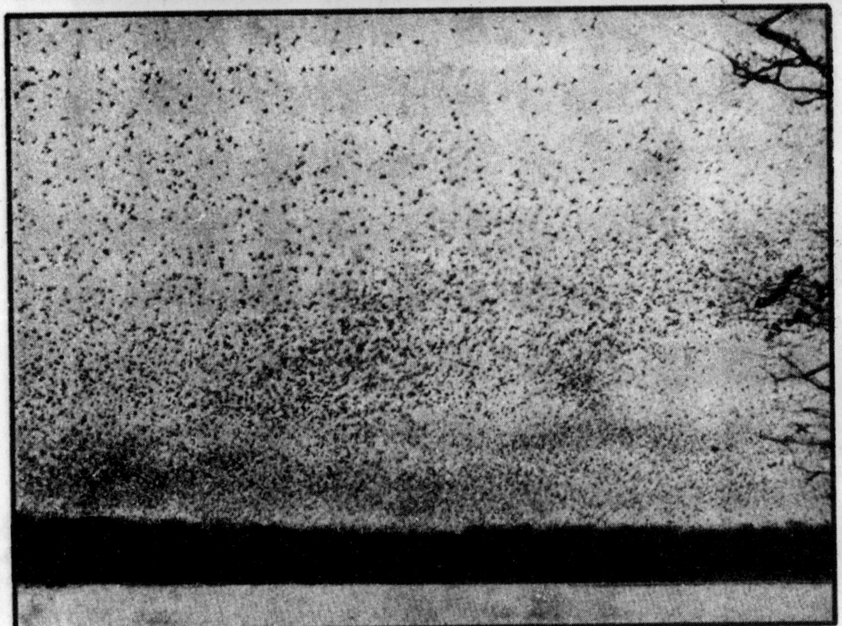

E. N. A.

MALLARDS AND A GREAT CONCOURSE OF GULLS

Most abundant of the fresh-water birds of Britain, the mallard or wild duck resides in considerable numbers in England throughout the year. But much greater numbers arrive from Europe during the winter (bottom), the mallard being a very strong and swift flyer. Gulls (top) are all either wholly or partly migratory in their habits—restless wanderers over the face of the sea.

horde was always small. Essentially the raiding habit here is a form of response to the enormous and virtually continuous productivity of the hot-wet lands of the earth. The bands may appear to destroy everything in their passage, but nature repairs their ravages so rapidly that growth—in the absence of any marked seasonal check—can keep pace with destruction and new resources are always available in some part of the zone of operations.

Many other types of mass-movement exist. The swarming of the hive bee, the nuptial flights of many kinds of true ants and of termites, or white ants, for example, illustrate the way in which sedentary social insects ensure the spread of the species. But none of these movements is comparable in

W. S. Berridge

KITE, CURLEW, CRANE AND STORK THAT FOLLOW THE SEASONS CHANGES

Birds which migrate have the instinct very deep-seated, and all its workings are not clear to us. But some of the causes which prompt these great journeys are obvious enough. The arrival of a bird in the land where it chooses to nest coincides with the natural multiplication of its food—insect, vegetable or animal. In going north, too, birds get more hours of daylight in which to find food for their hungry young. These photographs show (bottom left) a kite; (bottom right) a curlew; (top left) a crane, and (top right) a stork.

Natural History. N.Y

SWARM OF BUTTERFLIES RESTING DURING MIGRATION

Under normal conditions there is a tendency for races of animals to spread over the earth This tendency is checked by the interaction of one species upon another. Our photograph shows a swarm of monarch butterflies in the U.S.A. during the great southward flight they make every autumn.

interest to true migration as illustrated by birds. Bird migration may indeed be said to be one of the most wonderful phenomena of the animal world, and of it, as yet, we are able to give no completely adequate explanation.

The main facts are now fairly well known. A great number of different kinds of birds travel northwards in spring to nest and rear their young in cool, temperate or even Arctic latitudes. As autumn approaches these birds manifest great restlessness, often collecting together in bands. At certain dates, more or less fixed for the species, and showing no very close relation to the prevailing weather, mass movements to the south set in. The migrants follow definite lines, which can now be more or less accurately plotted on the map, and often travel enormous distances, so that birds which nest in Northern Europe or North-West Asia may winter in Africa south of the Equator, and others nesting in North-East Asia may winter in the Malay region or even in Australia. There is no corresponding large-scale movement of nesting forms into south, temperate or Antarctic latitudes, a fact which may be associated with the narrowing of the southern continents, their limited extension into temperate latitudes and the general unsuitability of the Antarctic continent for land plants and animals. Further, it should be noted that not all forms which breed in high northern latitudes migrate across the Equator in winter. The redstart is an example of a bird which breeds as far north as the North Cape in Europe, but does not in winter extend beyond the northern half of Africa.

The migrating instinct, where it occurs, is clearly both deep-seated and long-established. Though we do not know all the causes of its origin, part at least of its value is easily realized. The nesting process results in a great and sudden increase in the bird population, with a resultant heavy demand on food supplies. In temperate and even Arctic latitudes the spring renewal of life means just such a sudden increase of resources as is required. Insects in particular—a very important element in the food of birds—become very abundant.

An even more important factor is probably the length of the day. Most birds, like many insects, are active only by day, and the former require daylight to find food both for themselves and their nestlings. It has been found that in parts at least of areas in the higher latitudes, broods are larger and nestlings grow more rapidly than in the case of the same species when nesting in lower latitudes. This is associated with the greater number of hours during which feeding can be carried on. Again, it is found that some small tropical birds will not live through the winter in the north, even in well-warmed aviaries, unless artificial light is supplied so that they can feed during the hours of darkness. This makes it probable that the curiously punctual departure of many summer migrants, which so often seems independent of the weather, is caused not by falling temperature but by diminishing daylight. Such a view helps to explain why the adults not uncommonly leave before the young birds, for the latter, which have been fed by their parents, must have greater reserves than the breeding adults, who have expended much muscular energy in obtaining food from which they derived no benefit.

Chapter XCV

Marvels of Animal Craftsmanship

By Lewis Spence

THE nature of that which we call instinct in animals is still as dark to us as the secret of the origin of life itself. Those who have investigated it have too frequently been under the impression that the mental processes of animals are bound, in a measure, to resemble those of man himself. However that may be, instinct in animals appears more as a hereditary and native quality, like that of self-preservation, than reason pure and simple. That animals do employ reason on occasion is a proven fact, but this seems to occur more in sudden encounters with exceptional situations than in the round of their everyday existence.

Men, to excel in any craft, must labour for years in an apprenticeship of hard-won knowledge; but the beaver, the spider, and the bee enter into a phase of journeyman skill at an age when humans are still helpless and infantile. That in many cases they are actually instructed by their elders in the natural crafts which their several species have developed is scarcely to be disputed, but the aptitude with which they learn is eloquent of the presence of natural and inherent qualities the origin of which is still dark to us. There are no unskilful builders among the bees, no imperfect carpenters among the beavers, no second-rate spinners in the spider world; and in none of the teeming cities of the ants has the question of unemployment been known to present itself.

Still, amazingly clever as the craftsmanship of many animal and insect societies may be, they are nearly all limited to one particular direction of effort which, in the majority of instances, is associated either with their methods of procuring food, or is designed for their self-preservation. They resemble the craft-castes of India, in that their generations adhere to the one trade; they are like Mr. Wells's men in the moon, who herded in craft colonies.

Natural History, N.Y.

MUD-WASPS' NESTS LIKE PAN'S PIPES

Though the mud-wasp never sees its children it makes very careful provision for their welfare, constructing these wonderful nests from mud, stocking each one with stung and paralysed caterpillars, and leaving the eggs to hatch and the larva to feed on them.

But although the motive power of these activities is attributed to that mysterious inspiration which, for want of a better definition, we call instinct, they are frequently of such a nature as to excite our utmost admiration, and even our envy, and we are forced to confess that we superior beings have learned not a little from the subtly clever, intricate and often beautiful creations of animal artificers. Nor do these architects and engineers, these decorators and jewellers, invariably rely on inherited and natural skill. They have been known to think for themselves, to break away from tradition, to evince mental traits which seem to show that other forms of life save man are capable of some degree of conscious self-development.

Surveying first the craftsmanship of the mammalian world, we find ourselves most naturally observing those artificers whose engineering skill must, at an early era, have supplied man with more than one useful hint, the beaver family. The Canadian beaver is a naturally gregarious creature, although his reputation as a "good mixer" seems to be limited to the family, yet it frequently takes a tribal turn. His "villages" consist of a congerie of "lodges," situated in running water, each of which contains some half-dozen individuals—father, mother and little ones—and the work of construction proceeds as these set up house for themselves and the site becomes congested. These lodges are in reality dome-shaped gateways to one end of their burrows, the other being under water; and as the main design is to keep the stream in which they are situated at a constant level, so that the subaquatic entrance may not be exposed, it becomes necessary, in order to effect this, to build a dam right across the river.

A sluggish stream is dammed straight across, but swifter-running

Mondiale

water is crossed by a V-shaped construction not unlike the shape of the piers of a Roman bridge, in order that the force of the current may be broken more gradually. The logs are laid horizontally, covered with mud and stones, and bound together by withes and branches from the felled trees for greater security. Some of the larger dams actually cover a distance of three hundred yards, and may be as thick as ten or twelve feet. The lodges are usually contrived of twigs and branches, plastered with mud and lined with grass, and here the beaver folk huddle during the long Canadian winter.

Many mammals, like some races of early man, live as much beneath the earth as upon it, and this habit of self-protection has endowed them with wonderful powers as sappers and miners. The fox, the mole, the badger and the gopher are all professional tunnellers whose very lives depend upon their skill and prowess in this direction.

The mole, with his gimlet-shaped proboscis and shovel-like feet, works much nearer the surface than might be supposed; so near, in fact, that his progress may frequently be noted directly under

E. N. A.

BEAVER CRAFTSMEN AND THEIR DAMS

As aquatic engineers the beavers know all about their business, adjusting the formation of their dams to the exigencies of swift or slow-running water. We see two at work on a dam (bottom) and a big dam in Montana (top). Beavers are very shy and difficult to photograph.

E.N.A.

Mondiale

WEAVER BIRDS' NESTS IN AFRICA AND A TAILOR BIRD AND ITS NEST

Superficially the weaver birds, which are very widely distributed from Africa to Australia, much resemble finches. The bottom and top right photographs show nests of African varieties from Sierra Leone and Tanganyika. One kind builds in a tree with a company of its fellows so that it looks as though the branches bore some strange new fruit. The other builds long, slender, flask-like nests. The top left-hand photograph shows a tailor bird and its remarkable nest, from the Dutch East Indies.

AUSTRALIAN BUILDERS OF WONDERFULLY DELICATE NESTS: MISTLETOE BIRD AND FANTAIL

Mistletoe birds, which live in Australia, build their nests of wool or, failing that, wool-like fibres from plants. These fibres, or the strands of wool, are short and quite unlike the long strands which other birds use, and the whole substance of the finished nest has the texture of felt. But it is strong, for it supports several young birds and one or other of the parents at the same time, as we see above (left). The right-hand photograph is of another Australian bird, the fantail. This constructs an exquisitely delicate nest out of bark and spiders' webs. It is shaped roughly like a pipe bowl, and this idea is strengthened when a branch projects from one side of it, as happens when the base of the nest is built round a twig of the stem which supports it.

the turf. In constructing his subterranean nest, he first digs a round hole slightly below the surface, pushing the earth upward as he proceeds. But he is not content with one tunnel for entrance and exit. He requires at least another from which to eject the ever-falling soil which dribbles into his nest, and for a bolt-hole; and this is usually designed in corkscrew form, for the double reason that the earth may not drop down so readily and that he may the better be able to elude pursuit. Should the soil where he has elected to nest be of a boggy nature, he digs still other galleries for the purpose of bringing earth to heap over the nest. The nest itself is spherical in shape and about the size of a large melon. It is composed of a ball of grass or leaves, every scrap of which has to be conveyed to it in the mouth. It is invariably closed, even when it contains the family of young ones.

A. S. Berridge

HOW THE NESTS OF THE WEAVER BIRDS ARE BUILT

Below we see a red-billed weaver bird of East Africa in the process of building its nest. Certain kinds of weaver bird make communal nests of twigs, so closely interwoven as to bar the entrance of anything save a very small snake. The same nest is used year after year, dilapidations being made good by all tenants. Above are weaver bird nests from Bengal.

A SAPPER peculiarly expert is the Arctic fox, which, unlike the English Reynard, is communal in its habits, dwelling in large subterranean societies or "villages," but keeping nevertheless to its own compartments. Because of the Arctic cold, its burrows are extraordinarily deep, with a kind of "living-room" at the end of the entrance tunnel, from which lesser "apartments," nurseries and dormitories, branch off. Not infrequently the entire "house" is connected up by the most complex passages.

But an American tunneller, the prairie dog, has him beaten to a frazzle in the matter of cunning excavation, for his plans are as precise and as well-laid as that of the engineer of a London "tube." "Underground to anywhere" is indeed his native motto, the very philosophy by which he lives. Entering the earth at an angle of forty-five

H. Bastin

E.N.A.

BOWER-BIRDS THAT CONSTRUCT ARBOURS TO ATTRACT MATES

Bower-birds are related to the birds of paradise and are confined to Australia, New Guinea and the adjacent islands. The satin bower-bird (bottom) of the New South Wales waste lands builds a wonderful "bower" of sticks and grass, adorned with stones and shells and the bright feathers of parrots. The bower is really a tunnel about twelve inches long, and is built by the male as a kind of pleasaunce for the hen bird. Above we see bower-birds at work. Their practice of making arbours is unique among birds.

INCUBATORS BUILT BY BIRDS WHERE THE EGGS HATCH BY THEMSELVES

Certain Australian birds do not sit on their eggs but make a mound of vegetable matter and bury their eggs in that. The heat of the mound, decomposing in the sun, hatches out the clutch. The lower photograph shows the mound made by the hen of the mallee fowl. The eggs are laid in layers, separated by sand, and in very hot weather the top of the mound is removed by the bird, as we see here. Above is the incubator of a brush turkey which is equivalent to many cartloads of vegetable matter and takes several weeks to collect.

H. Bastin

NEST OF THE EDIBLE SWIFT

Despite the name, it is not the swift which is particularly edible, but its nest, made of the secretion from the salivary glands which the Chinese make into soup. The photograph shows how a kind of cup made of solidified saliva is fixed to its support.

degrees, and extending downwards for about five feet or thereabouts, his main passage takes a sudden sharp turning, ending in his reception room. But as he is a sociable little fellow, he burrows into the parlours of his next door neighbours. His cities are spread over enormous areas in the deserts of North America, and the odd thing is that he seems to be able to carry on with almost no water supply.

The pocket-gopher, another North American animal, burrows expressly to find the roots of plants. Armed with formidable claws, he tunnels down to the roots of a tree in short order, and constructs his nest of dried grass between its fibrous walls, hollowing out two chambers, a nursery and a larder.

Some animals are as expert in nest-building as their feathered neighbours. The bettong, or brush-tailed rat-kangaroo of Australia, is an ingenious architect which seeks a hollow in the ground, and roofs it over with grass and leaves, which she gathers and carries back to the nest, by rolling them into a bundle with her tail. The squirrel's nest has been described elsewhere, but those of the man-like apes deserve passing mention. The chimpanzee builds his of branches bent to shape, forming a substantial platform about 28 feet from the ground, and frequently secured to the trunk by the stems of creeping plants. Some of these structures are, however, mere canopies to keep out the heavy tropical rain. But, on the whole, birds certainly exhibit a higher degree of craftsmanship than most animals, and frequently extraordinary skill is to be observed in their methods. The humming-bird, for example, employs the web of the spider as a building medium, not only to hold the mossy fabric together, but also to attach it to the leaf on which it stands. This tiniest of the winged people also exhibits much skill in producing an exact balance for its nest, so that the eggs may lie securely, and to effect this it daubs mud or even introduces small stones into the structure so that the proper degree of equilibrium is secured.

The British chaffinch is a model nest architect. She invariably selects a firm foundation, and by interweaving wool with moss, thistle-down and spiders' webs, produces a marvellous structure, both firm and elastic, which is always wonderfully camouflaged. Some weaver-birds build a communal nest in harmony with their social instincts. Indeed, these birds live under one roof, often to the number of three hundred. The structure is built of bushman grass in an acacia tree, and looks like a mass of matted hay pierced by holes.

The "pedrero" or stone-mason bird, found in the south of Spain, builds a dry-stone "dyke" along the front of the space which the nest is to occupy, and the stones of which it is composed are frequently so heavy that how it manages to convey them to the spot is something of a mystery. Inside this barrier it builds a well-upholstered nest. But foundations of "masonry" are not uncommon even among British birds; for example, the ringed plover, and the blackbird and magpie, whose nests often have a base of dried mud. Swallows and house-martins build by sticking together pellets of prepared road-mud, obtained from drying puddles on the highway, and mixed with a mucous secretion from the bird, which acts as mortar.

Many foreign birds build hanging nests of extraordinary form, pear-shaped, bottle-shaped, and so forth. The Baltimore oriole, an American bird, suspends its nest from a branch, weaving it piecemeal until it takes the form of a straw hat half-finished. The basis is strong fibre surrounded by finer material and lined with horsehair, nor will the little builder be content with anything but the correct and appropriate materials, looting the entire countryside for bleaching threads and hanks of silk.

The pied granilla is a worker in clay, mixing the muddy basis with twigs, feathers and grasses, to form a stiff plaster which is hardened to a brick-like consistency by the sun. Its dome-shaped sides have a tiny opening, a mere gash in the clay, and a partition of mud gives it further strength and consistency, the male and female birds occupying separate chambers during the period of incubation.

The edible nest of the swift, which is considered so great a luxury at Chinese dinner-tables, is formed by the saliva of the bird which somewhat resembles isinglass. These are found in limestone and volcanic rocks, and as often as the birds build, the collectors remove their nests, which, in the Chinese markets,

NEST-CRAFT OF HARVEST MICE AMONG POPPIES AND YELLOW CORN

An acre of standing corn is a close-set forest of mystery wherein a secret, transitory life goes on until the reaper comes. There are rabbits and many birds there and, of course, the pretty, small harvest-mice. These twist straws together round three or four stalks to form a nest. Here we see young ones in the nest, and adult mice, their tails curled about the corn stems, eating the fruit of these miniature "tree-tops".

M. Duncan

WONDERFUL CRAFTSMANSHIP OF LOWLY SEA CREATURES

There are more kinds of sponges in the sea than ever were seen in a bath. It was not till the early nineteenth century that it was definitely known that the sponge was a colony of living creatures and not a sea plant. The forms and shapes are extremely varied and it is only those which, like the Turkey sponges of commerce, form horny skeletons, that are used for washing. On the right of this photograph are some sea fans contrived in beautiful lace-like patterns.

are worth their weight in silver for the purpose of making the far-famed birds'-nest soup.

For a long time the material from which the nest of the fiery topaz is made was a mystery to ornithologists. The small horn-shaped structure, with the point adhering to a branch, seemed to be made of leather, but it is actually contrived from a fungus of the genus Boletus, a tough and leathery growth, which the bird shapes deftly into the required mould.

Of cunning nests there is indeed no end, but to provide a worthy example a description of that of the tailor-bird will suffice. He builds his snowy structure in the folds of a leaf, sewing the edges together, using his beak as a needle by boring holes along the outer rim and then inserting plant fibres in the interstices. The leaf (or, perhaps, two leaves) is thus fashioned into a cone, the ends are knotted as a seamstress might do it, and the nest is introduced into the cavity.

AMONG bird carpenters the woodpecker is one of the few British species of this character, carefully excavating his nest-hole in a rotten willow, but seldom in sound oaks and elms, as popular fancy imagines. But he has, at least, once been badly cheated. In America the earliest telegraph poles were often damaged by woodpeckers, which mistook the humming of the wires for the buzzing of insects concealed in the poles and dug to find—nothing! He employs an oblique blow when he strikes for grubs, and his favourite prospecting ground is a tree which exposes a length of barkless wood, usually a Scotch fir. The ivory-billed woodpecker of the Lower Mississippi can chip off a piece of bark eight inches square with its powerful beak, and cartloads of bark thus detached from enormous pine-trees have not infrequently led explorers to believe that a gang of axe-men had been at work.

Eggs are productions which may legitimately be regarded as works of art, especially from the colour point of view. The eggs of the different species of birds have their especial peculiarities in surface texture and shape, those birds which lay in flat nests producing oval eggs which will not roll, and those which nest in holes, like the kingfisher or the owl, producing round eggs which roll easily.

The colour of eggs is usually a matter of protective camouflage, spots, veins and dyes usually agreeing with the natural surroundings of the species which lay them. The puffins, woodpeckers, kingfishers and

H Bastin

SCARAB BEETLES WITH THE FOOD PELLETS WHICH THEY MAKE

These large pellets—large, that is, when we compare them with their makers—serve the double purpose of providing food for the beetles and nurseries for their larvae. Dung is the material always used, and having moulded the substance into a ball, the scarab buries it and lays its eggs inside. In the above illustration we see how these industrious creatures manipulate their food supply. On the left two are co-operating, one pushing and the other pulling the pellet along.

owls—all those birds, in fact, which cover their nests—lay white eggs, but those birds whose eggs are not so carefully concealed usually produce spotted or coloured eggs. Birds of brilliant plumage seldom lay brightly-coloured eggs, but eggs of greenish hue are usually laid by birds which nest in the early spring among green trees and shrubs, such as blackbirds, thrushes and crows. However, the magpie, difficult as her nest is to find, lays a spotted egg, as does the jackdaw.

Naturally the ground birds, like the lark, the pipit and the plover, lay eggs which harmonise with their surroundings, but none has brought the business of camouflage to such a fine art as the nightjar, whose eggs, streaked with brown or grey, tone in wonderfully with the colours of the furze bushes under which she lays them. The ringed plover, which always nests in sand, lays an egg covered with fine sand-like points, and the tern, which broods on the verge between sand and beach, imitates the colour of its environment marvellously in the oval with large, bold blotches which it produces.

Hawks' eggs are coloured like the lining of the nest, and the sparrow's eggs shade in with the feathers which line her house. But the guillemot goes one better. She lays eggs of nearly a dozen different colours. These, in their exposed position on the ledges of rocks, are most conspicuous, and it must be in despair of imitating their surroundings that she colours them as she does; or else, trading on the inaccessibility of their position, she bursts out defiantly into a bizarre colour scheme.

On the whole, however, insects betray a much greater tendency to clever workmanship than either birds or beasts. The ubiquitous ant, whose social structure appears well-nigh human, is, as few are aware, a silk-spinner, weaving, while in the grub stage, those cocoons known as "ants' eggs" and sold as food for goldfish. Certain fungus-growing ants exist in tropical America which manure the soil in which they are raised with rotting leaves. Others harvest seeds which are stored in special granaries as food, and another Brazilian species actually designs and lays out gardens formed from earth carried into trees and built up into spherical sponge-shaped masses. In these certain plants are grown by the insects, so that the earthy particles may be held together by their roots.

The termites or white ants are most industrious carpenters or wood-borers. In the tropics it is well-nigh impossible to keep furniture free from their ravages, and in an incredibly short time they can reduce a solid rafter, chair or table to a mere shell of seeming timber. Teak and the resinous woods alone are free from their attacks. In Britain the goat-moth larva, so-called because of the odour it leaves, tunnels through trees with its powerful

G. Hearn

SHORT-TAILED AND LONG-TAILED FIELD MICE AT THEIR CLEVERLY-BUILT HOMES

Voles and wood mice, known indifferently and rather incorrectly as field mice, make their nests either in the banks under hedges or in bushes or cornstacks. Above we have four examples of these intricate little structures made of grasses and twigs, where the young are born and hidden. Notice in the case of the male short-tailed field mouse (or field vole) seen in the top right-hand photograph how the nest is almost invisible amidst the surrounding vegetation which it is cunningly made to match.

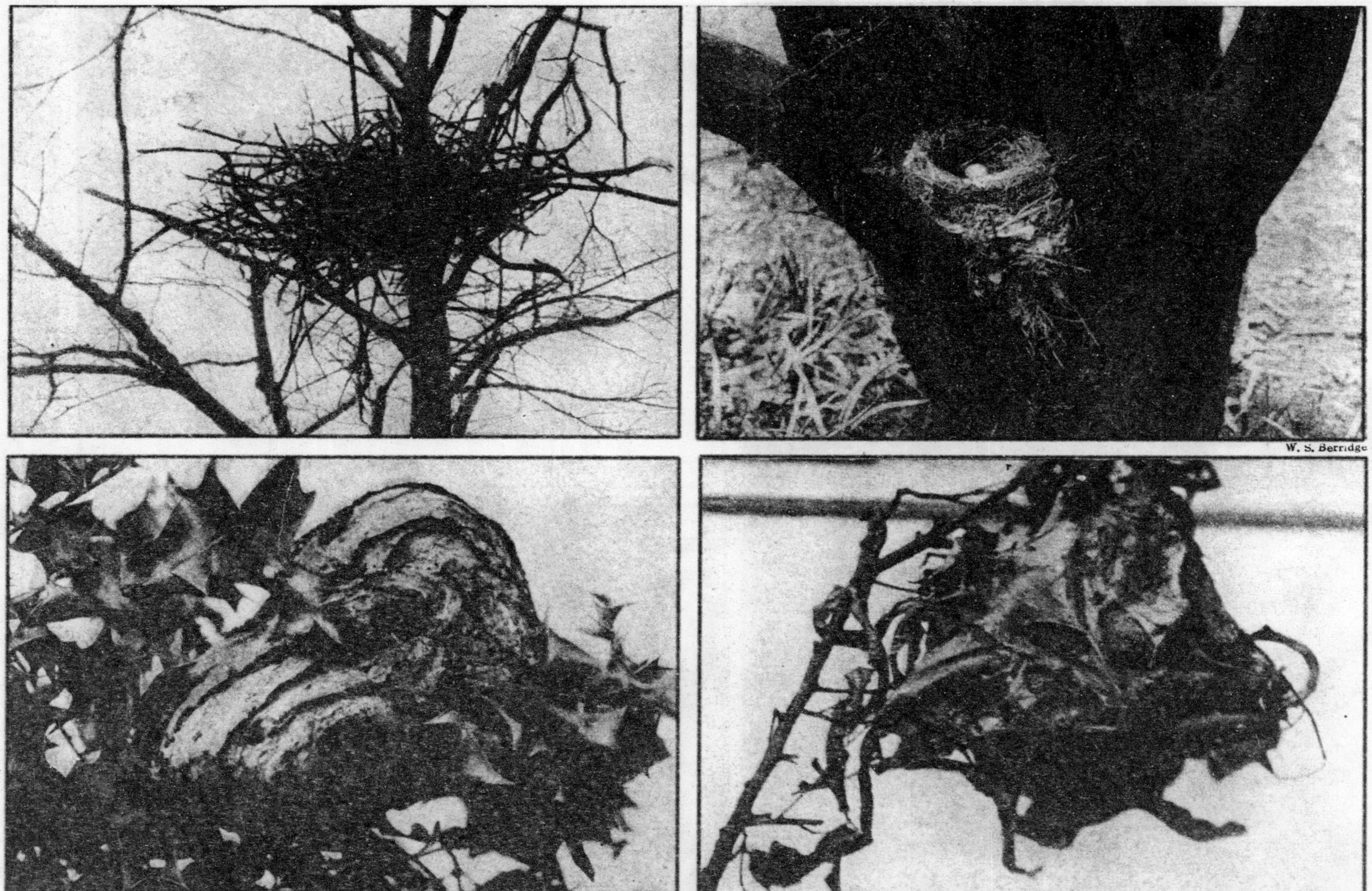

W. S. Berridge

J. J. Ward

W. S. Berridge

FOUR EXAMPLES OF THE TREE NEST BELONGING TO ORANG, BLACKBIRD, TREE WASP AND ANT

Various creatures have put their trust in the trees for safe sleeping and we have four widely-differing examples here. First a most interesting and unusual example of the home of the tree wasp (bottom left). Here two nests have been built together, a sight which is very rarely seen. The double nest is photographed from below. The bottom right-hand photograph shows a nest built by tree-ants outside Calcutta, while above (top left) is the nest built by an orang-utan which escaped once from its cage at the London Zoo. It made off and had built this sleeping place before being caught. Lastly, we have (top right) a blackbird's nest made in a very exposed position, a few feet from the ground.

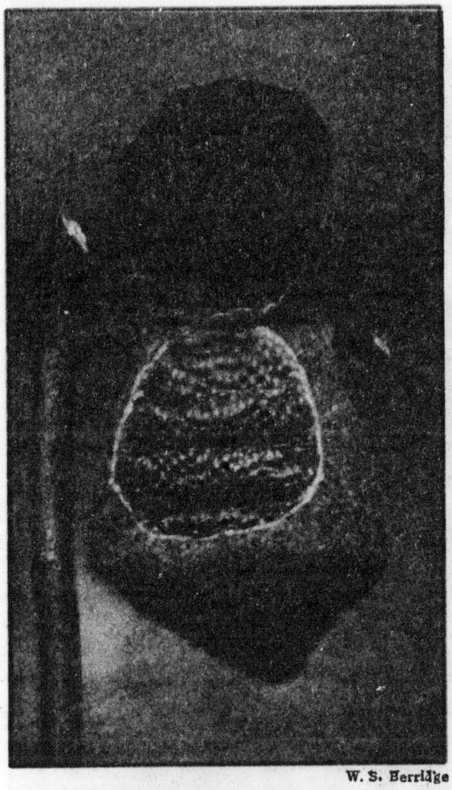

W. S. Berridge

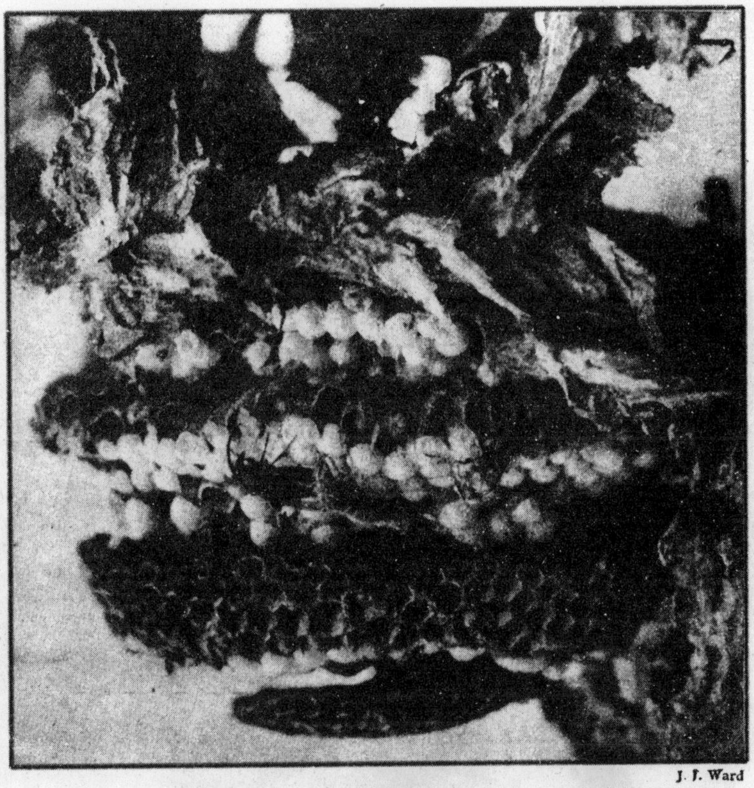

J. J. Ward

W. S. Berridge

TREE-WASPS AND THEIR ELABORATE HOMES
In the upper right-hand photograph we see a British tree-wasp's nest with the covering removed to show queen cells. On the left is a strange nest built by Brazilian tree-wasps cut to show the combs, and (bottom) some other tree-wasps' nest from S. America.

jaws, and exudes a destroying acid calculated to reduce the stoutest wood to an easily bored pulp. Similar in action, and equally destructive, almost, is the so-called death-watch, a wood-devouring beetle whose tappings are merely the call of the female to her mate, five ticks in rapid succession. This tiny pest eats into furniture, depositing its eggs at the end of the tunnel it makes, the young, when hatched, carrying on the work of destruction. The larvae of the wood-leopard moth, another British insect, construct a cell so near to the surface of a tree that the partition is as fine as writing-paper. This gives them the chance to break out at any time, and yet their presence remains almost unobserved. The giant wood-wasp is equipped with a regular gimlet, and the sawdust of the timber she bores passes through her body as through the hollows of that instrument.

THE resin-moth is a gall-maker, throwing out a long, fine, thread-like web, plunging it into the tissue of the leaf, and depositing there her eggs, accompanied by a drop of fluid which heals and seals up the wound in the plant, whether it be oak, willow or rose-bush. In each gall so formed there is a larva, and in autumn, when the leaves fall, the insect within is protected from frost and rain, hatching out in the spring as a chrysalis.

Cocoons are among the most beautiful products of insect life. Certain ants in tropical Africa actually employ the fine silk given off from the mouths of their larvae to repair the damaged sides of leaf-nests, using them as spools and shuttles, placing the mouths of the grubs against the leaf till the silk has adhered to it and sealed it up again. The silver water-beetle clings upside down to some water weed and spins a concave sheet of silk, which she attaches to the plant on which she stands. Then, assuming her proper position, she weaves a similar web and fixes both together so that they form a spherical cocoon in which she deposits her eggs. This tiny craft floats on the water, and in time the larvae are hatched out.

The egg-case of the cockroach resembles a diminutive vanity-bag. Within its horny structure her

J. J. Ward

GROUND-WASP AND TREE-WASP WORK COMPARED

Below we have a ground-wasp's nest excavated to show how a stone was built into the structure because it was too large for the wasps to move. Above are three examples of wasp paper, the material of which the nests are made; on the left that of the ground-wasp and on the right two examples of tree-wasps' paper.

sixteen eggs are deposited, the top being held close by its natural elasticity. The mantis exudes a similar egg-case of froth, which hardens like the shell of an egg through the action of the air. Within this the young spin a silken thread, from which they suspend themselves like spiders, until they have shed their first coats and emerge.

The bee has such a reputation for craftsmanship in architecture, and her methods are so well known that little need here be said of them, especially as they are described elsewhere. In the manufacture of combs, the wax is produced by the worker bee through certain perforated wax-plates in the lower part of her body. Through these, the wax oozes, and the insects, hanging together in groups, produce the scales, which are shaped into cell form by chewing and by the application of the nippers on the insect's hind legs. Some social wasps construct their nests from paper made of wood-pulp, in fact a South American wasp makes its nest of thick pasteboard, which is prepared by scraping the wood fibres from timber and chewing them up with saliva. Most curious as a piece of insect-craft

H. Bastin

H. Bastin

J. J. Ward

H Bastin

THE LEAF-CUTTER BEE UPHOLSTERS ITS HOME WITH ROSE LEAVES

This bee, when it wishes to make a home for itself, finds a piece of rotten wood, easy to bore, and makes a tunnel. Then it flies away to the nearest rose bush and begins to carve out fragments of leaf. For this is the material it uses to line its tunnel. The results to the rose leaves are seen in the top photograph. After cutting (centre left) the required amount the bee carries it, piece by piece (centre right) to its nest, where it constructs cells of the leaf in which to lay its eggs (bottom photograph).

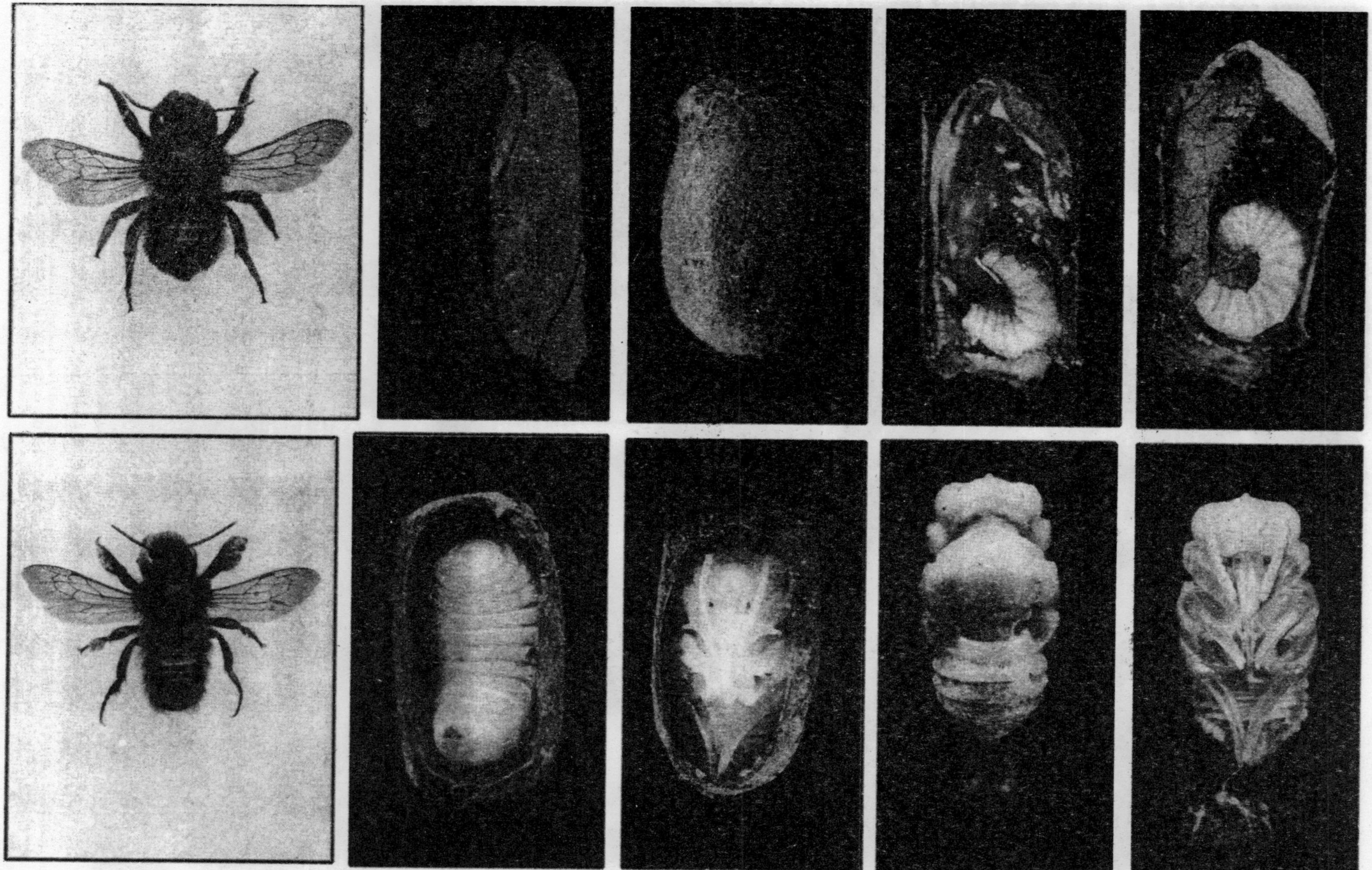

H. Bastin

CONSCIENTIOUS NURSERY WORK OF THE LEAF-CUTTER BEE AND SOME OF ITS RESULTS

From left to right these photographs show (top row) a male leaf-cutter bee; a leaf cell; a cocoon; the cocoon opened at one side to show the developing grub within; and (extreme right) the same grub getting fatter after having eaten nearly all the food supply put by the parent inside the cocoon. In the bottom row we have the female bee, and next a full-grown grub. Then come three illustrations of the pupa stage, first in the cocoon, then a top view, and lastly the underside. Notice the strange wax-like appearance of these immature creatures which are developing, each one in the dark of its rose-leaf cell in a tiny tunnel in a piece of rotten beam. This series of photographs shows a piece of craftsmanship that few people ever notice.

H. Bastin

J. J. Ward

UNTUTORED PROFICIENCY

Nobody teaches the spider to spin webs. Our photograph (bottom) shows a young one which is spinning its very first snare after emerging from its egg. Above are (left) a mason bee making a cell, and (right) the cells of sawdust made by a wood-boring bee.

is the work of the leaf-cutter bee, which papers the walls of her tiny tunnel in some old willow with rose-leaves. She bites through the leaf-tissue in perfect ovals or accurate circles, folds the fragment precisely in the middle, and flies off with it to her cell. Here she bends it to fit the entrance, and glues it to other leaf-fragments with wax until the entire passage is neatly lined. Sometimes as many as a thousand rose-leaf snippings are represented in her strictly utilitarian scheme of decoration.

The carpenter bee, after boring out a gallery for himself in a dead tree, going cleverly with the grain for nearly a couple of feet, mingles the thrown-out sawdust with his saliva and builds partitions and a roof with the mixture, each partition forming a roof to the cell below and a floor to that above. Equally cunning is the wool-carder bee, which constructs a nest of white wool, enclosing wax cells, and this it places in some cavity, an empty snail-shell or even a disused door-lock. The potter bee digs a hole in the soil, making a chamber at the end of the burrow, stamping the clay well down with her feet.

No insect surpasses the ubiquitous spider in artistic ingenuity. She is often capable of spinning two distinct kinds of silk, web and cocoon silk, the latter of which is actually capable of being woven into fabric. Of course there are many varieties of snare in the spider world. One British spinner constructs a trap of but four spokes, from which she hangs by a thread, awaiting her prey. When this appears, she releases her hold on the line, when the spokes fly outward and the insect is caught among them.

But the lace-weaver spider is a much more elaborate and conscious artist that the common spinner. Her foundational sheet-webs are much the same as those of her humbler sister, but across these run a number of fine, wavy bands which give the product a highly decorative effect. She is provided for this work with a special apparatus known as a cribellum, which consists of a plate situated in front of the foremost pair of feet, and perforated with a number of very fine holes. The silk produced from these is corded as it is spun and distributed into the lacy fabric of the web by means of extraordinarily fine combs situated in the hind legs of the female. The raft spider collects a few dead leaves, weaves them with silk into a miniature raft and floats over the surface of the water, an arachnian pirate to capture unwary passing insects.

Among the reptiles craftsmanship is not so rare as might be expected. The American gopher-tortoise is an expert burrower, which lines its sand-nest with fir branches, and the European pond tortoise is no mean engineer. She first moistens the soil with water to render it easily worked, and then, employing her pointed tail as a borer, makes a hole in the ground. This she enlarges with her powerful hind legs, laying her eggs within the cavity, and throwing her body on the loose soil with which she has covered the eggs until it is stamped down flat. The manner in which the Brazilian tree-frog constructs its nurseries of mud verges on the human, and observers have written of the extraordinary man-like way in which it uses its forepaws to smooth the exterior of those structures, " working like a mason with his trowel," and levelling the floor with its stomach.

The ingenuity of the finny tribe is confined mainly to nest-building, usually of a primitive kind. Perhaps the most ingenious is that of the goby, which inhabits sea pools and selects for its nest the shell of a limpet or crab, turning it so that it serves the purpose of a tent. The parents work their way out of this shelter through the sand, leaving a round entrance, over which the male lays a filmy secretion from his body

H. Bastin

BIRCH-WEEVIL MAKING A PURSE OUT OF A LEAF IN WHICH TO HIDE ITS EGGS

For the purpose of making a safe deposit for its eggs the birch-weevil seeks out a birch leaf and, towards the base, makes two cuts—each shaped like an "S"—one on either side of the midrib of the leaf (top left). The other photographs in the upper row show, in turn, the next stages. The weevil begins to roll up the leaf on one side towards the midrib. In the lower photographs we see—from left to right—how the egg case is completed. The other side of the leaf is now rolled up and the weevil disappears inside the purse thus formed. Then it tightens up the folds, tightens them again, and, finally, when all is accomplished, takes a rest from its tremendous task in the uncut part of the leaf.

M H Crawford

J. J. Ward & W. S. Berridge

WONDERFUL NURSERY BOXES IN WHICH SOME CATERPILLARS GROW UP

On the left is a lilac leaf ingeniously sewn together to hide the cocoon in which a caterpillar of the orange moth is developing. The centre photograph shows the nest of the processionary caterpillar. There are about two hundred individuals inside, and when they want food they crawl to the ground and set off in single file, each one joining up behind the next in front until the procession finds a suitable tree to feed on. After eating, the gang comes home as it went. On the right is a cocoon like a paper balloon, made by the larva of the golden plusia moth.

in order to hold the particles of sand together and keep the opening free. In this nest the eggs remain secure, the goby taking up a position near the entrance and waving his fins so that a fresh current of water continually passes over them.

The common stickleback's nest is perhaps as elaborate as any. It brings grass and aquatic weeds from a considerable distance which it carefully lays down on the bed of the stream, interlaced so as to form a neat and compact structure, smooth and rounded inside, but rough and unfinished without. It is held together by a secretion from the male, which acts as a natural mortar.

AMONG the crustaceans there appears to be little ingenuity, but the mollusca make up for the deficiencies of their greater cousins. Originally naked and defenceless, the molluscs developed shell coverings in which to lie at armoured ease from cunning enemies. The calcium carbonate from which these shells are made is derived from the water in which the marine molluscs dwell, and, as in the case of the piddock, is so strong, that it can be used for burrowing through rock. The piddock is, indeed, responsible for much of our coast erosion, and wherever he is common chalk and limestone cliffs are usually riddled with his galleries, which in the end undermine the cliff-face.

Among the land molluscs one at least has solved the problem of aeronautics. The prickly snail is able to climb trees, but has usually some difficulty in making a descent, so he mounts a leaf which is about to fall, clings firmly to it, and gradually descends as by a parachute.

No result of molluscan or, indeed, of animal activity equals the pearl in beauty or symmetry of construction. It is merely a protective secretion thrown out to prevent injury to the mollusc from a foreign body. Any bivalve may produce "pearls" of sorts, and they are by no means confined to the true pearl oyster, which is more of a mussel than an oyster proper.

When a foreign body, such as a grain of sand, introduces itself, or is introduced, within the shell of the oyster, a growth in the lining of the shell is caused. Some authorities believe the irritant agent to be a parasite, although this is doubtful, but in all likelihood the causes of irritation are various. In the Ceylon pearl, for instance, the exciting cause is certainly a tiny worm whose larvae batten on the bivalve. The finest pearls are admittedly those which grow just inside the edge of the shell.

The method of extraction is somewhat nauseous. The oysters are simply left to be eaten by the maggots of a rather nasty species of blow-fly, which in time devours the edible portion. The shells are then washed and the pearls detached from their lining of nacre.

Those little moons of the sea are scarcely more lovely than the nacre from which they come, the beautiful substance known as mother-o'-pearl, that irridescent membrane which is perhaps the most fairy-like element our planet affords. The manufacturers of this substance, both oysters and the humble mussel, have surpassed even man himself in the radiance of their achievements Nacre is composed of the same substance as the pearl itself, but has a rather different purpose, to enable the bivalve to lie smoothly in its flinty house.

But in ingenuity of craftsmanship as well as in beauty of production surely the coral polyp is preeminent in the animal world. It has indeed been left to the least of creatures to create forms which vie with the most enchanting of flowers.

British Museum (Natural History)

FISH FREAKS FROM THE SALT SEAS WHICH CATCH THEIR PREY WITH ROD LINE AND BAIT

These angler fishes differ from all other fish in that the foremost spine of the dorsal fin is situated on the head and used as a fishing line. Some of the fish live at the bottom in fairly shallow water while one group, that of the Ceratioids, live in mid water in the open sea at depths of from 250 to 1,000 fathoms. Here we have *Giganticus* (bottom left) which has a fishing rod and line much longer than its body ; and (bottom right) *Lasiognathus* with a rod like a broken trolley-arm on a tram-car. Notice the amazing contour of the body. Above we have (left) *Melanocetus* ; (centre) an angler fish photographed to show the astonishing distension of the stomach possible to these creatures—it has swallowed a fish larger than itself ; and (right) *Linophryne* which is all head.

Chapter XCVII

Nature's Strange Show of Freaks

By W. S. Berridge

Author of "Marvels of Animal Life"

THE old adage that "beauty is but skin deep" is certainly true, but considering that what one person may admire another may regard with indifference, it is quite obvious there is no true standard as to what really does constitute the beautiful. In a like manner what constitutes the ungainly and grotesque cannot be clearly defined, and is largely a matter of opinion, for some of us may appreciate that which may appear quite repulsive to others.

Such being the case, we feel we may be acting rather rashly in selecting certain members of the animal kingdom and placing them under the heading of "Nature's Freaks," but, be that as it may, the fact remains that some creatures are so remarkable-looking as to justify fully such an epithet.

Among the monkeys there are quite a number that arrest attention on account of their extraordinary appearance. In the group known as guenons there are two kinds, often spoken of as putty-nosed monkeys, that have a large, triangular mark on the end of the nose that looks like a dab of paint; another species is adorned with a pale-blue line across the upper lip suggestive of a moustache; while the Diana monkey grows a long pointed beard of white hair, which it has been known to hold on one side when drinking so as to prevent it from getting at all soiled.

None of the baboons can be regarded as being blessed with good looks, and the mandrill is certainly the most repulsive-looking of all. In scientific nomenclature it is called "mormon," meaning "spectre," a term that is certainly a very appropriate one to apply to the beast. It possesses a very large head, deep-set eyes, and projecting eyebrows. A crest of hair is present upon the crown of the head, and the chin is furnished with a short, pointed, orange-yellow beard.

But the most astonishing feature in regard to this baboon is to be noted in the large, ribbed swellings on either side of the face, these being blue in colour, and forming a vivid contrast to the bright red lips and nose. This colour scheme is continued on the animal's hind quarters, though in a somewhat modified degree, the red callosities thereon being thinly veiled with pink, heliotrope, azure, and lilac hairs. Owing to its remarkable appearance, an adult mandrill not only proves a great attraction at zoological gardens, but it is also a source of much merriment to the beholder. Indeed, it may well be said that "its face is its fortune."

The snub-nosed monkey and the proboscis monkey must certainly be included among the freaks of Nature. The former, found in Eastern Tibet and China, possesses a small, upturned nose that imparts a most comical appearance to the beast, while the bluish-grey skin of the face is encircled by a band of bright orange hair which also extends to the neck and chest.

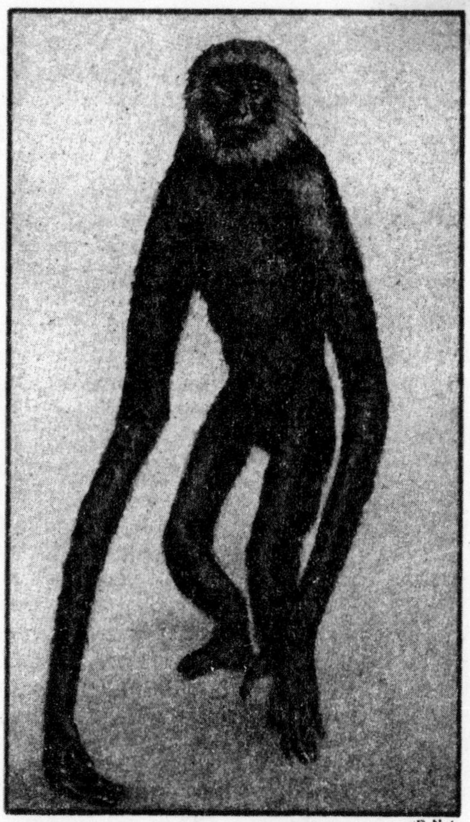

E.N.A.

AN APE OF BORNEO

With the long-armed ape of Borneo we seem to come to a case where Nature has laid herself out to fashion the grotesque. But, in reality, of course, these elongated arms have been evolved for a purpose and to meet a need

THE proboscis monkey, which comes from Borneo, goes to the other extreme in nasal development, for its large, drooping nose projects for four or five inches beyond the level of the face, the under surface being flattened, and the nostrils being situated beneath. This monkey, which was first brought to the notice of zoologists in the year 1781 by Baron Wurmb, Dutch Governor of Batavia, attains a length of about two and a half feet, exclusive of the tail, which measures some two feet or more.

Another most remarkable-looking monkey is the South American saki, a heavily-built creature with a large, bushy tail, suggesting the brush of a fox. Its entire face is clothed in short hair of a pale ochre tint, and that of the rest of the animal is jet black—the contrast between the two colours being so great and so clearly defined that the beast looks exactly as if it were wearing a mask. In spite of its forbidding appearance, however, this saki monkey is reputed to be of a very inoffensive disposition, a fact that was fully borne out by a specimen exhibited at the London Zoo many years back—the sole individual of its kind ever imported alive to the British Isles.

HEAD OF THE UGLY AARDVARK WITH ITS SPECIALLY ADAPTED SNOUT

Here we see the head of the aardvark, a Dutch word meaning " earth pig ", in the position in which it digs into ant-hills. We see that the head is, in fact, merely the broad end of a very long and specially adapted snout, whose purpose it is to eat up the tasty termites when the strong claws have scratched a hole in the exterior of the nest. Notice the slope of the eye and the way in which the very long ears are laid back. The aardvark is a nocturnal animal, and hails from South Africa.

Closely allied to the typical monkeys are a group of animals called lemuroids. They rank as the lowest of the primates, and most of them are nocturnal in habits. Among them are to be numbered several peculiar types, the most remarkable being the slow loris, which comes from India, Burma, the Malay States, Siam, Sumatra, Java, and Borneo; the slender loris, found in Southern India and Ceylon; and the tarsier, an inhabitant of Celebes, Borneo, Sumatra, and the Philippine Islands.

The scientific name of the first mentioned is *Nycticebus tardigradus*, the former word meaning " night ape," and the latter " slow step." The name " loris," from the Dutch " loeris," signifies " a clown," while in Malaya the animal is variously called the kokang, kongka, or kukang. By the Bengali natives it is known as the " chirmundi-billi " or bashful cat, and " lajjar banar " or bashful monkey, these names being given to it because of its habit of sleeping with its face tucked in between its knees. The Siamese sailors call the creatures the " ling lom," meaning wind-monkey, and regard the whistling noise it occasionally utters as a sign of approaching rain. They also state that if a live loris be kept on board their sailing vessels, the craft will never be becalmed. But the most remarkable belief held in regard to this little beast is that if a man buries the body of one under the threshold of an enemy, the latter will unconsciously be forced to commit a crime, a somewhat roundabout way of getting him into trouble.

As implied by its name, the slender loris is characterised by the extreme slenderness of its body and limbs, a feature so pronounced that the animal almost looks as if it were suffering from some wasting disease. The Tamils call it " thavangu " or thin bodied, an expression they also employ when alluding to a deformed or very thin person. The animal is very deliberate in all its movements, and in Ceylon it often goes by the name of " Ceylon sloth." Like the slow loris it has no tail, and its enormous eyes are remarkable for their close proximity to one another. Sir Emerson Tennent tells us that the " large and intense eyes of the loris have attracted the attention of the Singhalese, who capture the creature for the purpose of extracting them as charms and love potions, and this they are said to effect by holding the little animal to the fire till the eyeballs burst."

THE tarsier receives its name because of the great length of the upper bones of its ankles. It is the rarest of the lemuroids, and no living example has ever been imported into Europe. About the size of our brown squirrel, it reveals several peculiarities

W. S. Berridge

W. S. Berridge

EXTRAORDINARY MONKEYS OF NEW WORLD AND OLD

The snub-nosed monkey from China and Eastern Tibet (bottom) has a face which is mostly upper lip, while its nose is a mere isolated lump. A fringe of orange-coloured hair surrounds the face, which is of a grey-blue tint. The white-headed saki (top) has a face shockingly like that of a stout, elderly man. It is a native of South America, haunting the Amazon basin.

not found in other creatures. The extremity of each finger, for instance, terminates in a large, rounded disk that acts as a sucker and enables the animal to adhere to any object upon which it may alight. When moving about the dense bamboo jungle amidst which it dwells, it jumps from one stem to another with a rapidity so great that the eye can scarcely discern its passage, its leaping power being likened to that of a flea. The large eyes are rendered exceptionally conspicuous owing to the smallness of the face and jaws, while the long tail is remarkable because it is quite devoid of fur, except at the extreme base and tip.

Pigs have never been noted for their beauty, and it is not surprising to find that among this group is to be found an animal that has earned the reputation of being the ugliest beast on earth. Known as the

arises as to why the females also are not endowed in a similar manner.

In olden days it was believed that the animal employed its curved upper tusks for the purpose of hooking itself to a branch of a tree when retiring to rest, but it is hardly necessary to state that this quaint conception is not based upon fact. The babirussa dwells in the neighbourhood of rivers and lakes, and feeds chiefly upon aquatic vegetation. It takes freely to the water and swims with facility, a fact of special interest in view of the common supposition that pigs cannot swim, but only cut their throats with their sharp hoofs whilst in the act of striking out and making the attempt

W. S. Berridge

BRINDLED GNU AND A MEXICAN HAIRLESS DOG

The gnu of the South African veldt is a freak in that it seems to be in doubt as to whether it ought to belong to the horse, the ox, or the antelope families. The nostrils are noticeably weird in shape, as is, indeed, the whole head. The upper illustration is of one of the absurd-looking Mexican hairless terriers.

Although babirussas are rarely seen outside their native home, they have been exhibited at the London Zoo in the past, and young ones have been born there—the babies, unlike those of the majority of wild pigs, being unstriped at birth, and there never being more than two in a litter. The animals become quite tame, and in Celebes they are sometimes kept as pets and allowed to roam at their own will about the natives' houses.

Among the group of animals known as the edentata, so called because they do not possess front teeth, and are sometimes quite toothless, we have in the aard-vark, the sloths, and the ant-eaters some creatures of very grotesque appearance. Also called the ant-bear, or earth-pig, the former is an ugly-looking beast measuring about six feet in length. Its long head terminates in a pig-like snout, and the ears are of enormous size. The thick, stumpy limbs are provided with powerful claws employed for excavating a subterranean home wherein to sleep during the daytime. In spite of its large size, the animal feeds entirely upon ants and termites, of which it laps up enormous quantities with the aid of its long tongue.

Although possibly of a more prepossessing appearance than the aard-vark, the sloths are to be numbered among the curiosities of the animal world. Arboreal in habits, they spend practically the whole of their lives hanging back-downwards from the branches of trees, suspended therefrom by their long, curved claws. On the rare occasions when they do descend to the ground they can only progress by dragging themselves along by clutching on to any inequalities of the surface, such as a stone or the root of a tree, that may lie in their path. They are clothed in thick, coarse, fluted and somewhat brittle hair of a brownish-grey colour, but often the fur assumes a greenish tint owing to the presence of a powdery fungus that grows thereon. Another curious feature in regard to the fur is that it lies in the reverse direction to that of other creatures, so that when the

W. S. Berridge

PROECHIDNA AND THE GREAT ANT-EATER THAT BOTH POSSESS PHENOMENAL SNOUTS

From New Guinea comes the strange proechidna, or black-spined porcupine ant-eater (bottom). The epithet "black spined" refers to the spikes which mingle with the hair of its body and can be made out here amid the short, woolly-looking hair which covers it. But the most remarkable thing about the proechidna is that it has a nose like a carrot. This imparts a touch of the bizarre to an already weird animal. The great ant-eater (top), has abnormal prolongations at both ends, for it has a tail like a vast feather fan.

THE HEIGHT OF UGLINESS AMONG THE PIG FAMILY: BABIRUSSA AND WART-HOG

Two Malay words—" baba," meaning a pig, and " rusa," a deer, are the derivatives of the name of the babirussa (bottom), which is found in the great island of Celebes. The babirussa is built on very slender lines for a pig and has a narrow, small head. The specimen seen here seems to have shrunk in its skin, which is very wrinkled about the neck and the shoulders. The upper photograph shows a wart-hog with one of its great curved tusks broken. There is a large lump or " wart " below each eye, and two others lower down.

W. S. Berridge

FOUR BIRDS WITH FREAK ORNAMENTS ON THEIR HEADS

Never did the most wild designer of feminine hats ever beat these birds for queerness of head ornament. The Javan peacock (bottom left) bears a horn like a crest upon its forehead, while the great bustard (bottom right) has a brush of feathers jutting out from under its beak. The Californian quail (top left) has strange plumes standing out from its head and resembling a peak half torn off a cap. Finally, we have the white-headed bell-bird (top right), which has three wattles protruding from it like banderillas from a bull's neck at a bull fight

W. S. Berridge

W. S. Berridge

Otho Webb

FROGMOUTH WITH A ONE-WATTLED AND A RAZOR-BILLED CASSOWARY

One of Australia's many strange-looking birds is the frogmouth (bottom), which we here see trying to look as much as possible like a piece of the branch on which it is perched. In page 979 we have another photograph and a description of this interesting and weird-looking bird. The upper photographs are of cassowaries. On the left we have the one-wattled cassowary with the distinguishing triangular lump on its beak, and on the right, a razor-billed cassowary with a very distorted-looking beak.

W. S. Berridge

its body is clothed with hair that forms an upstanding mane along the top of the neck and body, and the tail is developed into an enormous fan-like appendage, the longest hairs of which measure as much as sixteen inches in length. When sleeping, the animal lies on one side, turns its head inwards, and then throws its tail over itself as if it were a blanket.

Brief mention must be made of the proechidna, an animal of almost freakish appearance, and one that shares with the platypus the unique habit of laying eggs from which its young are hatched. Found in New Guinea, it is sometimes called the black-spined porcupine ant-eater or the three-toed echidna; but although normally possessing but three toes to each foot, the number appears to vary in different individuals, one specimen having been recorded with five claws on each of its fore feet and four on each of the hinder ones. Like the great ant-eater, the proechidna possesses a very elongated and slender snout, at the extremity of which is situated a tiny mouth It has no teeth, but

torrential rains fall the moisture merely drips off instead of soaking through to the skin, as it otherwise would do if the hair grew in a normal manner.

Although all other mammals have but seven vertebrae to the neck, some of the sloths are unique in possessing either more or less than the usual number, Hoffmann's sloth having only six, while the three-toed sloths are provided with nine. The animals feed exclusively upon leaves, the shoots of trees and fruit, but in an old Natural History book we read that they "live onely on aire." Moreover, it is further stated that they have very little mouths and are unable to bite.

Of the several species of ant-eaters, the great ant-eater is probably the most remarkable. Were it not for the attenuated proportions of its head, its immobile features, and general imbecile appearance, it might be regarded as quite a handsome creature, for

C. A. House

BIZARRE BIRDS, DOMESTIC AND WILD

Man has been busy in producing freak birds from the original rock-dove stock, and, as a result, we have such queer pigeons as the tumblers and fantails, a specimen of the latter appearing in the lower photograph. Above is a male cock-of-the-rock.

E. T Manly

OCELLATED BLADDER FROG AND AN OLM FROM THE SUBTERRANEAN WATERS

In the lower photograph is an ocellated bladder frog with immensely fat forelegs, while the upper photograph is of the strange creature called the olm. It is found in the dark waters of certain caves in Dalmatia where no light penetrates, and its skin is consequently white and the eyes covered by skin. When exposed to the light, however, colour appears, and, in certain circumstances, the eyes appear too. It has four little legs, the front pair possessing fingers which, however, have lost the ability to clutch

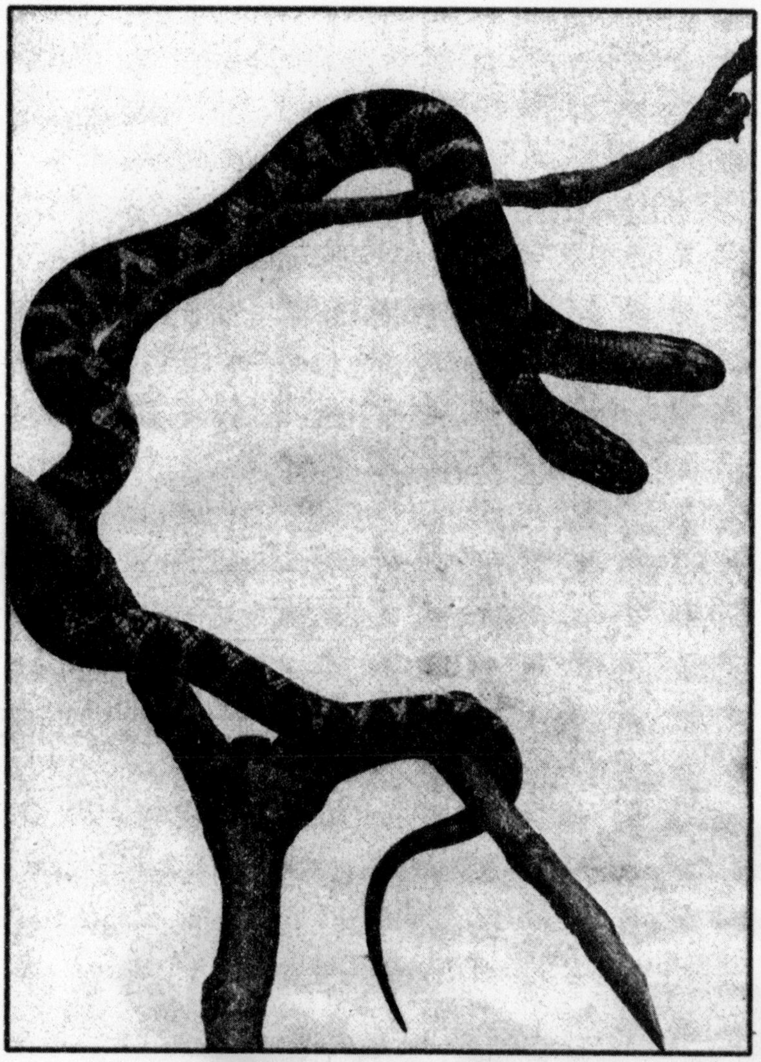

dwelling birds, it is of a very unsociable disposition, for, although several individuals may be seen standing in a comparatively small sheet of water, each one keeps as far as possible away from its fellows. Called by the Arabs "Abu markub" or "Father of a shoe," it is a large, heavily built bird that attains a height of about five feet.

Although spending most of its time wading in the water in search of its food, which consists chiefly of fish, it is well able to fly, and when so doing it arches its neck over its back and rests its cumbersome beak upon its crop. The bird thrives well in captivity, but can hardly be regarded as a desirable pet. The young are clothed in blue-grey down, and their bills resemble those of their parents, though being smaller in proportion. Mr. Petherick records that after two years' experimenting he succeeded in rearing some young ones from eggs placed under domestic hens, but we can well imagine the patient sitters had the surprise of their lives when they first caught a glimpse of their foster-children.

Other birds with abnormal beak development are the boatbills, the hornbills, and the toucans. The boatbill is a moderate sized bird, belonging to the heron family, which comes from South America. Its beak is very large, but the upper mandible, unlike that of the shoebill, is convex in profile instead of concave. The native name for it is "savaku."

employs its worm-like tongue for gathering up its food. One of these animals is housed at the London Zoo, where it has been for quite a number of years, but as it is nocturnal in habits and lies hidden within its sleeping-box during the hours the Gardens are open to the public, very few people have ever seen it, or even know of its existence.

PASSING to the birds, although the vast majority of them can only be described as beautiful, a few prove an exception to the rule. The shoebill or whale-headed heron, for instance, is a creature that one might expect to envisage in a nightmare rather than in the flesh, its enormous beak, terminating in a sharp, hooked claw, imparting to it a most weird appearance. It lives amidst the swamps of the White Nile, but is nowhere plentiful. Unlike other marsh-

Natural History, N.Y.

SNAKE MONSTROSITIES FROM U.S.

Accidents of birth occasionally produce freaks and here we have two cases, among snakes, where two developing embryos failed to become individualised and a double-headed snake was born. Below is a copperhead and above a milk snake. The latter lived for some months in the New York Zoo. The former was found in the woods of Pennsylvania.

W. Saville Kent

EXTRAORDINARILY SHAPED LIZARDS FROM THE AUSTRALIAN BUSH

Western and southern Australia have, among a varied fauna, these extraordinary lizards which look at a distance more like some kind of prickly leaf than animals. The spines which cover them are purely defensive and never used for attack. These lizards are found mostly in dry, sandy localities, and their chief food is ants. As ants at times become a nuisance to settlers these lizards often prove a blessing, since the numbers of ants they can capture by lightning movements of their tongues is prodigious. They are known as Thorny Devils.

J. J. Wa d

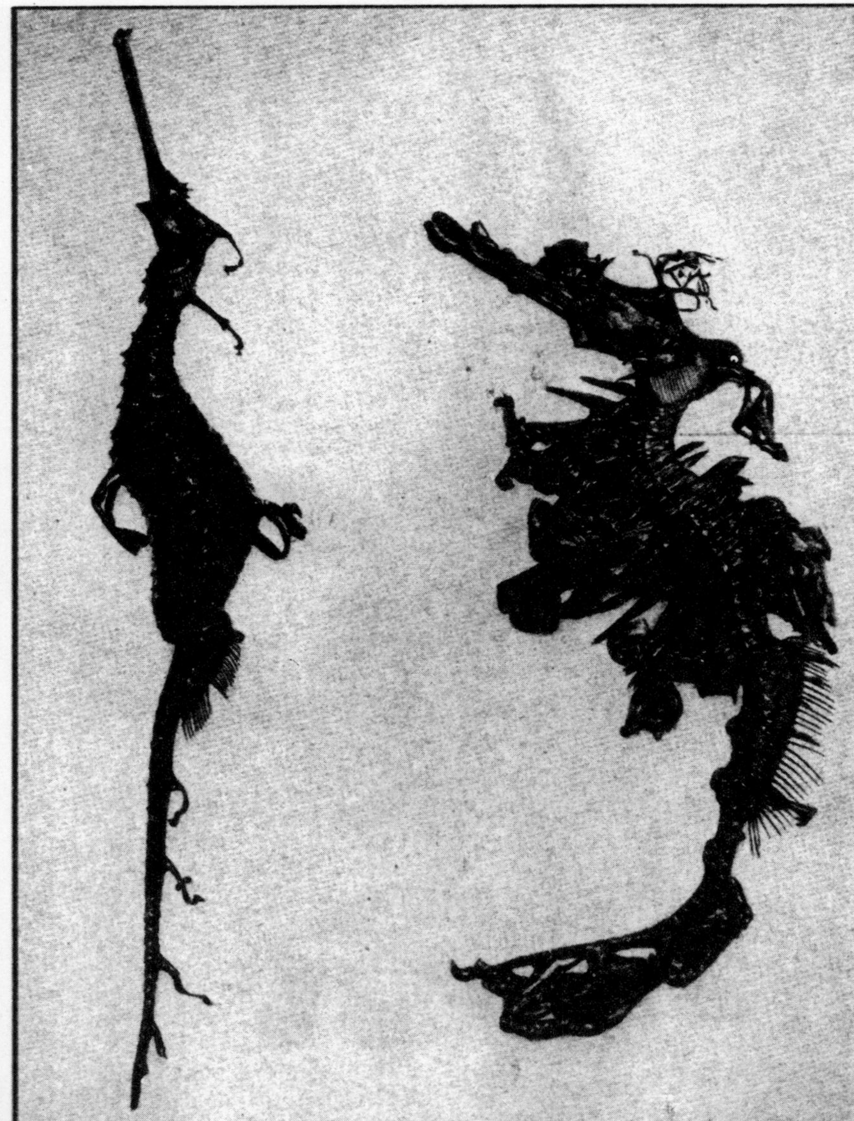

Natural History, N.Y.

QUEER FISH WHOSE QUEERNESS HELPS THEM TO HIDE AMONG THE SEAWEEDS IN WHICH THEY LIVE

Among fish the sea-horses (left) have evolved a most interesting abnormality which is responsible for their popular name. The head, instead of being in line with the spine, as in most fish, is bent at right-angles to it, thus giving the little creature a horse-like air. Even more, perhaps, it reminds one of a "knight" in a set of chessmen. The tail lacks the characteristic fin of other fishes and instead of being used for swimming is prehensile and coils round the stems of the seaweeds among which the little sea-horse lives. The sea-dragon (right) which comes from Australian waters, has the contours of its body remarkably broken up by various spiny processes which all tend to make the fish inconspicuous.

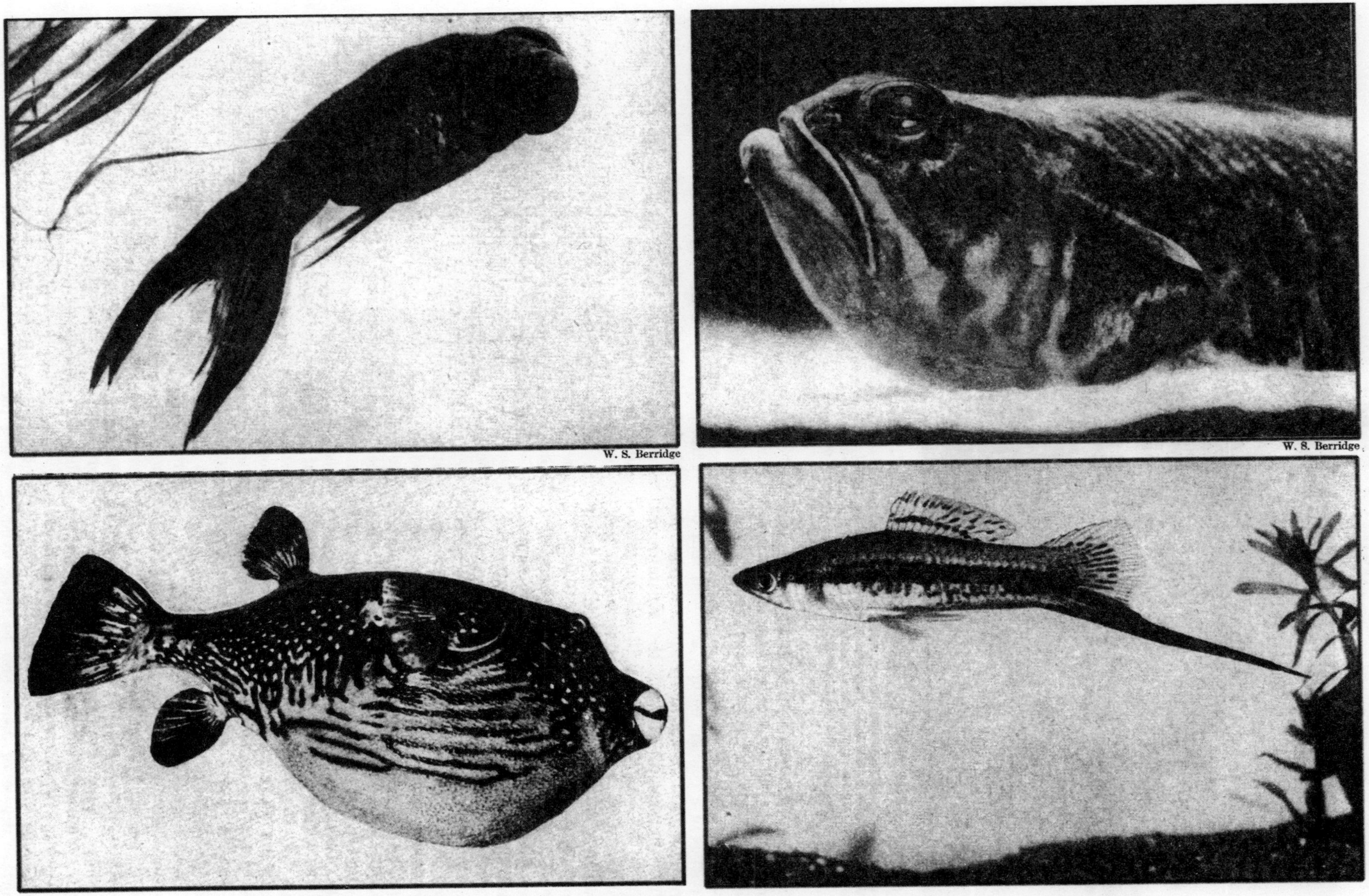

W. S. Berridge

W. S. Berridge

QUARTETTE OF QUAINT SEA CREATURES FROM NATURE'S MENAGERIE OF FREAKS

Nature seems to become most extravagant in fancy where sea creatures are concerned, for the oceans continually yield a fresh crop of marvels to those who seek them. The globe fish (bottom left) and the sword-tail (bottom right) are a pair of marvels such as would have graced any old-fashioned freak show. The sword-tail is a small fresh-water fish of Mexico, and the specimen here is the male of the species, which has a very elongated tail. The sword-tail is viviparous. In the upper left-hand photograph is an example of the telescope-eyed goldfish. We have a side view in this photograph, and the eye is about as large as the rest of the head. The greater weaver (top right) has its mouth in a vertical instead of a horizontal position, more usual with fish.

W. S. Berridge

GLOBE FISH OF THE EXPANDING AND PRICKLY SKIN

While the globe fish or puffer, of which there are a great many varieties, look surprising creatures in the ordinary way, they can make themselves more astonishing still by filling themselves with either water or air so that the skin is stretched tight and numerous spikes and bristles become erect. This is a safety device. Some species are very poisonous.

It is, however, the hornbills that attain the greatest development of the bill, for, besides being of enormous size, it is often surmounted by a large casque. But this structure is not so heavy as it looks, for the greater part is of a cellular nature, although that of the helmeted hornbill proves an exception to the rule inasmuch as it is solid. Indeed, the substance of the casque of the latter bird is of such a close texture as to look like ivory, and it is interesting to note that the Chinese employ the substance as a medium upon which to execute their carvings.

Of the sixty or more different species of hornbills, the largest is the great Indian hornbill, or homrai, which measures about five feet in length from the tip of its beak to the end of its tail; while next in size is the rhinoceros hornbill, a bird that receives its name from the fact that the front part of its large casque terminates in an upturned protuberance suggesting the horn of a rhinoceros. The ground hornbills, of which there are two kinds, are curious for the prominent eyelashes they possess. The Boers call the South African species by the name of "bromvogel." The kaffirs believe that if one of the birds be killed rain will afterwards fall for a lengthy period, consequently, during times of drought it is the custom to throw the carcase of a captured individual into the river-bed so as to bring about the longed-for return of the waters.

The toucans have aptly been described as "birds behind beaks." Their bills are often almost as long as their bodies, and are invariably decorated with bright colours. That of the toco toucan is of a deep orange tint, with large, black, oval spots near the extremity; while yellow, green, red, blue, and black are the prevailing tints in those of other species. To add a further degree of distinction to these avian grotesques, gaudy colours are often displayed upon the throat, breast, and tail. Toucans feed chiefly upon fruit, but they will readily devour any grubs, small birds or reptiles that may come within their reach.

With the adjutant storks we come to some birds that look as if they were suffering from a chronic state of depression. They will stand motionless for lengthy periods, their heads sunk back upon their shoulders, and an expression of utter boredom illuminating their countenances. Perhaps the only time when they assume an air of dignity is when they walk, their measured stride as they slowly proceed on their journey and their resemblance to a military figure on parade, giving rise to their name. Found in India and Africa, they are very efficient scavengers, and in the former country they will not hesitate to enter the large towns to feed upon the filth and garbage that litters the streets.

There are quite a number of birds with curious embellishments of the beak. In the comb duck, or black-backed goose as it is also called, the male possesses a large, fleshy prominence that arises abruptly from the upper mandible; the globose curassow has a large, bright yellow, rounded knob in a similar situation; while the male rough-billed pelican grows a thin, erectile, horny excrescence thereon during the mating season.

Other birds reveal peculiarities by the presence of wattles or fleshy growths upon the head. The snowy bell-bird, for instance, possesses a long, sparsely-feathered, rod-like wattle situated at the base of the upper mandible, and this can be erected at will; while the white-headed bell-bird has three of these curious appendages, one on the upper part of the beak, and one on either side at the corner of the mouth. Then we have the umbrella bird, which receives its name from the large crest upon the top of its head, the elevated feathers thereof curving outwards and downwards at their extremities, thereby forming an umbrella-like shield extending from the back of the head to the tip of the beak. But in addition to this curious decoration, the bird also has a long, pendant, bib-like lappet of feathers arising from beneath the throat and from the sides of the neck. The cassowaries must also be included in our survey because of the curious upstanding helmet surmounting their heads, an embellishment that, although of a somewhat freakish nature, imparts a distinct air of dignity to the birds.

In regard to the reptiles, it would be easier to single out the more attractive species rather than those of a less pleasing aspect, for none can be described as

beautiful, except perhaps in their colouring. Among the snakes with unusual characters mention must be made of the shield-tails in which the caudal appendage terminates in a blunt-ended, flattened disk, instead of tapering to a point as in the case of all other serpents. As they live underground, burrowing through the soil like a worm, they are not often seen, but in the tea and coffee plantations of Ceylon and India, from whence the reptiles come, they are sometimes brought to light when the ground is being tilled.

THERE are so many curious types of lizards that it is only possible to mention a few in the space at our disposal, so we must content ourselves with selecting the frilled lizard and the moloch lizard as noteworthy examples. Both come from Australia, the former being remarkable for the large, scale-covered frill of skin that surrounds its throat and neck. Under normal circumstances this lies folded up and in repose over the shoulders, but when the creature is alarmed or irritated, it opens wide its mouth, expands the frill, bringing it forward so as to form a shield-like cuirass almost completely surrounding the head. In spite of its formidable appearance and defiant attitude, however, the reptile is quite harmless.

MONSTROUS CRABS FROM HOT CLIMATES

Japan produces the largest crab in the world. A horrid sight it is, for it spans a distance equal to twice an average man's height between the ends of its two great claws, and the other legs are in proportion. It is called the great spider crab. Above is a tropical crab, with one enormously developed claw

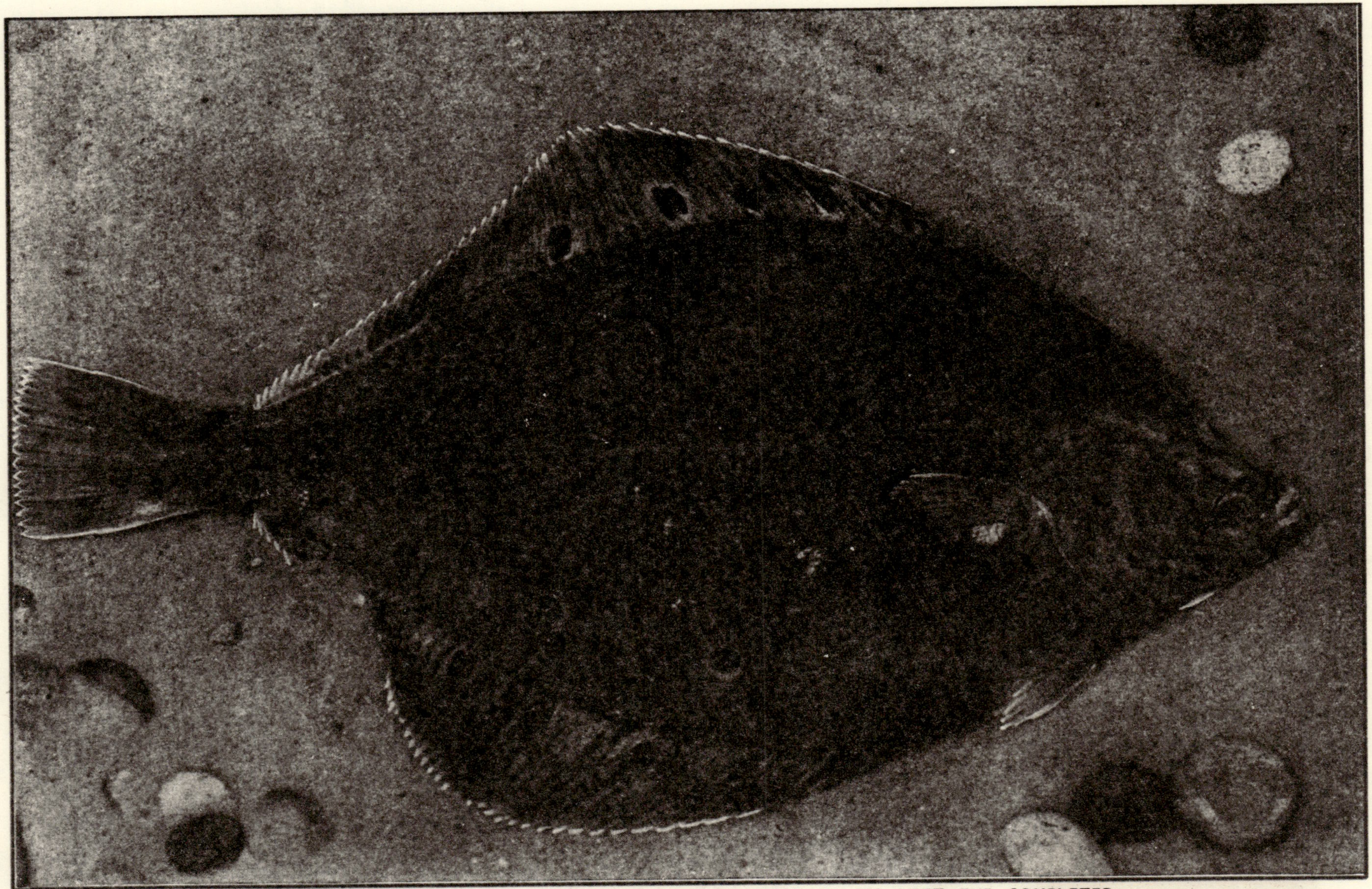

ADULT PLAICE WITH THE WONDERFUL TRANSFERENCE OF ITS LEFT EYE COMPLETED

At the age of two and a half or three years a plaice is adult and has reached a length of about a foot. Both eyes are then on the same side of its body although, in the early stages of its life, this fish had one eye on either side, as we shall see in the illustrations that follow. The plaice is a very important food fish, and is found in the North Sea and the Atlantic from Iceland to the Bay of Biscay. It does not reach the American coasts. The story of its strange metamorphosis from a normal to an abnormal fish form is also true of a great number of other flat fish of which there are about five hundred classified kinds. The best known beside the plaice are the dab, flounder, sole and halibut

Chapter XCVIII

The Wonderful Story of a Fish's Moving Eye

By Henry Neil Milligan

Zoologist of the Horniman Museum

EVERYBODY must have noticed the wry countenances of the flat-fishes in a fishmonger's shop, but probably there are few people who know the story of those peculiar faces. The story has to do with a shifting eye, and some other curious matters.

Let us consider for a moment the body of a fish which is not a flat-fish. Almost any one will serve, provided it is of ordinary shape, such as a cod-fish. It is smooth and rather spindle-shaped, that is to say, it is of a form which is fitted for easy motion through the water. It has a head, a back, a belly, right and left sides, and certain fins. Its eyes are in the usual place in the head, one on the right and one on the left, so that the fish can see on both sides.

We may now turn to examine one of the flat-fishes. There are about five hundred different kinds of such creatures known and named. The plaice, the dab, the flounder, the halibut, the turbot, and the sole are well-known sorts among the five hundred. However, they are all very much alike, and any one of them would doubtless be recognized at once as a flat-fish. The plaice may be taken to serve as our chief example in the following account, as it is a species which is very well known. The difference of its form from that of an ordinary fish is seen at a glance. Instead of being rather spindle-shaped, it is flat. Instead of having an eye on one side and an eye on the other, it has both its eyes close together on the upper surface. We may note, too, that the upper surface of the plaice is brownish in colour (with red spots), whilst the lower is white.

If anybody should be asked to say which is the back and which is the belly of a plaice, he might reasonably regard the question as quite unnecessary, or at all events as one which is very easy to answer. " Clearly," he might reply, " the brown surface must be the back, and the white surface must be the belly." If some proof be then demanded that the brown surface really is the back and that the white surface really is the belly, he could reply that the plaice, whether it is swimming or whether it is resting, always keeps its brown surface upwards and its white downwards. Moreover, he might add, the two eyes are there, on the brown surface, on the back, where they might naturally be expected to be in such a flattened fish. It is obvious, is it not, that the brown surface is the back ?

But the student of nature must always be vigilantly on his guard against accepting the obvious without enquiry. It is obvious that the earth is flat—until it is shown to be round. It is obvious that the brown surface of the plaice is its back—until it is shown to be truly its right side. But, it might here be objected, if the brown surface is truly the right side of the fish, then the animal must have both its eyes on its right side, and this seems to be absurd. Nevertheless, the plaice really has both its eyes on its right side, and how and why they come to be in such an extraordinary position is the strange story to be told.

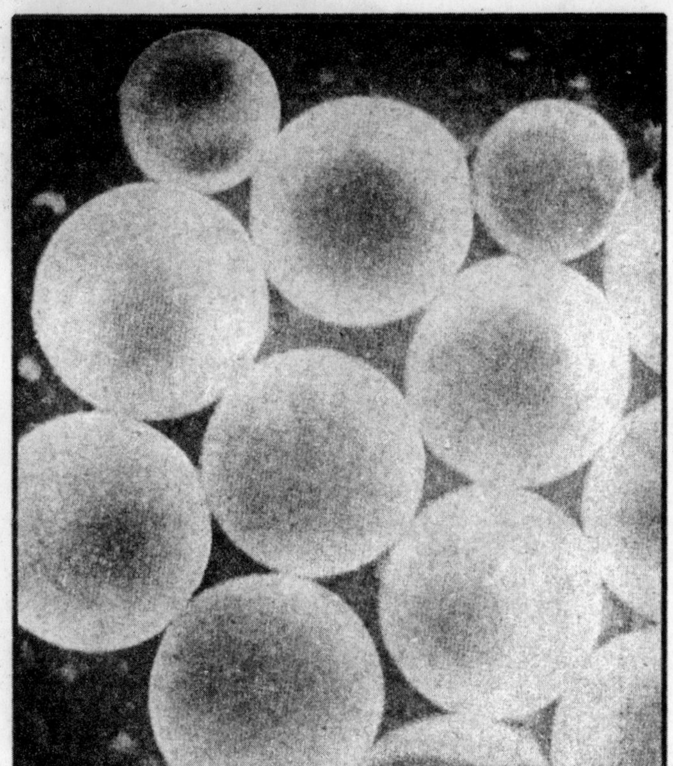

F Martin Duncan

FIRST STAGE IN A PLAICE'S LIFE

About a quarter of a million eggs, of which we see a few here, are developed on an average by the ordinary female plaice, and these semi-transparent globules, with opaque matter at their centres, float near the surface till they eventually hatch. The young plaice make for shallow water.

The tale begins with the hatching of the plaice from the egg. A baby plaice, just hatched, is not in the least like a flat-fish. It has essentially the form of an ordinary fish (with, in its earliest stages, a bulging bag of yolk, or reserve food-material, in the region of its stomach). Its eyes are not both on one side, but are on opposite sides of the head as in an ordinary fish. It is not brown on one side and white on the other, but such colour

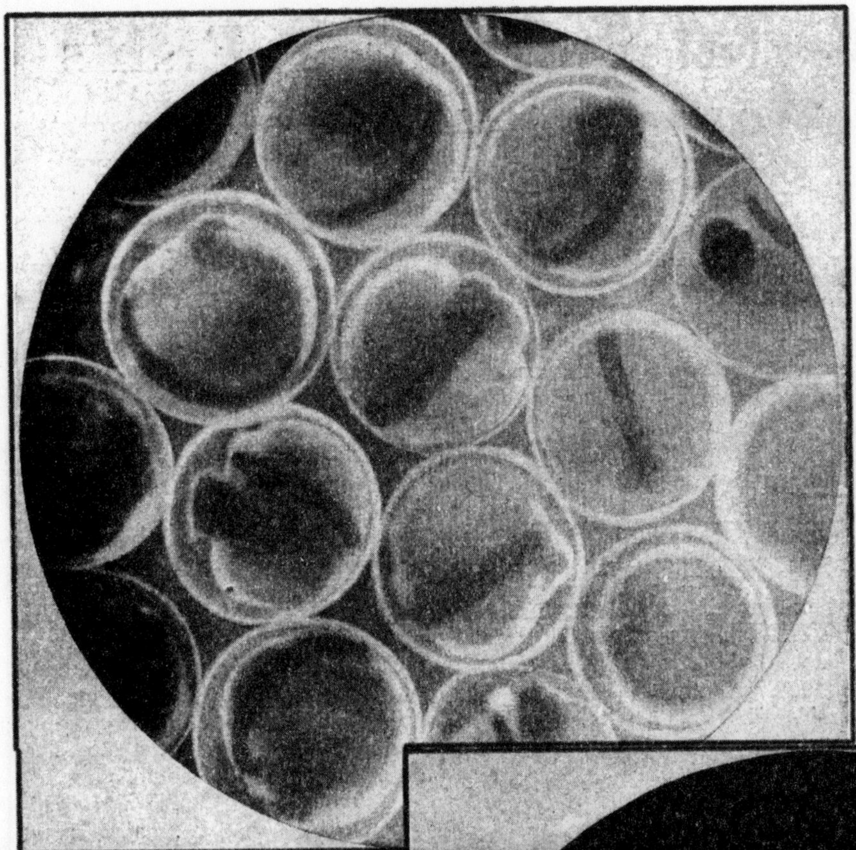

the position of the left eye, that is to say, the eye which, if the fish lay on its side, would be underneath, gradually becomes shifted, the eye seeming to pass over the top of the head and thence on to the right side of the animal. There is besides a distinct tendency towards a deepening and spreading of the darker colours on the right, or two-eyed, side, and a tendency towards development of the white colour on the left, or eye-less, side.

The reader should be careful not to suppose, as he might easily do in the absence of warning, that the left eye of the fish casts off all its moorings and then creeps away to settle in a new position. The phrase in the paragraph above, about the eye "seeming to pass over the top of the head," was written advisedly. Now

as it has (for it is translucent at this time) is practically the same on both sides. Such a newly-hatched plaice is not more than about a fifth of an inch in length.

THE little creature becomes flatter and more plaice-like as it grows older. It has already begun to lean more and more to one side, and presently it lies wholly on that side. It is a most curious fact that the side to which it leans is the left one, though occasionally it leans to the right. Why the inclination should be to the left rather than to the right provides food for thought. There are some flat-fishes, such as the turbot, whose eyes are on the left and whose bodies lean to the right; and there are others which have eyes either right or left and which lean either to the right or the left. Here is more matter for thought.

As the habit of toppling to one side develops in the plaice

F. Martin Duncan

EMBRYONIC FORMS AND THE BEGINNINGS OF GROWTH

The nucleus of the egg soon begins to take form until a recognizable creature (bottom) appears with a large bulge in its slight body where the yolk sac—a legacy from the egg—provides nourishment created originally by virtue of the parent fish. The upper photograph showing the embryo taking shape should be compared with that in the preceding page.

as the left eye does actually come to lie on the right side, we may seem here to be unnecessarily cautious, and a few words of explanation must be added. What really happens is that there is an alteration and a shifting of all the structures, including the bones, of that portion of the head which lies around and about the left eye, and the result of the changes is that all these parts become twisted over towards the right side, the eye being thus brought into a new position. It is more appropriate to say that the eye shares in a general shifting rather than that it passes to a new place.

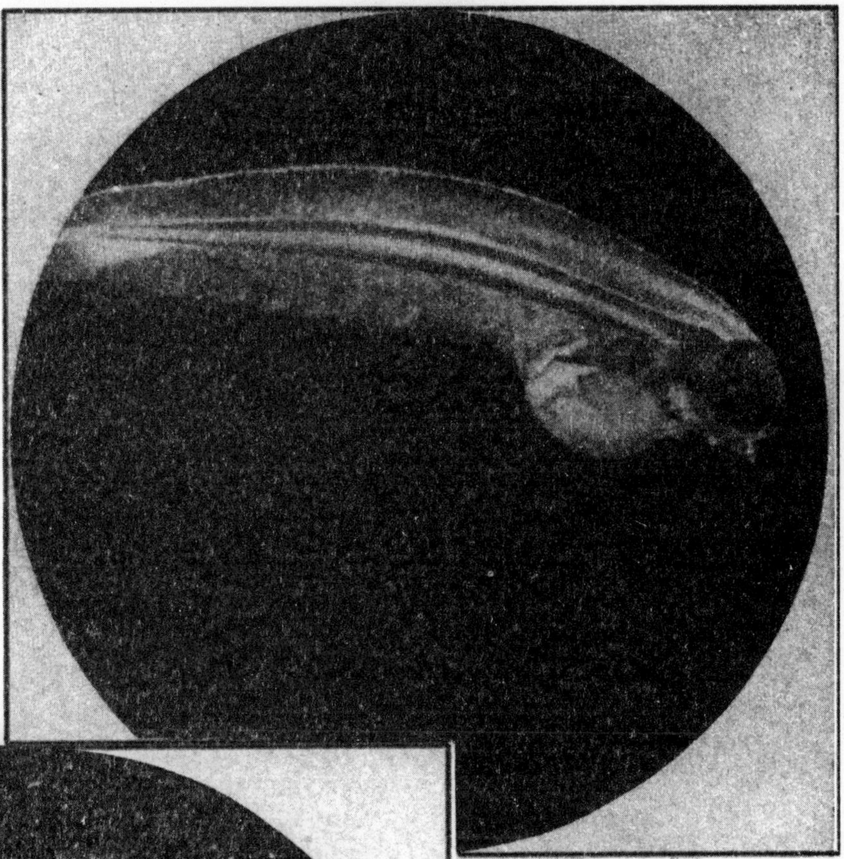

It will be seen from the explanation given above that there is considerable twisting of the head and, as will be supposed, signs of this twisting can plainly be seen in the skull of the plaice. It may here be opportune to suggest that, if a skull of a plaice or other flat-fish be within reach, it will repay examination. It is distorted, and distorted in such a way that at first glance it is difficult to understand its arrangement; but the distortion chiefly affects the facial parts, and one look at its hind end, at the place where, in life, it joined the backbone, will show that it is essentially very much like the skull of any ordinary fish.

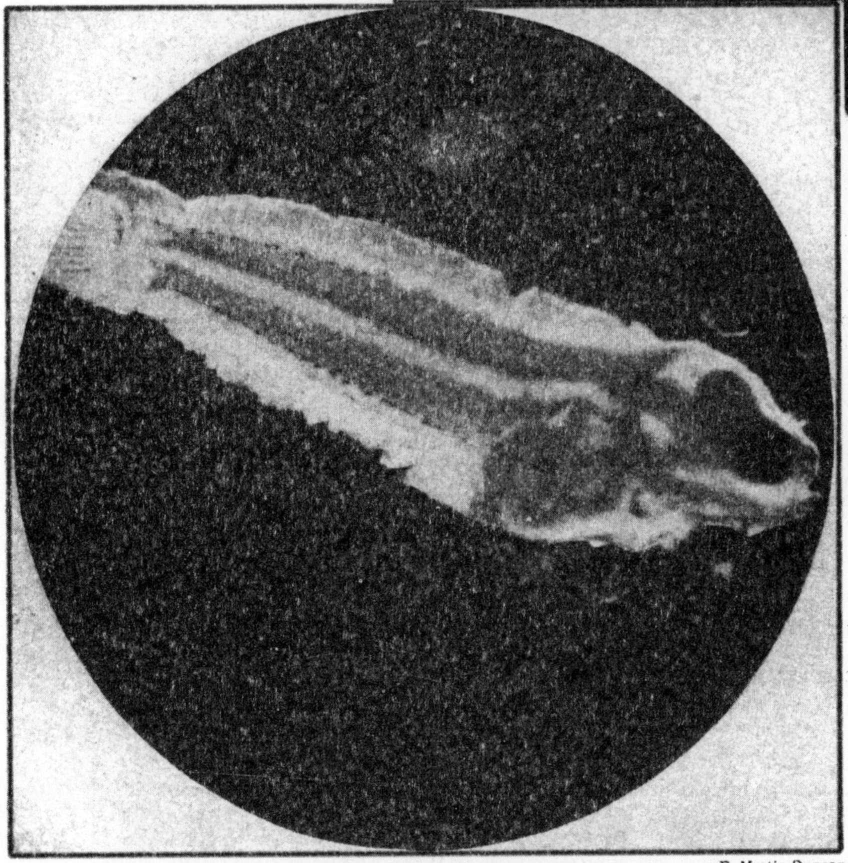

F Martin Duncan

ABSORPTION OF YOLK: BODY BEGINS TO FLATTEN

Here we have the developing plaice growing rapidly into an ordinary fish form with two normal eyes. The upper photograph shows the yolk sac partially absorbed and the mouth beginning to form in preparation for the moment when (bottom) the sac is absorbed and the plaice must feed itself. Notice that the body is starting to flatten in the lower illustration.

Flat-fishes are sometimes found in which the eye has failed to change its position and which have grown up with the eyes to right and left as in ordinary fishes. In some specimens the migratory eye has succeeded in getting only part of the way round the head.

By the time a plaice has grown to about half an inch in length it is, except in size,

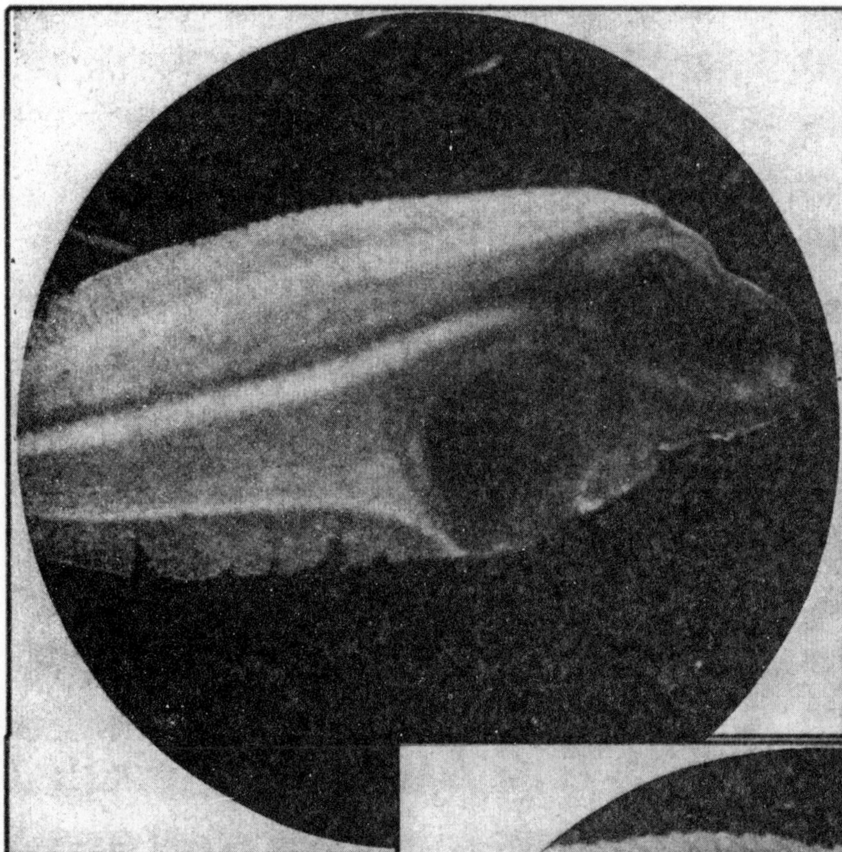

chiefly of sand or mud. The flat plaice, with its brownish upper side, is plainly adapted for life on such a sea-bed. Not only can it lie flat against the bed, but its brownish colour, harmonising with that of the bed, helps to conceal it from the eyes of possible enemies. Further, a plaice will not only lie on the sea-bed, but also partly in it. When the fish sinks down to rest on the sand, it may make peculiar flappings with its body. By this means a little cloud is raised, and as the grains almost at once fall back on the outlying parts of the fish, the animal's outline is lost in the sandy bed. Only people who have watched flat-fishes concealing themselves can understand how effective the concealment may be. The writer of this chapter well remembers putting a sole into

essentially like the adult, having one side brown, one side white, and both its eyes on the brown side. It swims and rests always with its brown side uppermost. It is clear from all that we have learned of the plaice that it is to be regarded as a fish fitted for lying flat on one side, and that the carrying of the eye over towards the opposite, or exposed side, is a device for bringing into employment an eye which would otherwise have been underneath and useless. There is no doubt at all that flat-fishes have evolved from fishes with more ordinary forms and eyes.

But there is more in the story than this. The eyes of a plaice are flat when the fish lies dead at the fishmonger's, but in life those eyes can be raised at the will of the animal somewhat above the level of the surface of the head. Now, we shall find on enquiry that the plaice and most flat-fishes inhabit seas whose beds are

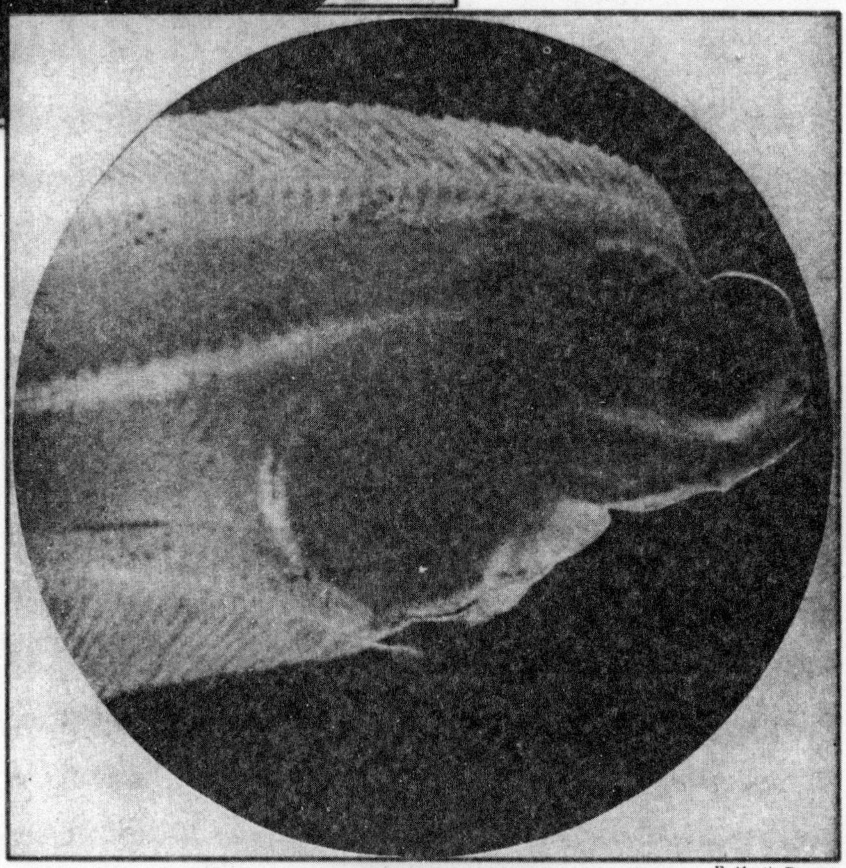

F. Martin Duncan

BEGINNING OF THE EYE'S TRANSMIGRATION

As the young plaice begins to feed for itself and to grow it gradually loses its transparency and its body starts to lean—usually towards the left—and to become dark on the right side. As it leans and the left eye tends to point always to the bottom of the sea, this eye and the whole surrounding part of the head become twisted. We see the start of the movement here.

an aquarium, whose bed was of mixed sand and fine shingle, and the fish, which rarely moved in the daytime, remained undetected in the bed for about three weeks. Those who were in charge of the aquarium had in the meantime supposed that the sole had died and been removed by somebody else. But to return to the eyes of the plaice. When the fish lies on the sea-bed, and particularly when it lies partly in the bed, it is clearly an advantage that the creature should be able to raise its eyes at will above the level of the surface of the sand, and this, as we have seen, it can do. It is then able to see enemies and prey.

The mouth of the plaice is awry, like its eyes and face generally, its jaws having a marked twist towards the left, or eyeless and lower side of its body. The reason for this is that the plaice takes its food, which is mostly living shell-fish, from the bed of the sea, and a mouth so turned is well fitted for picking up prey.

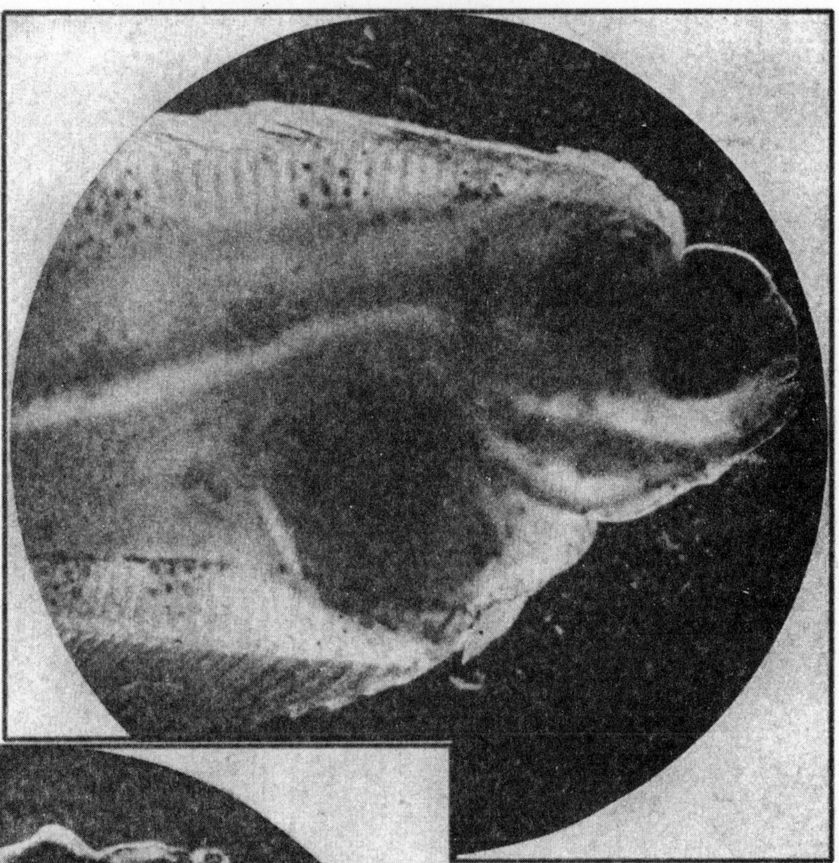

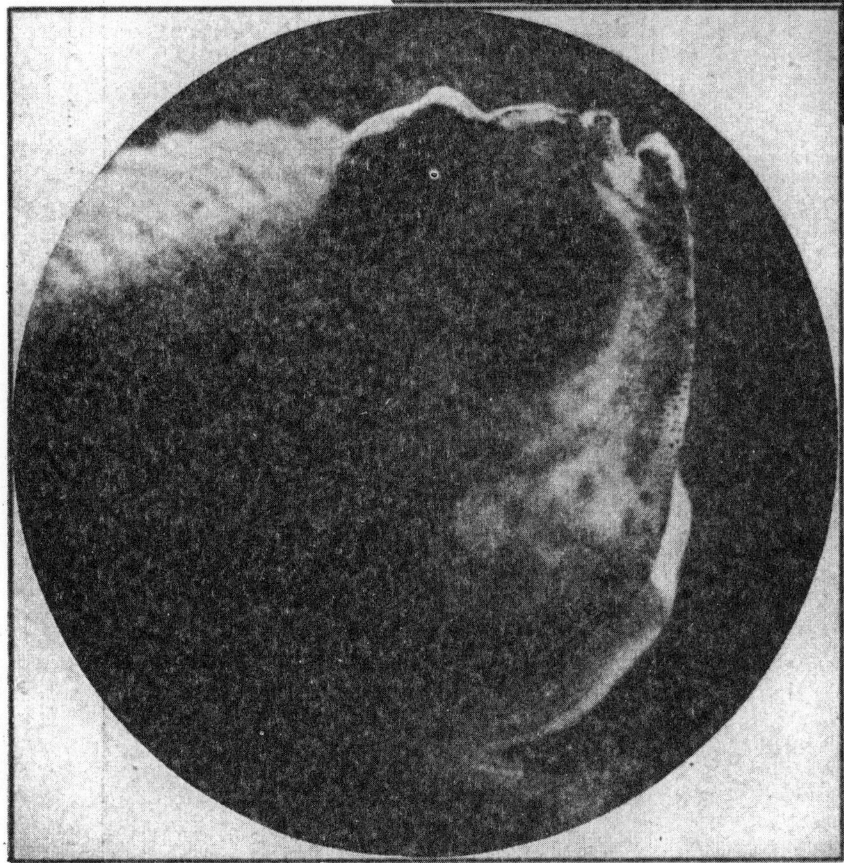

F. Martin Duncan

LAST STAGE THAT ENDS THIS EYE'S STRANGE HISTORY

Finally, when the plaice is adult, the facial twist is complete and the mouth has assumed the familiar contortion. The upper photograph shows the eye in the midst of its migration and the pigmentation—brown with red spots—developing on the right side. Below we see the plaice's head as it remains for life. As the fish grows it moves gradually into deeper water.

The reader will now be in a position to understand the why and wherefore of the peculiarities of the plaice: the reasons for its flat form, its brownish upper side, its shifted eye, and its twisted mouth. The fish is adapted for life on sandy sea-beds. It needs to be flat, so that it may lie close upon the sand; its upper side needs to be more or less sand-coloured, for the sake of concealment; its left eye needs to be carried to the upper side, where it can be used; and its mouth needs to be twisted, so that food may readily be taken from the sea-bottom.

And all this strange story has come to be told because we wanted to understand some wry faces on a fishmonger's slab!

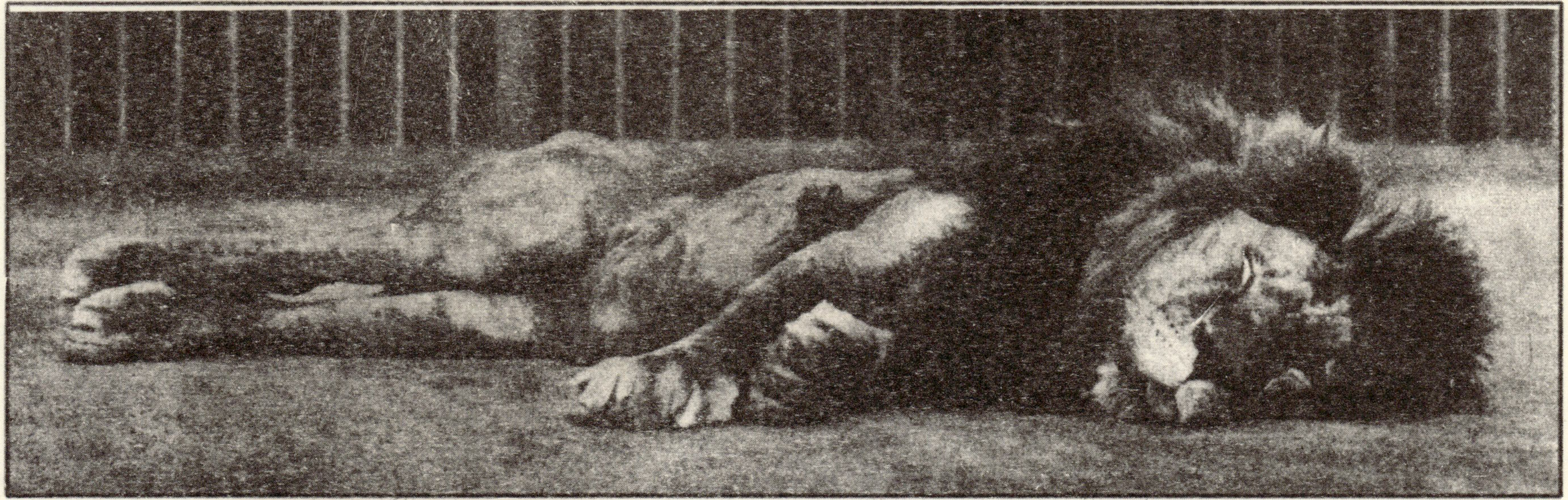

Autotype

ATTITUDES OF LORDLY EASE: THE LION AND TIGER SPENDING THEIR HOUR OF REST

When the big cats decide to take their ease they do it thoroughly. Every line in their bodies, as we see them here, betokens utter relaxation. These great animals, so powerful and ferocious, spend very much of their lives in cultivating the gentle art of being really comfortable, and they are so constructed that the hard ground, whether it be a rocky ledge in the wild or only the floor of their cage, makes for them as comfortable a resting-place as any feather bed and down pillow to a tired human being. There is something imposing in this complete contentment and the spectacle of strength in repose when one considers the size of these great creatures.

Chapter XCIX

Rest Hour in the Animal World

By Frank Finn

Author of "The World's Birds"

It will be noted, even if one confines oneself at first to familiar domesticated and captive animals, that these present very great and often unexpected differences in their notions about rest.

To take indoor animals first, it is not unnatural to find the slim little canary, which, as a bird, is a member of the warmest-blooded class of animals, pretty constantly on the move during the day, and only settling down to rest at night; but it is rather surprising to find that the cold-blooded gold-fish seems never to rest at all, and displays quite twice as much activity as its feathered rival.

The highly-organized cat, whose splendid suppleness makes other creatures look jerky or stiff, sleeps a great deal, and even when not asleep sits still for long periods at a time. That it commonly devotes the night to the thrilling pursuits of love and war with their accompanying wild music may partially account for this, but not entirely; for the cats, as becomes the aristocrats of the animal world, are pre-eminently a leisured class. The tiger, if lucky enough to kill a large beast, will eat his fill, go to water to drink and then retire to bed; next day he will do the same, probably finishing off his cold meat; the day after he will also spend in repose, though not refusing any easy chance of another kill, and not till the fourth will he begin seriously to hunt once more.

The dog, like the cat, sleeps a great deal—probably more than he ought, for he is by nature a more strenuous animal than the cat, having a more energetic method of hunting, often in company, and seldom enjoying a great surplus of provisions. Under our care, he does not usually get enough exercise, as is shown by his excitement on hearing the word "walk," which to his simple mind means a very discursive run in which he works off a lot of pent-up energy. The humanitarian legislation which forbids the use of dogs for draught is probably mistaken kindness, and we should most likely hear less about the unpleasantly wolfish eccentricities of Alsatians if these animals were given harness-work to do.

John Roberts

WATER BOATMAN AT ANCHOR

Anchored to a water plant by its usually very active legs the little water boatman takes its pleasure in a quiet rest, inconspicuous, at any distance, among the protecting fronds. It provides a good contrast to the huge animals in the opposite page.

Going outdoors, we find the pig putting in more hours of sleep and rest than are natural, owing to his restriction to a sty or yard, and copious rations of rich food; allowed to roam in a pasture he is no more sluggish than most other animals.

Cattle and sheep rest a great deal, but one does not often see them actually asleep by day; and they are fortunate in being able to combine rest and feeding by chewing the cud, which, as everyone knows, is simply eating their hastily-swallowed food over again. This necessity for cud-chewing is one of the drawbacks of the ox as compared with the horse as a working animal; he must have time to chew the cud as well as to feed.

Horses, it will be noticed, though they rest a good deal in the standing position, lie down far more rarely than the ruminants; in fact, some horses have so confirmed a habit of sleeping in a standing position that their legs suffer thereby, and they have to be slung when in the stable.

It is noticeable that none of these hoofed animals lie down squarely, so to speak, but always recline to some extent. The elephant is never seen to lie down by day; at night he will lie down for three hours, get up and eat some fodder, lie down on the other side for another three hours, and then get up and finish his food.

A few mammals have the very exceptional habit of sleeping on their backs, at any rate at times; this has been recorded of the large Indian flying-squirrel in hot weather, and the writer has seen the hairy armadillo, the only species of these queer armour-plated beasts at all common in captivity, reposing in the same position.

A peculiar characteristic of seals in repose, noted by Mr. J. G. Millais in his fine

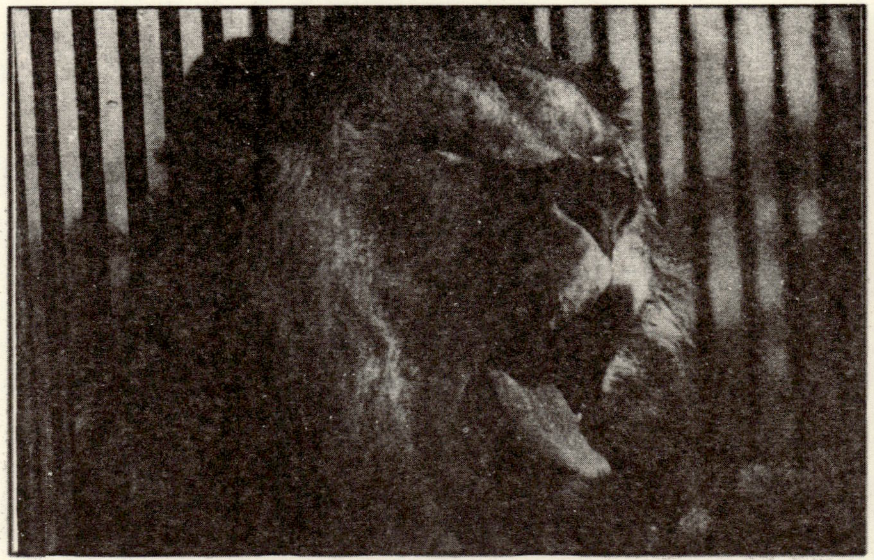

F. W. Bond

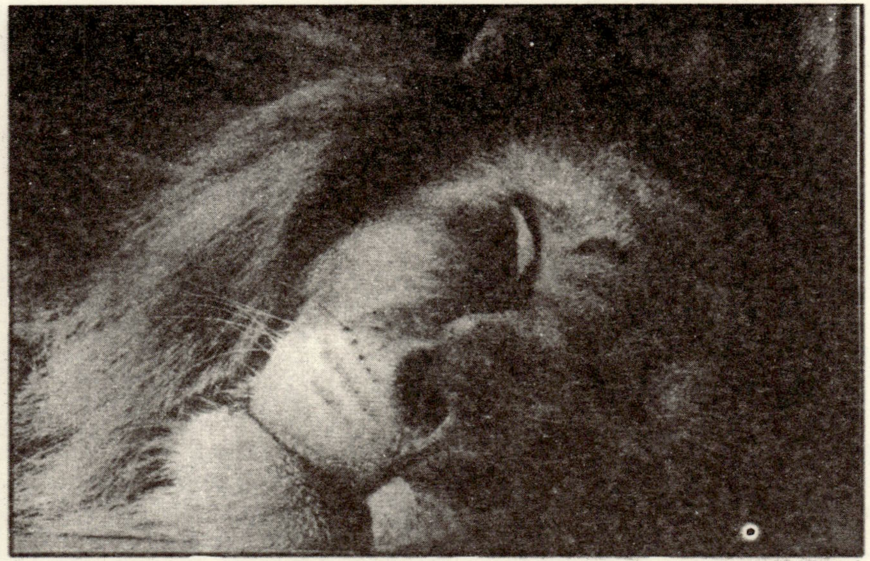

F. W. Bond

WHEN THE KING OF THE BEASTS TAKES HIS EASE: FOUR STUDIES OF LEONINE LEISURE

All lions spend much time in resting, but in captivity this proclivity is especially marked, the animals lying for hours with only an occasional lazy movement. It is probably boredom as much as anything that causes these prodigious stretchings and vast, protracted yawns, though the lack of natural exercise may help to induce a constant feeling of lassitude. Hunger wakes the lion very successfully even though it knows that the next meal is a certainty which will occur at the usual fixed hour. It is the resulting restlessness causing the worried pacing up and down so familiar to the crowds at the Zoo, which excite most interest, many people passing the sleepy lion with only a glance. But this somnolence is worth a little study as these photographs show.

F. W. Bond

F. W. Bond

TIGER AND PUMA: BIG CARNIVORA AND HOW THEY LOOK DURING THEIR AFTERNOON SIESTA

Although they are among the most active of animals the cat family—from tabby to tiger—spend a great deal of time in sleeping, curled up with heads comfortably tucked in or lying lazily stretched out. In its wild state the tiger, having made a large kill, will gorge itself, find water and drink and then retire to some place where it may be fairly sure of being undisturbed. In this page the bottom right and the two top photographs show some expressions and poses of the resting tiger while the bottom left-hand photograph is of a yawning puma. This very interesting beast has been dealt with in a previous chapter (see p. 241).

work on the British Mammals, is their extreme dislike of getting wet when they have hauled out for a doze on a tidal rock. As their coat dries they get sleepy, but when the rising tide begins to wet them again they show by their attitudes considerable distaste for what one would consider their more congenial element.

The sea-otter, which is far more aquatic than the more familiar fresh-water otters, will sleep on its back at sea. Ordinary monkeys sleep perched on the boughs, sitting upon their haunches ; in the case of a pair of Japanese monkeys that became the parents of a young one at the London Zoo before the War it was noticed that the old ones slept face to face, with the baby nestled in between, so that it had the benefit of their thick coats.

THE great man-like apes sleep reclining, on beds which they make for themselves in the trees, something like wood-pigeons' nests on a gigantic scale ; in such a bed a great orang-utan which escaped from the Zoo bivouacked for one night of freedom, making his couch in a surprisingly short time.

The male gorilla, however, in some localities at any rate, makes his bed on the ground. The orang appears to use bedclothes of some sort—presumably large leaves, as it seems to have a strong instinct in captivity for putting things on its head, though this may be merely " aping " human headgear.

Some of the hoofed animals make beds in a more or less crude way ; wild pigs construct shelters by biting off grass or cane and then pushing themselves in under the heap that they have made. The chiru antelope of the bleak uplands of Tibet scrapes out a lair for itself in which it lies covered except for its tall upright horns, the purpose apparently being to get a wind-break rather than to conceal itself. Lichtenstein's hartebeest in South Africa, too, also makes a " bed," out of which, according to Mr. Millais, it is often unscrupulously turned by the better-armed sable antelope.

In the Himalayas the musk-deer, which is more like a hare than a deer in its habits, follows the hare-like custom of establishing for itself a " form " or squatting-place, which may also be called a bed, as it is resorted to for rest. The lower animals love routine, and resort to the same places for rest, whether by day or by night, whenever possible.

The writer noticed this particularly in the case of a common kingfisher which haunted the pond in the Indian Museum grounds, Calcutta. At one end of this a tree grew out of a mass of masonry, and on a twig of this the bird always perched when not fishing, so close to the wall that his forcibly ejected droppings made a white patch on it against which he stood out like the bull's-eye of a target.

STERNDALE has also recorded a case in his "Mammalia of India," in which a wary black buck which he hunted about for three days before he could shoot it, never left its ground, and even slept every night in a field near his tent.

The otter is peculiar in often changing its lair, but even here there are certain " holts " well known to otters generally, which use them as places of call when travelling. Gadow, in his volume on reptiles in the Cambridge Natural History series, gives instances of the love of routine repose displayed by reptiles, notably in the cases of eyed lizards, tree-frogs which haunted particular spots, and of a tortoise which after hibernation went straight to a favourite basking spot which it had used the year before.

Tortoises display interesting intelligence or instinct in their poses when basking : though disliking really hot sun, they will make the most of feeble sunbeams by tilting their shells against a wall to get the utmost amount of heat, a habit which was noticed in the case of the common land tortoise by Gilbert White, and has been observed by the writer in that of the common European water-tortoise. Reptiles at rest display a remarkable power of sustaining the most rigid and apparently awkward-looking poses without such mechanical help, and often look as if they had fallen asleep while in the act of walking.

Land poultry rest a good deal by day, but do not sleep ; like the ruminants with their cud-chewing, they can combine repose with another needful activity, in this case a toilet performance, the dust-bath. This begins, indeed, with much expenditure of energy in scratching and wing-scuffling, but, once well worked into a dust-hole, the bird reclines more or less and takes things easily. It is only when so occupied, or when basking, that the birds do recline ; otherwise they stand if on the ground, or squat if perched, when resting.

AQUATIC poultry sleep a great deal by day, but then, like the dog and cat, they are quite active by night, and in fact, foxes permitting, ducks are best left out then, as this is their best time for hunting slugs, worms, and so forth. The land poultry go to roost at different times : the guinea-fowl earliest, perhaps because it is on the trot all day and seldom seen to rest ; the peacock latest, for his leisurely strolling is not calculated to tire him much. Both peafowl and guinea-fowl are much lighter sleepers than ordinary poultry : at any rate, they are always ready to give the alarm if anyone approaches, and peafowl at any rate are not helpless at night like ordinary fowls, but, if then alarmed, will fly to another perch. A pea-hen which escaped from a dealer's premises which used to be on the terrace in Covent Garden, thus lived at large for several months, and was only captured at last by flying at night to a known window-sill where she was seized.

The Muscovy duck, now coming to the front again after being neglected for half a century, offers a very curious case in being a bird with the lethargic habits of a reptile. Although it swims as well as the ordinary duck, walks better, and flies strongly, it spends its time much as most reptiles do, being mostly quiescent, though not actually sleeping ; yet it is capable of vigorous action when roused by anger or any other emotion. It often perches, being descended from a

F. W. Bond

F. W. Bond

LION AND LIONESS SUNNING THEMSELVES AT THE LONDON ZOO

When the summer weather brings a genial temperature to the London Zoological Gardens and the animals are able to enjoy, out of doors, climatic conditions more approximating to their natural ones than usual, the lions soon avail themselves of the change. We see above two views of a handsome pair, lion and lioness, taking a sunbath in the outside portion of their cages. Lions enjoy sleeping in the sun as well as any human does, and will lie contentedly dozing for a long time—too long for some visitors, who had expected to see a little ferocity.

F. W. Bond

LITHE GRACE IN REPOSE: JAGUAR AND LEOPARD DOZING

What the lions and tigers possess in size the jaguar (bottom) and the leopard (top) make up for in grace and lithe movement. A jaguar cannot be ungainly, and when, as we see it here, it curls its handsome head round upon one paw and dozes, one can only think of the most handsome cat that was ever created seen through a magnifying glass. The leopard in the upper illustration was photographed while having a rest in the middle of the road at Bengoli, in the Belgian Congo. It was the pet of some native children there.

W S Berridge

HIMALAYAN LYNX AND A WAPITI STAG IN RESTFUL ATTITUDES

This lynx (bottom) comes from the Himalayas, and lives at an altitude of ten thousand feet. The lynx is probably the fiercest of all the cat tribe, its rage being really demoniac to watch and its claws terrible in their operation. In repose it only just suggests the spitting, clawing devil into which it can, in a moment, turn. Above we see a wapiti stag curled round like a dog, but with one of its forelegs stuck out in front. This is a strange attitude to choose for resting.

J. T. Roberts

tropical American species which, like most tropical wild fowl, is a percher; and then, like such birds generally, stands up, though it sits down when resting on the ground, thus behaving in exactly the reverse way to the land poultry. Parrots differ from other cage-birds in remaining awake as long as the family is about.

THE mechanism by which a sleeping bird unconsciously retains its grip on the perch is very interesting; by bending the leg of a dead bird up against the body the toes will be seen to contract, so that when it sinks down on its perch it automatically, by the arrangement of the muscles of the tendons, clamps itself on to its support. Many birds, however, sleep standing on one or both legs, but the shanks in such cases are often a little inclined from the perpendicular, which must give some pull on the toes; probably little actual grip is required unless the wind begins to blow, when the percher would no doubt wake up and consciously hold on.

Perching waterfowl, however, as has been said, generally stand in repose, but in any case these cannot depend much on grip; their hind toes being usually too small to be of the slightest use, and also placed too high up.

That curious South American bird, the Cariama, perches with a foot even less adapted for grasping than a duck's, the hind toe being so high that it could not possibly be of use, while the front toes are very short. This bird sits down on its perch, and when basking by day rolls over so far that it lies almost on its back, but not quite.

Its compatriot the rhea, the so-called "ostrich" of America, has a most curious and unique way of taking its ease at times,

F. W ond

STRANGE POSTURES OF PANGOLIN AND GIRAFFE WHEN RESTING

When the pangolin (bottom) is tired of climbing about among the trees it just curls itself round a branch, presenting merely the appearance of a suit of scale armour when seen from behind. The giraffe is awkward to look at when it is resting. Even when taking its ease the neck is at full stretch in a restless, watchful way.

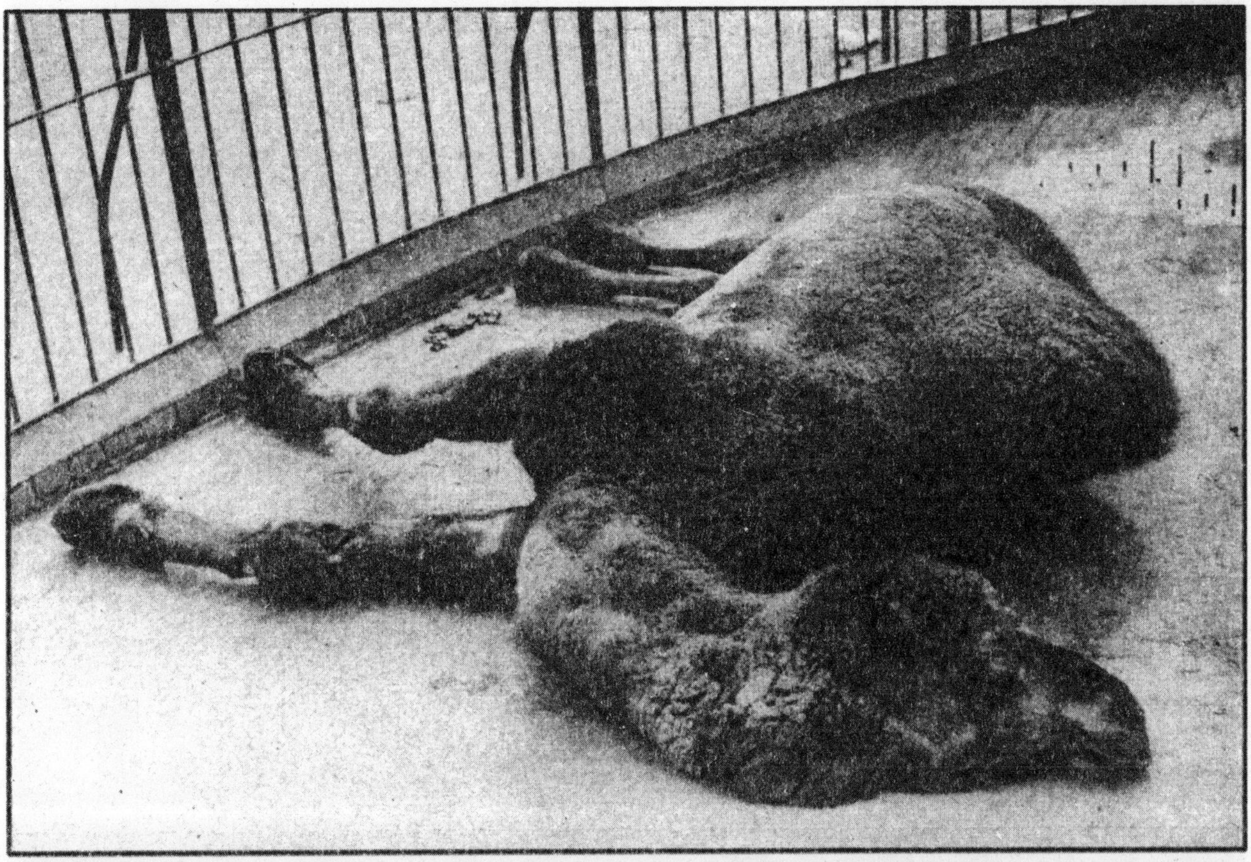

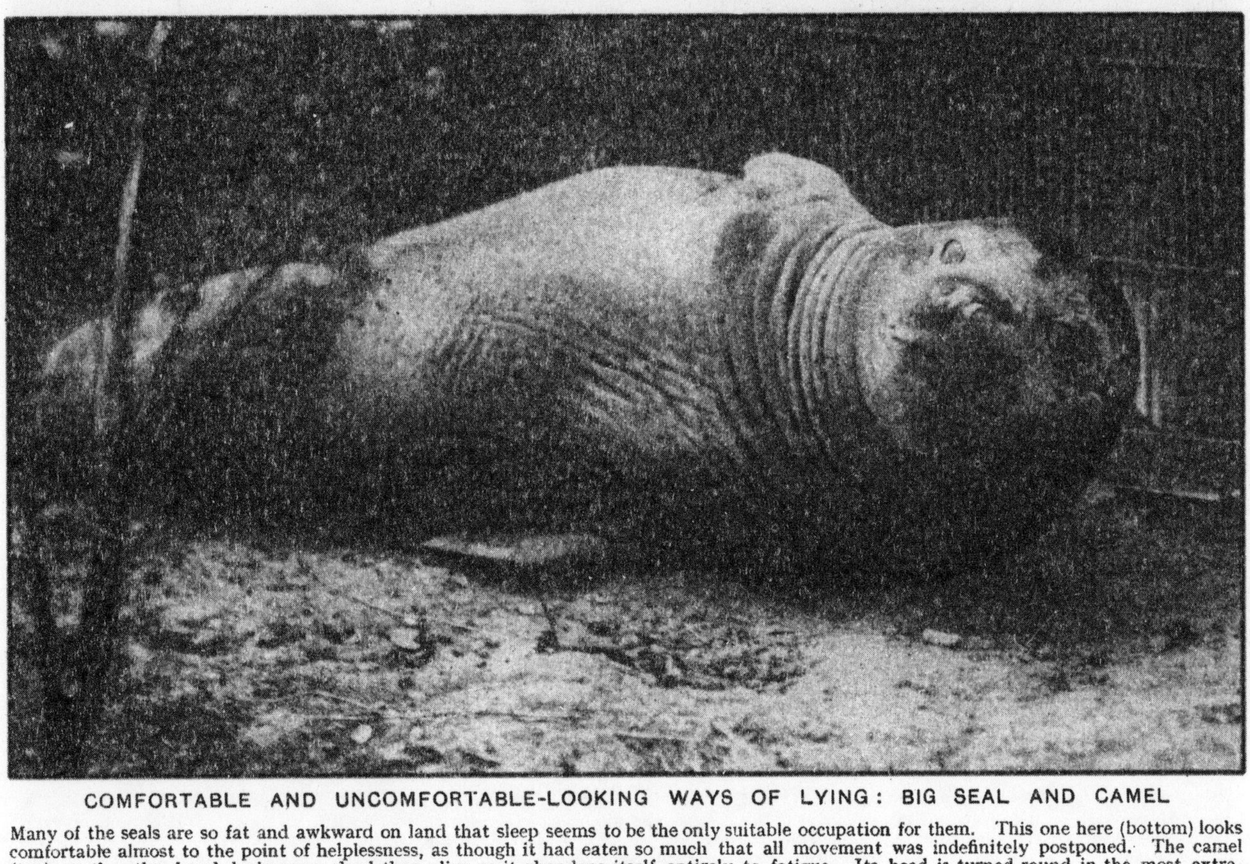

COMFORTABLE AND UNCOMFORTABLE-LOOKING WAYS OF LYING: BIG SEAL AND CAMEL

Many of the seals are so fat and awkward on land that sleep seems to be the only suitable occupation for them. This one here (bottom) looks comfortable almost to the point of helplessness, as though it had eaten so much that all movement was indefinitely postponed. The camel (top), on the other hand, looks more dead than alive as it abandons itself entirely to fatigue. Its head is turned round in the most extraordinary way so as to look right away from the rest of its body.

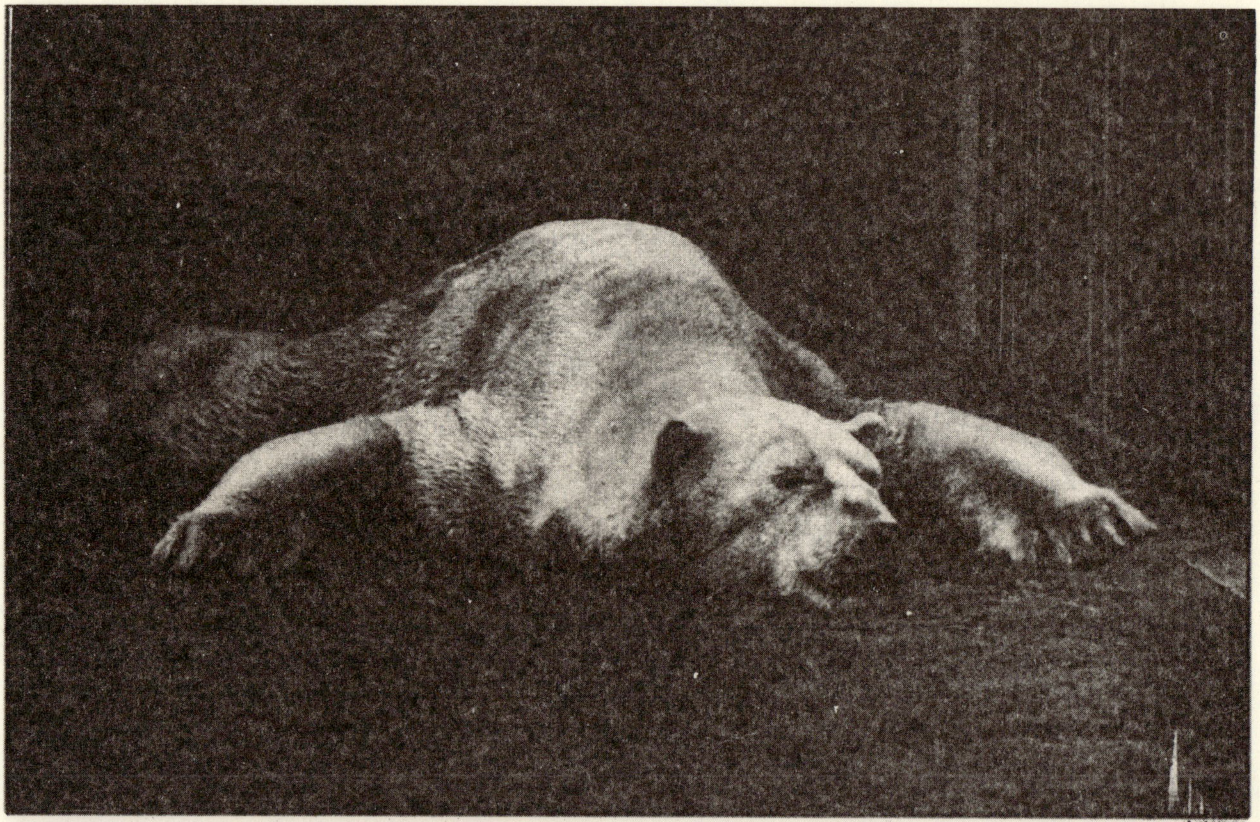

TWO POSTURES IN WHICH POLAR BEARS MAY BE FOUND ASLEEP

In the upper photograph the polar bear looks more as if it had been just shot than as though it were merely sleeping. The strange spread-out, swimming position is seldom seen in animals, and it contrasts strongly with the attitude of the other polar bear (bottom). This one makes a fine picture as it lies on the edge of the deep concrete trench that defends one of the Mappin Terraces at the London Zoo, dreaming, perhaps, of the unconfined spaces of the Arctic and a whole seal for supper.

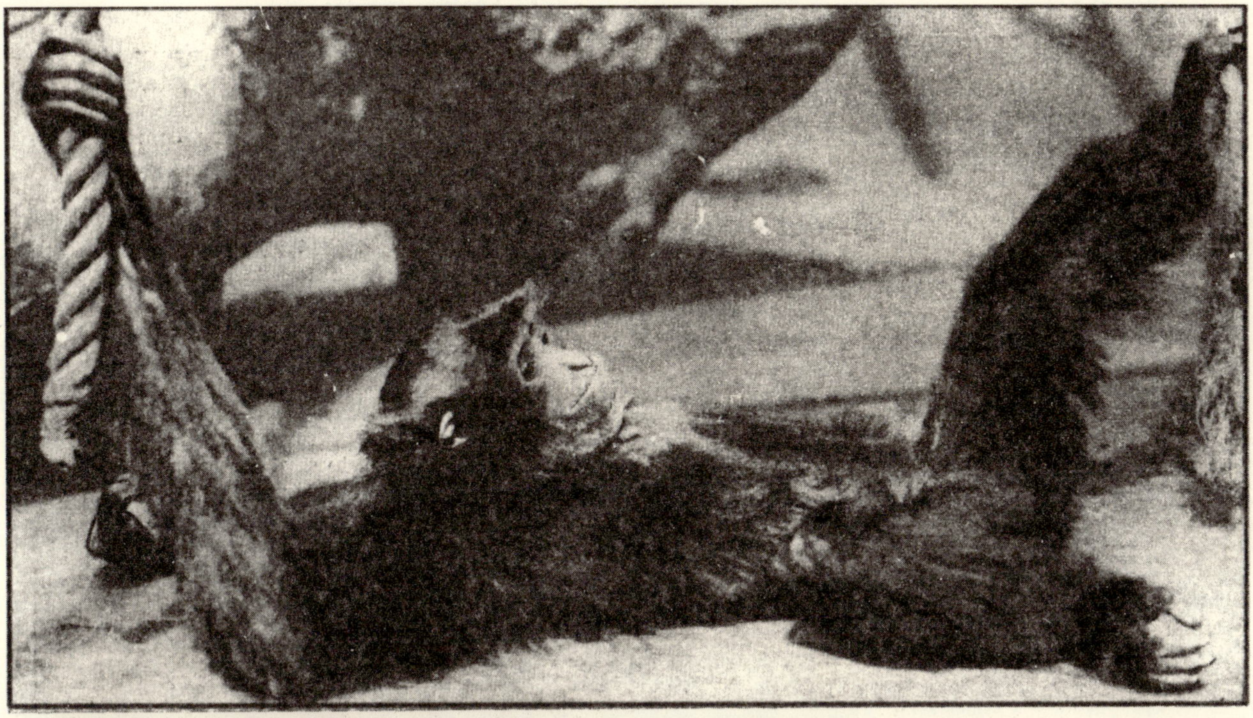

E.N.A.

BEAR AND GIBBON MAKING REPOSE COMFORTABLE EACH IN ITS OWN WAY

The bear (bottom) lies rather quaintly with all its four feet placed firmly together, and has a neat appearance as it takes forty winks. The gibbon, on the other hand (top), spreads itself over this business of resting, and has elaborately made a hammock of itself by grasping one rope with a foot and another with a hand. For this method of resting it can at least be said that, so far as concerns the gibbon, it looks comfortable. It is quite common for the monkeys at the London Zoo to use for rest the apparatus given them for exercise.

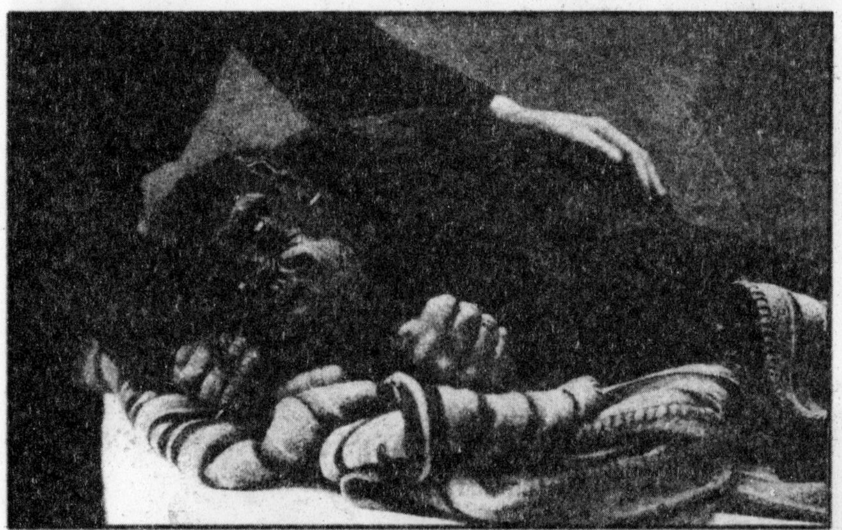

F. W. Bond

turtles in particular, in an aquarium at any rate, are hardly ever still. The little wall-lizard, too, is pretty constantly in motion.

No reptile, however, will remain long active in a really low temperature, and this would make their general hibernation in winter easier to understand, were it not for the fact that many of the warm-blooded mammals also hibernate, and that tropical reptiles will "aestivate," that is to say, become torpid during the long dry season, when it is hot enough in all conscience. The same cause evidently brings about both aestivation and hibernation—terms which mean prolonged sleep under droughty and frosty conditions respectively. Certain animals overcome the difficulties of finding food attendant on extreme drought or frost by passing into a state of torpor until favourable conditions obtain once more. It may be remembered that extremes both of heat and cold produce sleepiness even in ourselves.

The daytime sleep of the British bats, at any rate, is particularly sound, and forms a sort of physiological link between ordinary sleep and hibernation, as they are practically torpid rather than asleep till the time comes for them to wake up, being very cold, and taking ten minutes or more to become active.

Flying-foxes do not hibernate, but then they do not live in climates with a cold winter, and are fruit-eaters; and they probably sleep less by day than most other nocturnal mammals, for they quarrel so

F. W. Bond

TAME APES IN SOME OF THEIR "OFF MOMENTS"

By the expression on its face one might conclude that this chimpanzee (bottom) curled up on the flat top of a sawn tree stump, was not finding this resting-place very comfortable. But hard surfaces do not worry any but domestic animals, as a rule. The gorilla in the upper photograph is enjoying the height of luxury with a blanket and a lady to caress its back

lying down with its long legs stretched out behind it, while the long neck is erect and the eyes closed. No other bird ever assumes this position, which would be a most dangerous one to recover from in case of surprise. At other times the rhea will sit with its legs tucked under it in a normal way, and its long neck resting on its back; but it seems never to "tuck its head under its wing," nor do any of the specialised flightless running, or "ratite," birds do this except the kiwi. The kiwi is such a sound sleeper that it can be picked up before it will untuck its head—which, by the way, cannot be put under the tiny wing. But birds in this repose posture do not actually put their heads under their wings, but rest them on the shoulder, snuggling them in between the long shoulder-plumage and the basal joint of the wing lying parallel to the body and concealed by this cloak of plumage. In fact, the writer was only enabled to find the exact position by observing an unfortunate parrakeet in India which was a feather-eater—a very rare parrot-vice in that country—and had stripped himself all but his head, so that it was possible to see exactly what part of his anatomy he used as a pillow.

MANY birds like to repose by day sitting down on their hocks, the species which do this being usually large and long-legged species like the carrion-feeding storks—adjutant and marabout.

Although, as above hinted, most reptiles are very lethargic, some are quite active especially the tortoises, in spite of their heavy shape; the sea-

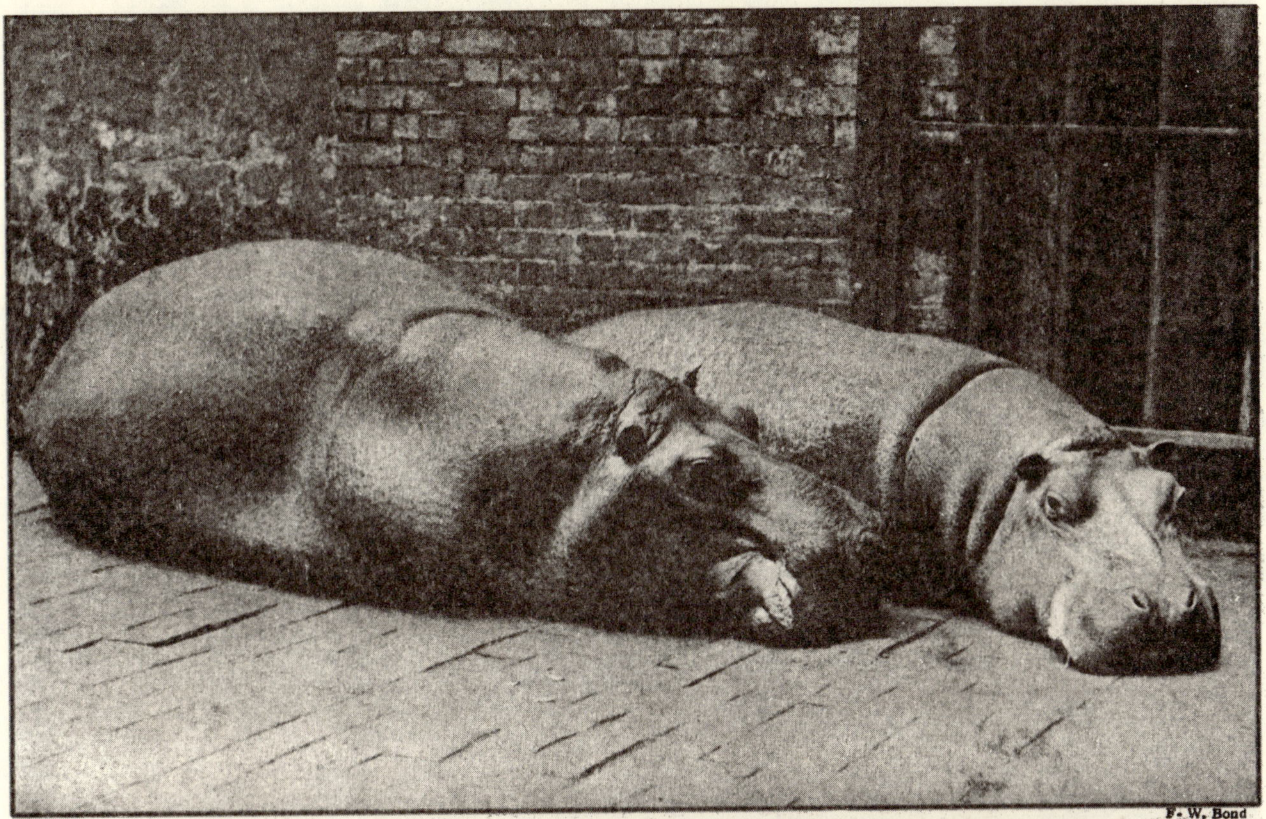

F. W. Bond

RHINOCEROS AND HIPPOPOTAMUS IN RESTFUL ATTITUDES AT THE ZOO

This young rhino (bottom) has adopted an apparently uneasy pose for lying in. The forelegs are doubled up under the body and brought over to the same side. But whatever this attitude seems to us, the young animal finds it suitable to its needs, and we can see by the way the nose is dropped contentedly to the ground that the animal is enjoying its rest. The upper photograph shows us two hippos sunning themselves side by side on the brick floor of their yard.

Autotype

W. S. Berridge

ONE LEGGED AND TWO LEGGED METHODS OF RESTING: EXEMPLIFIED BY MARABOU STORK AND BOATBILL

When a perching bird sits on a branch the mechanism of its toes is so arranged that the sleepier the bird becomes and the more it sinks down upon its feet, the tighter becomes the grip of the claws round the branch. This may be easily illustrated by pressing the legs of a dead bird up against its body when the claw will be seen to contract. The large carrion-eating storks like the adjutant, or the marabou (left) often rest squatting on their hocks, though for sleep they seem to prefer standing on one leg. The shanks of the legs are usually inclined a little from the perpendicular, which probably applies a certain amount of pull to the toes. On the right is a boatbill which rests on both legs.

PIKE RESTING MOTIONLESS IN THE STILL WATERS OF THEIR AQUARIUM

It is still debated whether fish may be said to sleep as we understand sleep, but certain fish spend many hours almost motionless. Of these a familiar case to all who have watched rivers and lakes is that of the pike. This voracious fish will move out of the strong water in mid-stream and make for some quiet lay-bye—at the tail of an island or the mouth of a dyke—and float so still that one might mistake it for a sunk log. In the aquarium at the London Zoo pike may be seen thus, with only their greedy, golden eyes moving now and then.

much at their "camps" that they fall asleep late, and yet are on the wing again before dark when evening comes on.

An Indian vampire the writer once kept appeared never to sleep at all, for whenever he was awake at night he could hear it fluttering about in its large cage, and always found it awake when looked at by day. It may be that such creatures, like owls, which in captivity generally seem to be awake whenever one looks at them, only sleep in snatches, as has been noted in the case of some seals, and it is possible that the long-sailing albatross really dozes on the wing, as pictured in Moore's beautiful lines:

> A ruined castle towered so high
> That oft the sleeping albatross
> Struck the wild ruins with her wing,
> And from her wind-rocked slumbering
> Started, to find man's dwelling there
> In her own silent fields of air.

To return to the bats, a few species with a high northern range migrate south in autumn like birds, and it has been suggested that the reason why they do so is that the northern winter is so long that even a hibernator's endurance could not survive it; it is true that, except in the case of the pregnant polar bear, there is no hibernation among mammals in the Arctic. The lemmings remain active under the snow, as also does the Alpine mole.

The curious long-tailed bat, whose tail is free from the leg-web and looks like a mouse's, accumulates a mass of fat at its hinder parts as a reserve supply for hibernation; so do also the little mouse-lemurs of Madagascar, which are the only Primates or relatives of the monkeys which are subject to torpor, which is limited to a few groups in mammals.

In reptiles and amphibians, however, it is very common, and universal in climates with a cold winter; the more aquatic kinds seek the water at this time, and bury themselves in the mud; what little flicker of respiration that goes on being conducted, no doubt, through the skin, at any rate in the case of frogs which are known to be skin-breathers.

That the common European water-tortoise, so well known to pet keepers, can go for long without breathing, and even bear freezing, was proved to the writer by a specimen of his which wintered in a stone flower-basin sunk in the ground and containing about six inches of water; and on one occasion it must have been frozen, as the water became a cake of ice. Yet it survived and suffered in no way.

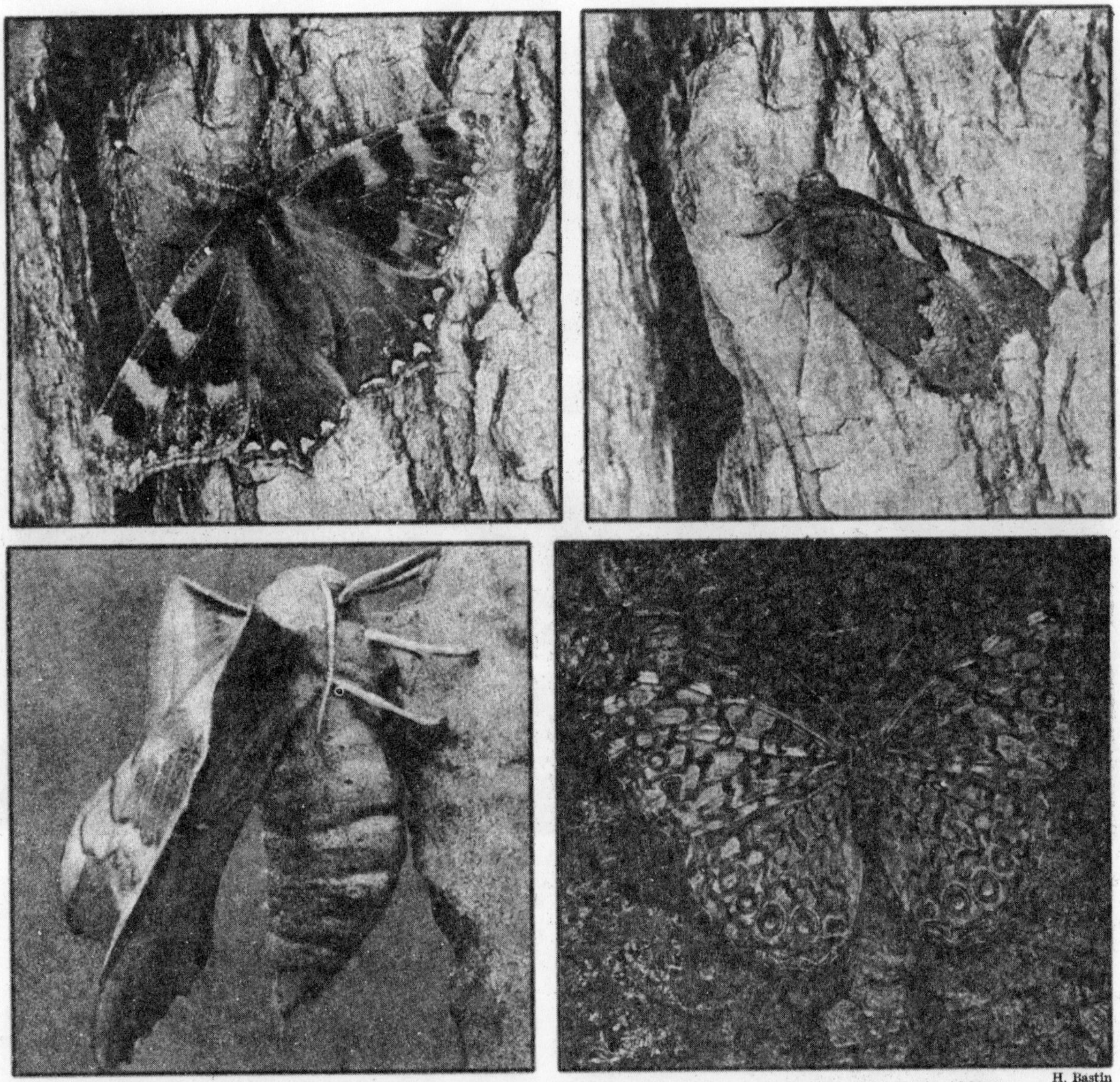

H. Bastin

WING POSITIONS OF MOTH AND BUTTERFLY WHEN RESTING IN THE SUN

The lower left-hand photograph is of a poplar hawk-moth, slightly enlarged, resting its huge fat body from the labours of flight. Next it (bottom right) is a specimen of ageronia, a South American butterfly which much resembles the irregularities and lichen on tree trunks. This butterfly rests with its wings open, whereas most butterflies keep their wings closed when resting. Moths, on the other hand, when asleep, open their wings out flat. The upper photographs show the small tortoiseshell butterfly (left) sunning itself and (right) in its sleeping position.

An opposite example of endurance was shown by an Eastern water-tortoise, the box soft-shell, which was found by a well-known Indian sporting naturalist, Mr. W. K. Dods, aestivating at a little distance below the surface of a previously-flooded plain which at the time was being baked by the sun so thoroughly that it was painful to walk over it even in shooting boots.

An instance of a peculiar and very aquatic frog, inhabiting a warm country liable to drought, nevertheless remaining active all winter under very abnormal conditions of temperature occurred in London during this century, when an East-end dealer got a number of the curious and highly aquatic African claw-footed frogs, and kept them in an outdoor unheated shed in a tank, where they not only did not hibernate, but fed; for some that died were devoured by their companions, the claw-footed frog differing from others in readily eating dead food.

Fish are usually killed, like air-breathing vertebrates, if frozen, but this is not the case with the Alaskan blackfish Dallia, which also inhabits Eastern Siberia. It lives in sphagnum-grown ponds, being content with the merest wetting of water, and undergoes freezing in winter with perfect equanimity. The Alaskan natives use it freely for food, though it is only about as big as a gudgeon, and it is found that specimens which have been stored frozen in baskets for weeks will be as lively as ever when thawed. The fish is also fed to dogs, one of which animals has been known to swallow the frozen fish and vomit it up alive, thawed out by the warmth of his stomach and no doubt provoking ejection by its activity.

Insects commonly become torpid when the temperature falls at all markedly, and many will not even fly when the sun is overcast, as is very noticeable in the case of some butterflies; the writer, however, once saw in a London street a Large White butterfly flying about and feeding at the flowers in window-boxes on a dull drizzly day. This, however, was a very exceptional case and it might almost be said that the butterfly's official hours are ten to five, the rest being spent in repose.

He has also seen the Painted Lady butterfly active on an autumn day when the temperature was decidedly cold, though the sun was bright. The few hibernating butterflies may occasionally be tempted out on warm days, and the writer has found that captive Red Admirals will live for weeks in winter even, if periodically awakened by warmth and fed, this butterfly being quite willing to move and feed, when the sun is not shining, and even fighting over food by flapping like an angry pigeon and pawing ridiculously with its tiny legs.

Natural History, N.Y.

BEARDED DRAGON IN REPOSE UPON A STUMP

When in repose, the bearded dragon lies with its " beard " as we see it above. But under the stimulus of alarm or anger this appendage is expanded, making this already hideous creature more frightful still. It is a little under two feet long, as a rule, and is very fond of basking on tree stumps. When photographed this particular " dragon " was at peace with all the world.

Butterflies and moths differ much in their positions of repose, the butterflies usually resting with wings closed over the back, exposing the under surface, while the moths draw their wings down to their sides or spread them out flat. Skippers, which are one of the groups forming the transition between butterflies and moths, exhibit a compromise when in repose, keeping the fore-wings erect and spreading out the hinder ones horizontally.

The different groups of dragon-flies exhibit a very similar difference in their repose positions; the larger and stouter-built kinds spreading out their wings horizontally, while the slim " demoiselles " fold their wings in butterfly fashion with the inner surfaces applied together, and the outer exposed.

The instinct for resorting to a given resting-place even by day is well known by the Purple Emperor which likes a certain twig high up on an oak tree, and, in fact, his special attachment to this gave almost the only chance of capturing him when, his taste for strong-smelling bait not having been discovered, his human enemies used to pursue him with preposterously long-handled nets.

The pupa stage of insects, in which this takes the form of a helpless chrysalis incapable of anything but a wriggle, is a period of absolute rest as far as the external world is concerned, but there is, at this time, a regular revolution going on in the creature's interior, for insects which pass through such a stage may almost be said to die and undergo dissolution and emerge in a resurrection. The chrysalis really is, as Shelley said

> An ante-natal tomb
> Where butterflies dream of the life to come

for the chrysalis stage sees the wonderful process of histolysis, or tissue-dissolution, in which the organs of the caterpillar break down into a sort of creamy matter to be reconstructed into those of the imago.

H. J. Shepstone

DEALING WITH THE TERRIBLE LOCUST MENACE IN SOUTH AFRICA

In South Africa hundreds of thousands of pounds worth of damage has been done by locusts periodically. Methods of dealing with this pest have now become standardised and one of the most effective is illustrated in this page. Locust traps (lower photograph) are made by sinking a box or a pit in the path of the locusts when they are in the nymph or flightless stage and guiding them into the trap between two converging lines of obstacles. The upper photograph shows both men and women turned out to drive the crawling host.

Chapter C

Insect Enemies of Man's Industry

By Dr. S. A. Neave

Assistant Director, Imperial Bureau of Entomology

THE realization that insects are perhaps the chief enemies and competitors of mankind has only quite recently received recognition in the history of civilization. Indeed, it is doubtful whether primitive man took any interest in insects at all except for the honey he obtained from bees and that some of the larger caterpillars and beetle larvae provided him with toothsome morsels. Even at the present day the natives of Central Africa are chiefly interested in insects from this standpoint and scarcely recognize them as enemies that take toll of their crops or affect their health.

Nor is this surprising since the fact that certain insects occur in such numbers as to reach the status of pests is entirely due to the action of mankind in upsetting the balance of nature by cultivating great quantities and large areas of one particular kind of plant. Consequently it is not until agriculture is widely and extensively practised in any country that insects become serious and obvious competitors of man so far as his food supply is concerned.

Under modern conditions, however, the most cogent insect problems, at least in more civilized countries, are concerned not so much with the native species, though these are serious enough, but with those that have been accidentally introduced from elsewhere. Everyone knows the result of importing the rabbit into Australia, and this is a classic instance of what may happen when a creature is introduced into a new country where the climate may be more favourable to it and where its natural enemies are few or non-existent. With the constant interchange of foodstuffs of all kinds and many other animal and vegetable products that occur under modern conditions, it is not at all surprising that many insects have escaped from their native country into new homes and have caused untold and incalculable losses. Though nearly every civilized country now maintains expensive quarantine services aimed at keeping out these invaders, it is a moot point whether they will be permanently successful, and the fact has to be faced that it is highly probable that every dominant insect pest will ultimately spread over the whole of its potential geographical range.

The most modern method of dealing with these invasions is to endeavour to introduce into the invaded country one or more of the parasites of the pest concerned which normally keep down its numbers in its original home. For it has been found that the absence of these natural enemies is in many cases an important cause of its huge increase in the country it has invaded. Such parasites are highly-specialised creatures and are usually only able to live in a single host; scarcely any risk therefore exists in establishing them in new countries.

In order to give some idea of the enormous losses involved and the vast sums that have had to be expended in dealing with these imported pests, we may now take some concrete instances. The continent that has suffered most in this respect is probably that of North America. This is, however, only in accordance with expectation. Agriculture in Europe has been carried on for many centuries, and a new equilibrium between the crops and the insect pests has been partly attained. In North America not only is agriculture relatively recent, but it has been carried on on a vast scale, and very large areas have been devoted to single crops, thus favouring the propagation of a particular insect in great numbers. Not only, therefore, have some of the indigenous insects been provided with an almost unlimited food supply, but invaders from Europe have, in many cases, had opportunities of spreading that did not obtain in their native land.

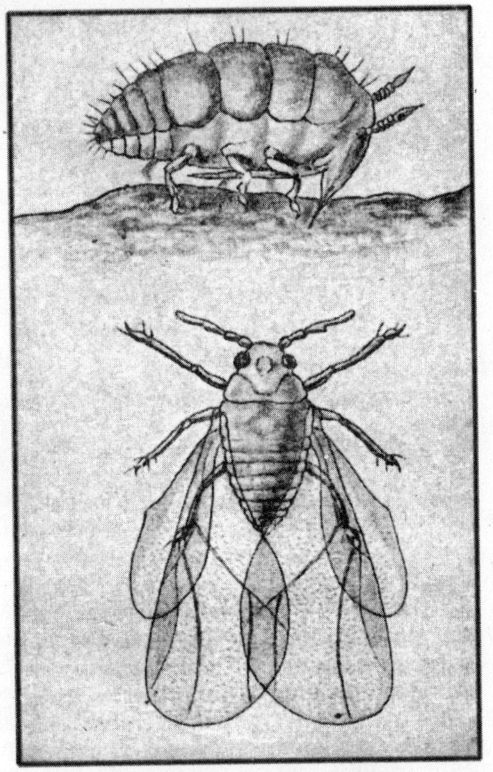

DESTROYER OF THE VINES

About the year 1863 the vine aphis or phylloxera was introduced into Europe from North America, doing enormous damage. In 1878 an international convention had to be called to deal with the pest.

Europe itself has not wholly escaped from American invaders. The dreaded phylloxera has spread throughout the vineyards of the Continent since the middle of the last century, and the woolly apple aphis (*Eriosoma lanigerum*) is now almost universal in European orchards. A more recent example is the invasion of the potato fields of south-western France by the Colorado potato beetle (*Leptinotarsa decemlineata*). This last pest made its appearance in Germany just before the War, but it was stamped out by the extreme

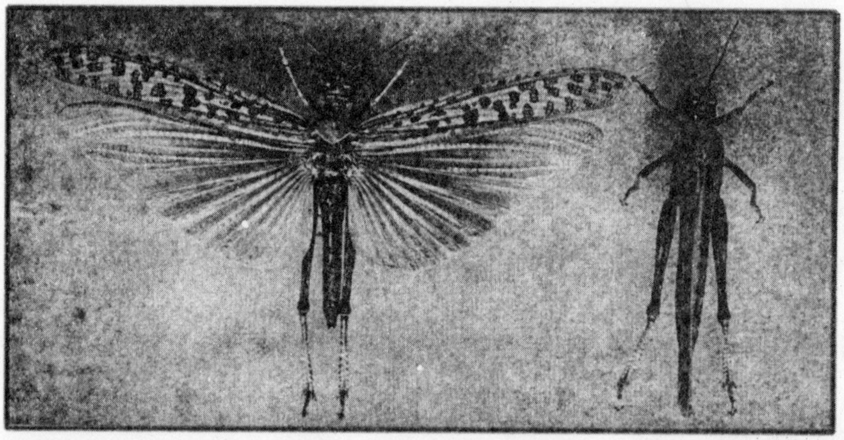

H. Bastin

F. Martin Duncan

WINGED LOCUSTS AS THEY FLY TO NEW FEEDING GROUNDS

The locust is a species of short-horned grasshopper belonging to the family Acridiidae, and though the term locust is applied to insects of other families, even the cicadas of America, strictly speaking only members of the short horned grasshopper family should be called locusts. Here are (bottom) a locust as in flight, and (top) migratory locusts with wings open and closed.

measures taken by the authorities, who turned out troops to deal with it! It was even suggested during the War that this beetle might be dropped from aeroplanes on to the German potato fields. This novel form of warfare, though it would have been quite practicable, would, however, only have ultimately resulted in permanently affecting the crops, and therefore the price of potatoes throughout the whole Continent.

In North America itself many striking examples occur of the enormous damage and loss that have been inflicted by insect pests. Costly routine measures against some of the indigenous ones, such as the cotton bollworm (*Heliothis obsoleta*), the San José scale (*Aspidiotus perniciosus*), the chinch bug (*Blissus leucopterus*), the various caterpillars known as army worms, and the many species of aphids that infest fruit and grain crops, such as the Southern grain louse (*Toxoptera graminus*), have in recent years become a commonplace in American agriculture.

But serious though these pests are, an even more alarming menace to that country is presented by some of the insects that have been imported from Europe and elsewhere.

Probably the best known of these is the gipsy moth (*Porthetria dispar*). On this side of the Atlantic, this moth is chiefly prevalent in Central Europe, where it has long been known as a pest in the forests. It is fortunately an uncommon insect in England. It first appeared in North America in Massachusetts about 1868. About twenty years later it had become so abundant and injurious that the Legislature of that State found it necessary to appoint a special commission to study the situation. It is now generally distributed over a very considerable percentage of the New England States, and though some isolated infestations have been exterminated by the energy of the authorities, the pest still appears to be spreading. The war on this enemy and the brown-tail moth (*Nygmia phaeorrhoea*), another imported pest of the same character, is, however, still in progress, and the methods of exterminating it continue to be improved upon. These have been considerably assisted since about 1905 by the introduction of numerous parasites and predaceous insects, chiefly from Europe, but also from Japan.

The direct cost of keeping this moth within bounds is stupendous. A calculation made in 1922 estimated that at that time the New England States had expended over four million pounds sterling in their efforts to control it. In Massachusetts alone the expenditure for 1921 amounted to over £165,000, and to these figures must be added the expenses of the Federal Government, which since 1906 has applied its efforts to checking the spread of the enemy into new areas.

Nor is this the only loss to the community that has been inflicted by its presence. The damage done to the forest areas in these States is in-

H Bastin

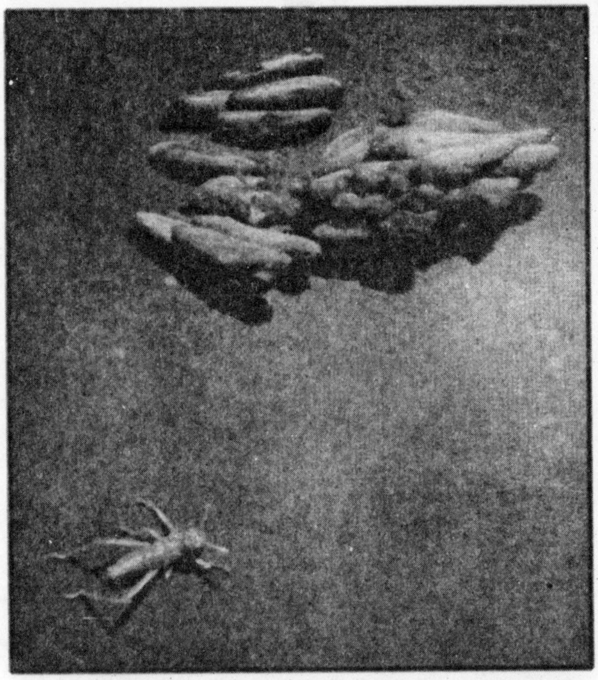

LOCUST EGGS AND A WINGLESS GRASSHOPPER
The female locust bores a hole in the ground and lays her eggs into it, sticking them together in a clump (bottom). The same substance which keeps the eggs together fills up the hole. Above is another pest, a large wingless grasshopper from Asia Minor.

calculable, and no serious attempt seems to have been made to estimate it at all accurately. In one relatively small area in Massachusetts, the oak forests of Cape Cod, 90 per cent. of the oaks have been killed, these trees representing 75 per cent of the forest land. It must be remembered that this moth's capacity for increase and for doing extensive damage lies in the fact that its caterpillars are very catholic in their tastes. Though they have a preference for deciduous trees, such as oaks and poplars, they will also attack several conifers and other valuable timber trees. Even where such trees are not killed outright there is a serious retardation of growth and consequent loss in the production of marketable timber.

In spite of all this, and though the best known to the public at large, the gipsy moth is perhaps not the most dangerous enemy that America has to face at the present time. Within the past ten or twelve years the so-called European corn borer (*Pyrausta nubilalis*), a small moth that bores in the stems of maize, sorghum, and similar plants, has been introduced from Europe, and is spreading with most alarming rapidity. So menacing is the situation that in the spring of 1928 the Federal Government voted no less than two millions sterling toward investigations and other measures for checking its spread. Vast though this sum is, it is clearly not more than the situation demands, when we remember that maize is one of the chief food crops of the United States.

This country has also had to face the attack of most dangerous invaders from the South. The Mexican cotton boll weevil (*Anthonomus grandis*) now causes tremendous annual losses to cotton, and has apparently increased the cost of producing this crop. The Mexican bean beetle (*Epilachna corrupta*), a kind of leaf-eating ladybird, is steadily spreading, and doing great damage in the Southern States. An even more alarming enemy is the notorious pink boll worm (*Platyedra gossypiella*). This is the caterpillar of a small moth which enters the cotton seed and is consequently very liable to be transported about the world in spite of all precautions. It is still a matter of dispute as to where this pest originated, but it has undoubtedly occurred in India for a very long time, and it is most probably indigenous there. Outside that country it first began to attract attention in Egypt about 1912. Since then it has spread rapidly, and it now occurs in most of the tropical cotton-growing areas of the world. A few years ago it crossed the Mexican frontier into the Southern United States, and the most strenuous efforts of the authorities to eradicate it have not yet apparently been entirely successful.

Canada is also menaced by some of these enemies, and a recent account of the situation respecting the spruce budworm (*Tortrix fumiferana*), another European invader, states that this moth has already

H. J Shepstone

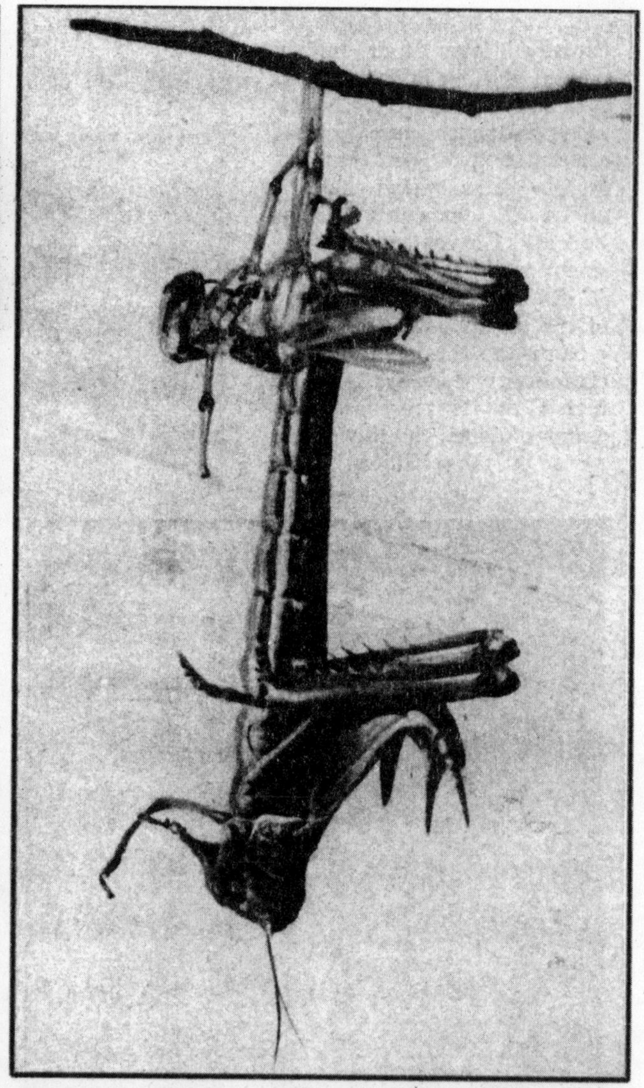

American Colony, Jerusalem

LAST STAGES IN THE DEVELOPMENT OF A PALESTINE LOCUST

Adolescent locusts undergo a series of moults, usually six between the time of emerging from their eggs and becoming fully developed flying insects. Here we see opening stages in the process of the final moult. The nymph has little, semi-developed wings which we see in the top left-hand photograph, folded in membranous cases which themselves resemble tiny wings. Hanging from a twig it begins to shake itself free of the old skin (bottom left), gets its hind legs free (top right) and then comes two-thirds of the way out (bottom right).

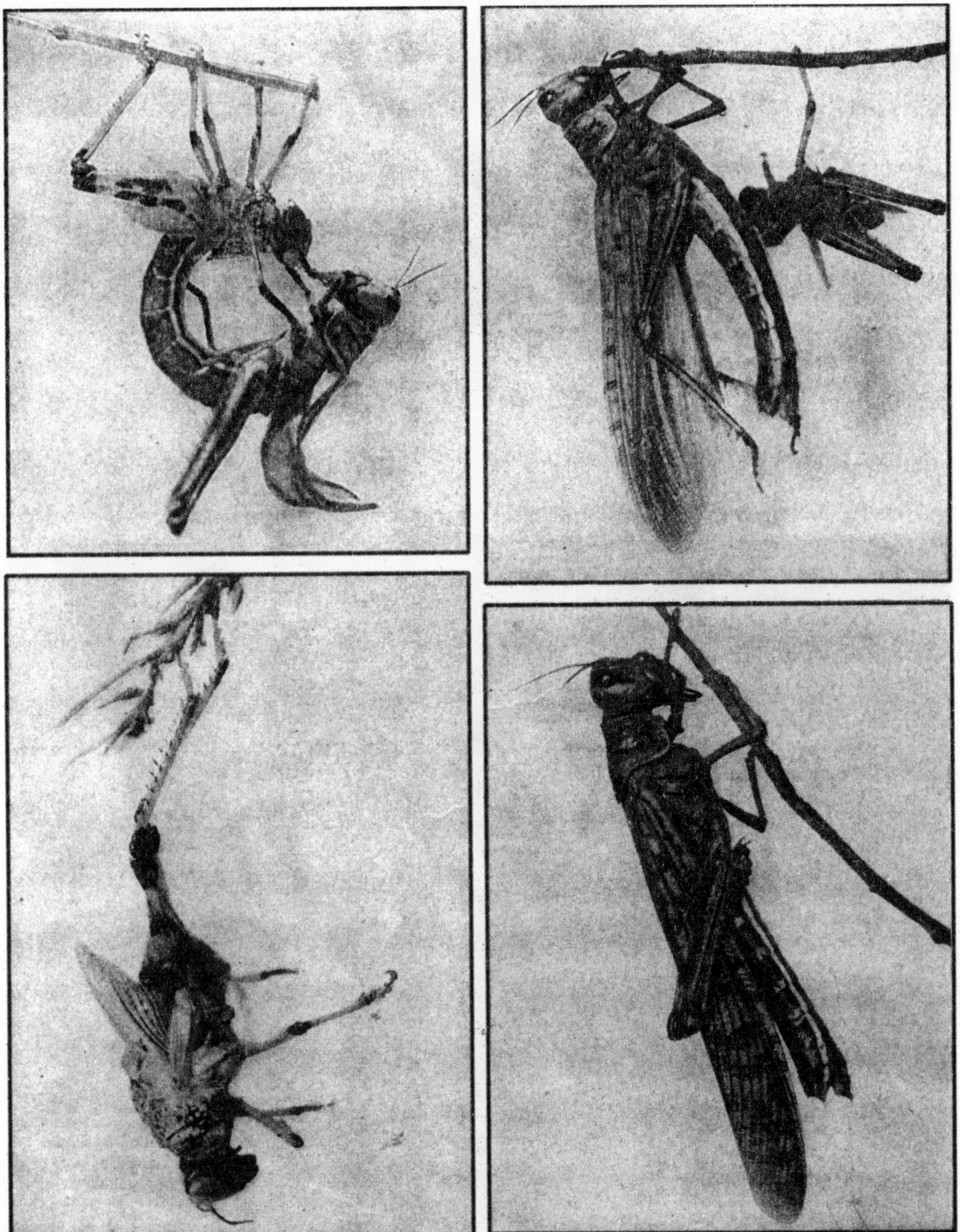

American Colony, Jerusalem

HOW THE DESTROYER ADDS WINGS TO ITS POWERS OF DESTRUCTION

Rapidly curving its new, lithe body (top left) the emerging locust writhes its way out of its old skin wherein it was doomed to be always on the ground. The discarded nymph case (bottom left), hollow throughout from the very tips of the antennae, is left hanging from the twig which it still grips with its hollow, lifeless legs. Having successfully completed the business of emergence the locust then proceeds to dry its wings very carefully, its long hind legs smoothing out the creases meanwhile (top right). At last all is ready (bottom right).

SPECIMENS OF THE SOUTH AFRICAN AND PALESTINE LOCUST COMPARED

It is in South Africa that the locust has made the greatest depredations, destroying in one year a million pounds worth of potential goods. It is in the nymph or crawling stage that the damage is mostly done since, when the insects can fly, it is usually the dry season when there is not so much to destroy. It is, of course, its terrible power of being able to travel from place to place over considerable distances that makes the locust the most appalling of pests. Below is a South African locust, and above a Palestine locust.

AMERICAN LOCUSTS, THEIR EMPTY EGG SHELLS AND THEIR ATTACK ON TREES

In the United States of America, as well as in Canada and South America, locusts have caused great harm to crops. Above we see some locusts of the true or grasshopper type, for it should be borne in mind that in America the cicada has been sometimes referred to as a locust. The lower photograph shows empty shells from which young ones have emerged while above we see insects attacking (left) the bark and (right) the branches of trees. It has been found that deep ploughing is a very efficacious way of dealing with the plague.

destroyed 150 million cords of pulpwood in parts of Quebec and the Maritime Provinces.

Though the above examples relate to insect invaders in North America, many other cases exist in other parts of the world. Within recent years very serious damage has been done to the coffee plantations in the Dutch East Indies and also in Brazil by a small beetle, the coffee-berry borer (*Stephanoderes hampei*), the original home of which is in Central Africa. Coco-nuts, which are the most important crop in the Fiji Islands, were recently threatened with extermination by the caterpillars of an imported moth. Fortunately the introduction of a parasitic fly from Malaya that attacks it has met with marked success, and there are good grounds for hoping that this pest is now under control.

Such instances of outbreaks of imported pests in tropical and sub-tropical countries are naturally less numerous than those in temperate zones, among which an interchange of commodities has gone on for so much longer. There is, however, every reason to think that as direct trade between the regions within the tropical belt increases, they will become

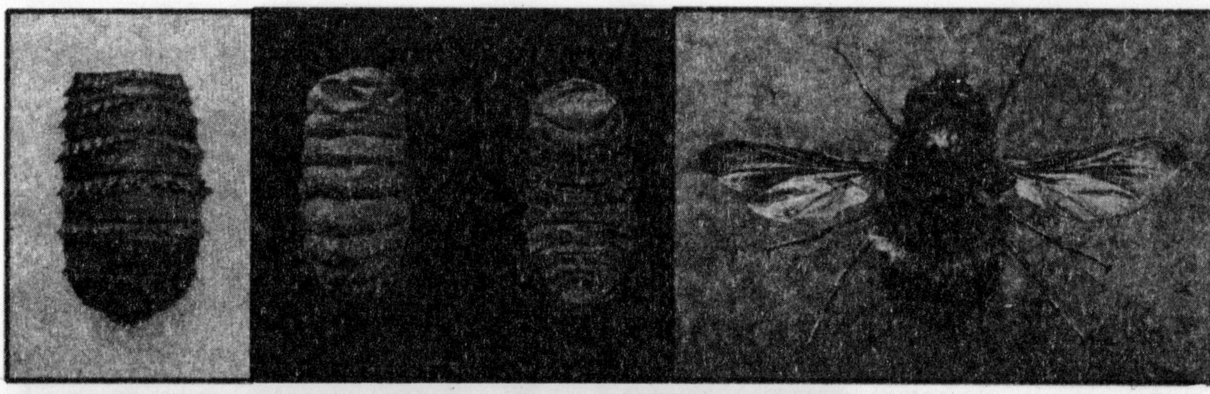

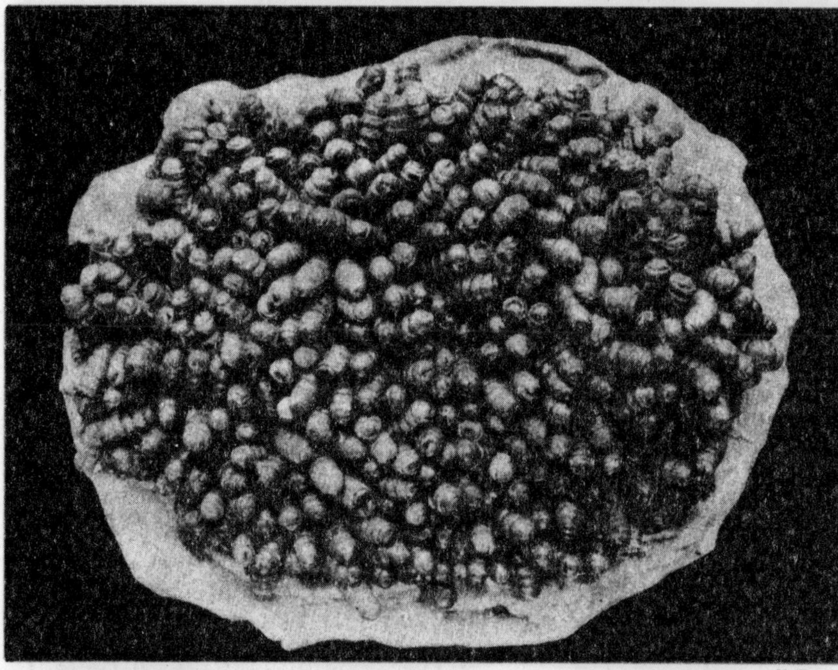

H. Bastin

HORSE-BOT, A HORRIBLE PARASITE AND ITS LIFE STORY

The horse-bot fly (top right) lays its eggs on the horse's fore-leg, which consequently begins to irritate. The horse licks itself and thus the eggs get transferred to the tongue and so swallowed. The larvae (top left) develop in the stomach (bottom) and eventually pass through the food canal and fall to the ground, where pupation takes place (top centre).

much more numerous. Indeed, as stated earlier, it may well be that, in spite of quarantine measures, all the more important pests of our staple crops will ultimately occur wherever the climate permits of their existence. It must be remembered also that quarantine measures themselves frequently cause serious disorganization of trade and may seriously affect commercial relations between different countries. For instance, great disturbance to Spanish trade has been created during recent years by an embargo on the importation of Spanish grapes into the United States, owing to the fact that they may be the means of introducing into that country the Mediterranean fruit-fly (*Ceratitis capitata*), a very dangerous pest in warm climates.

As regards the insects that transmit disease to man and animals, the instances of serious outbreaks due to imported insects are, for obvious reasons, not so striking, though many of them are of great and far-reaching importance. The ones most likely to invade new countries are those that are attached to their host either permanently or at least for long periods. Thus, some of the ticks that infest and convey disease to domestic animals have become cosmopolitan. The same applies to the "sheep tick" or "ked" (*Melophagus ovinus*), which is really a degraded wingless fly. Ticks themselves, though not true insects, are generally treated as coming under the problems dealt with by an entomologist. Other blood-sucking insects of outstanding economic importance are fleas. One of them is the principal carrier of bubonic plague in man and rats and, though probably originally confined to the Oriental region, has now been spread by shipping into many of the seaports of the world. A quite recent instance of an invasion by a disease-bearing insect may be seen in the island of Barbados, which, until the last year or two, has always enjoyed immunity from malaria. One of the malaria-carrying Anopheline mosquitoes has, however, now made its appearance there, having presumably been imported in shipping, and numerous cases of the disease have occurred.

No serious calculations have been made as to the huge economic loss due to insect-borne diseases in man and domestic animals, such as malaria, sleeping sickness, plague, yellow fever—to mention only a few. It is, however, obvious that any community, a high percentage of the members of which are annually incapacitated for some weeks or months by a disease like malaria, must lose heavily in efficiency and earning capacity.

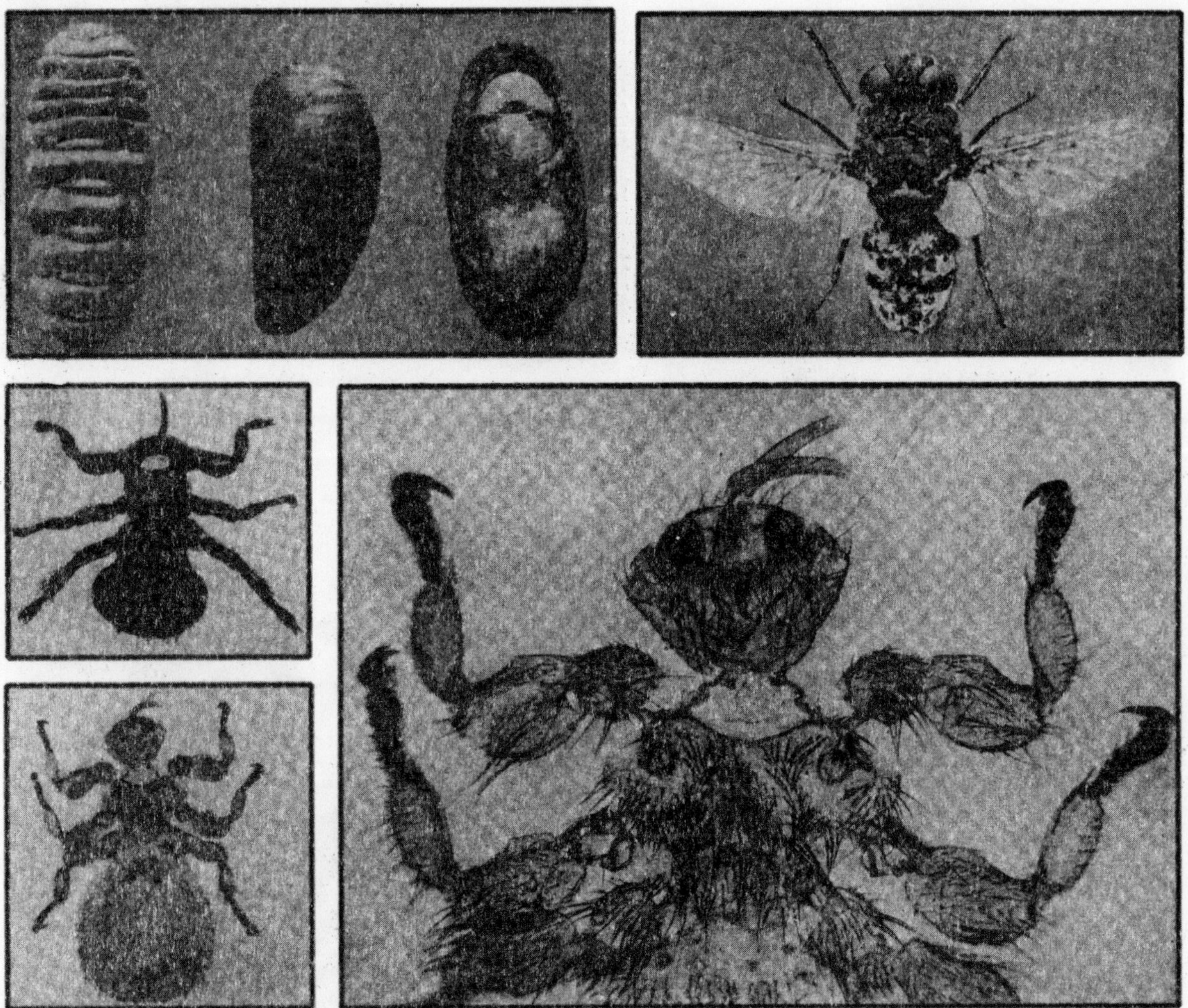

H. Bastin and J. J. Ward

TWO OF THE PESTS THAT INFEST SHEEP: THE KED AND THE NOSTRIL FLY

The so-called sheep tick or Ked is really a wingless fly which lives in the thick fleece of the sheep's wool and sucks blood. Here (bottom right) we see a ked's head, much enlarged, and the two small photographs to the left of it show the whole fly. Dipping when the wool has been sheared is the remedy. Above are five photographs of the sheep nostril fly. From left to right they show: a full-grown grub; pupa cases, one being opened to show pupa; the fly itself. The larvae are deposited on the noses of sheep and work their way inwards.

Enormous damage is also done by insects which, though not carrying disease, inflict direct injuries on domestic animals. Thus the warble flies in America are said to cause a loss of from ten to twenty millions sterling per annum owing to the damage they do to the hide industry, without reckoning a reduction of from 10 to 25 per cent. in the yield of milk. The blow-flies that attack sheep in Australia are calculated to cause an annual loss of three to four million pounds. Sheep bot-flies also do great damage in that country.

INSTANCES of the damage done to man and his multifarious enterprises might be multiplied almost indefinitely, and to mention them all in detail would be quite beyond the scope of this chapter. Much might be said about the gigantic losses all over the world due to the now nearly cosmopolitan beetles and moths that destroy a high percentage of stored cereals, pulses, cocoa and other foodstuffs, to say nothing of those infesting timber, hides and indeed all sorts of animal and vegetable products.

Though no accurate figures for the world as a whole are available, the total annual losses due to insects in the United States alone have been estimated to reach £450,000,000, and the figures for other parts of the world are proportionate to this. To these figures must be added the annual cost of maintaining the entomological services. These reach to nearly a million sterling in the United States, and the British Empire is at present spending about a quarter of a million in routine work. Special emergencies sometimes involve much larger sums, and a bad locust year has before now cost South Africa alone nearly half a million sterling.

It has been calculated that a conservative estimate of the world loss of agricultural products alone from insects is at least ten per cent, and probably a good deal more in tropical countries. In other words

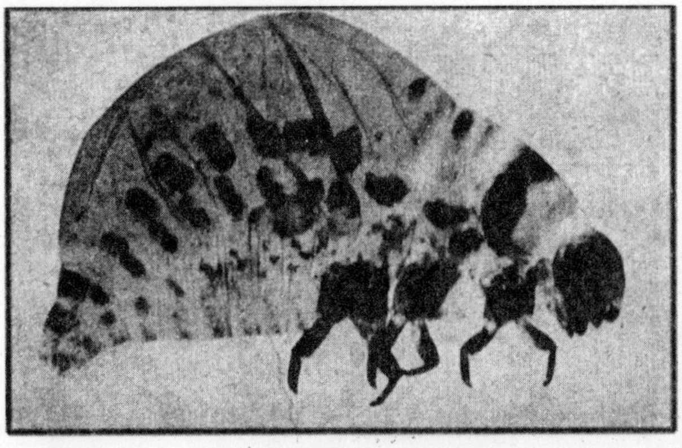

Larva of the Colorado beetle

Colorado beetle larvæ feeding

The Colorado beetle with its wings extended

Colorado beetle

Winged form of woolly aphis

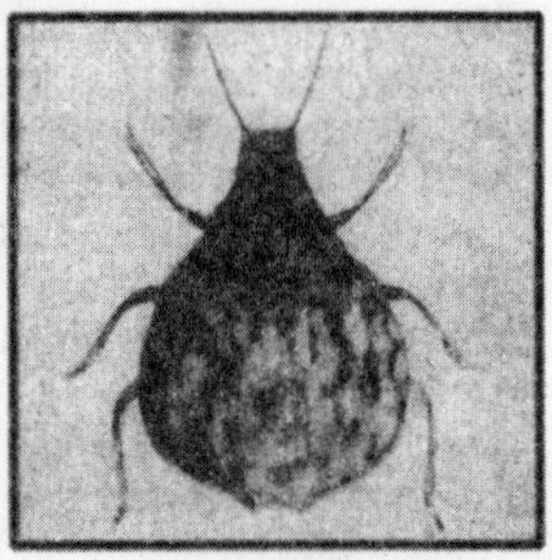

Wingless female aphis

INSECT INVADERS FROM AMERICA THAT HAVE DONE VAST HARM

When an insect pest is transferred from its normal habitat it often happens that its natural checks—other insects and birds—are absent from the particular part of the world to which the pest has been introduced. Also, suitable food may be unusually plentiful, for instance, where there are large areas of crops. Thus it has been with the woolly apple aphis (bottom centre and right). The Colorado potato beetle became transported to Europe just before the War. Photographs, enlarged to various degrees, by J. J. Ward and H. Bastin.

J. J. Ward H. Bastin

SOME OF THE LITTLE CREATURES THAT COME AS A PESTILENCE TO FLOWER AND KITCHEN GARDEN

All during the warmer days of the year when flower and kitchen gardens are in their full bloom a huge hidden system of destruction is going on, so that what to-day is a promising bud is to-morrow a withering bloom. In the kitchen garden one of the first things noticed is that the big leaves of the cabbages are riddled with holes. This is the work of the caterpillar of the cabbage white butterfly (bottom). Above are (left) a larva and (centre) a male and female of the brown tail moth; and (right) a larva of Hadena oleracea eating a rose bud.

H. Bastin

H. J Shepstone

J. J. Ward

J. J. Ward

WONDERFUL "PALISADE" MADE BY A SAWFLY GRUB: TWO PARASITES OF THE PEAR TREE

Before starting to eat the sawfly grub secretes globules of saliva and arranges them in a fence as a protection against ants. Each globule is drawn into a little pillar. Ants cannot cross the fence because the saliva contains noxious properties. This habit has earned for the insect the name of palisade sawfly. Both the upper (bottom left) and lower (bottom right) sides of this black poplar leaf are defended. Above are (left) the grubs of a tiny pear midge and (right) pear tree leaves attacked by a "black beetle" larva.

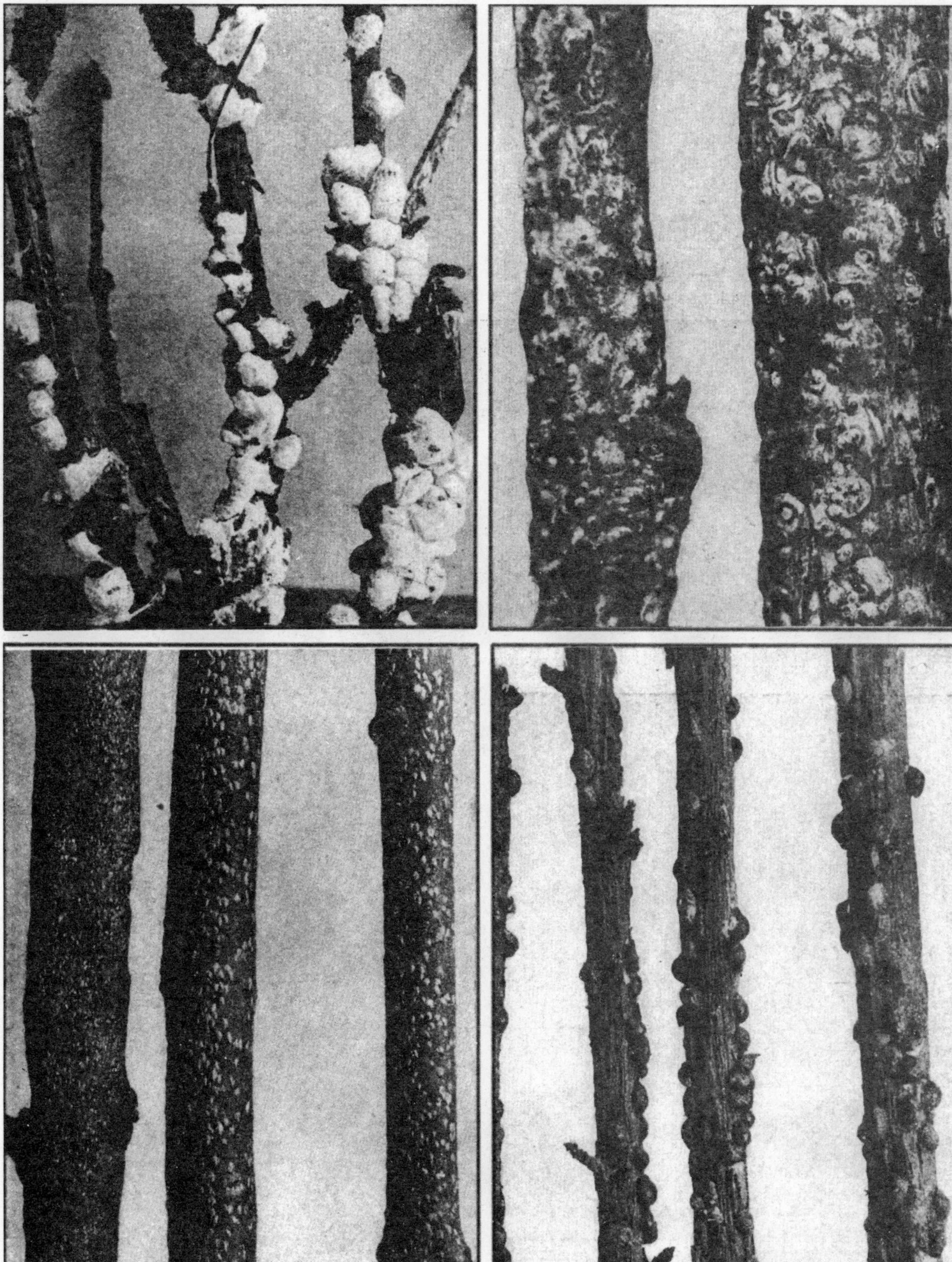

H. Bastin

SCALE INSECTS THAT DO IMMENSE DAMAGE IN NORTH AMERICA

When man upsets the delicate adjustments called "the balance of Nature" he is often the worst sufferer by the change, as has been seen in U.S.A. From Europe came a new race of men, sowing vast areas of wilderness with one kind of insect food—wheat or potatoes, or cotton or fruit. As a result the insects multiplied on a corresponding scale. Here are four among the worst offenders: (bottom left) the ash and willow scale; the brown currant scale (bottom right); the cottony cushion scale (top left) and the San José scale (top right).

Cockchafer feeding on a leaf

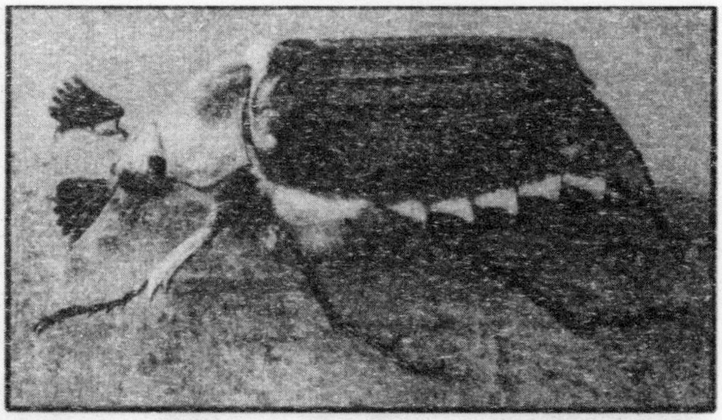
Cockchafer or may-bug, much enlarged

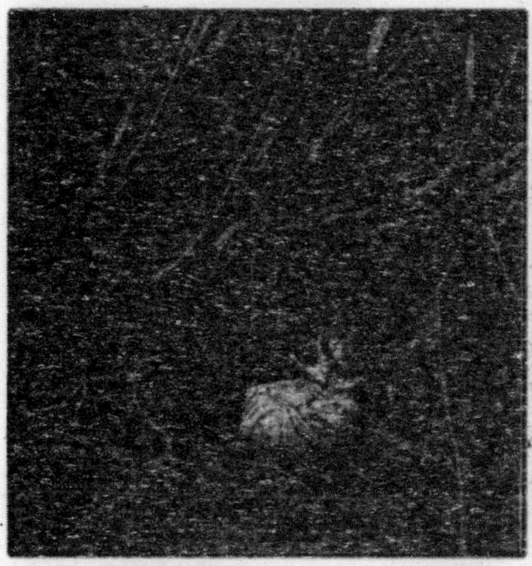
Cockchafer larva among grass roots

Leather jacket or grub of crane-fly

Larvae of celery fly

Shield bug on birch catkins

Pine bud moth pupa projecting from damaged shoot

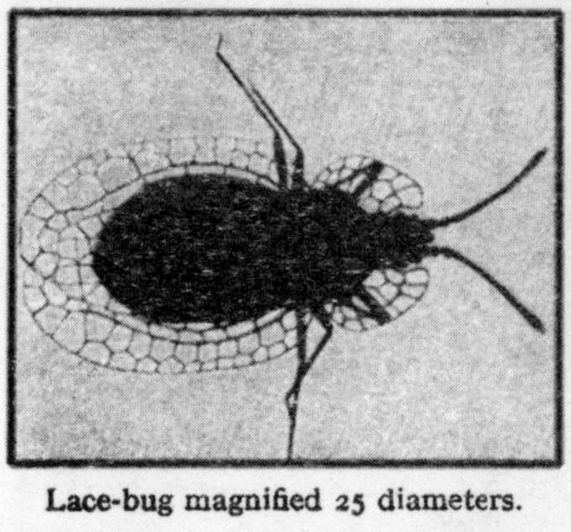
Lace-bug magnified 25 diameters.

Tortrix, twice its natural size

Shield-bug, natural size

DANGEROUS MARAUDERS OF MAN'S TIMBER AND AGRICULTURE

It is not only the sources of man's food that are attacked by insect pests. Some of the most destructive of his insect enemies live by feeding upon timber. The lace-bug (bottom left), for instance, lives on sycamore trees and betrays its presence by giving the leaves a crusty appearance. Another tree pest is the shield bug. There is also the tortrix moth which eats out the shoots of the pine tree. The roots of grass and vegetables are attacked by the leather jacket, and the cockchafer is a destroyer of leaves. Photographs by J. J. Ward and H. Bastin.

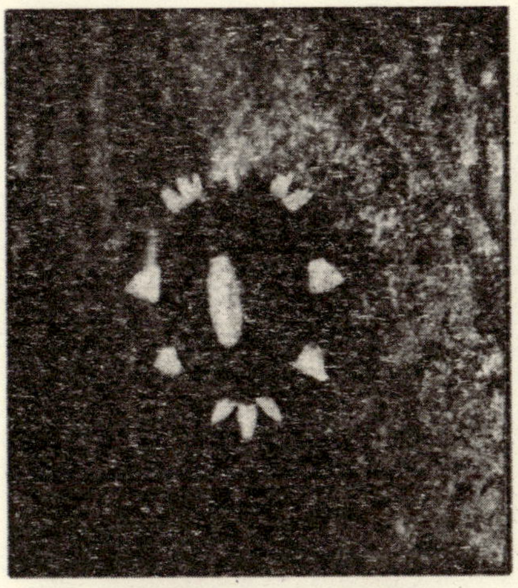

Scale insect from Trinidad

Orange tree scale insect

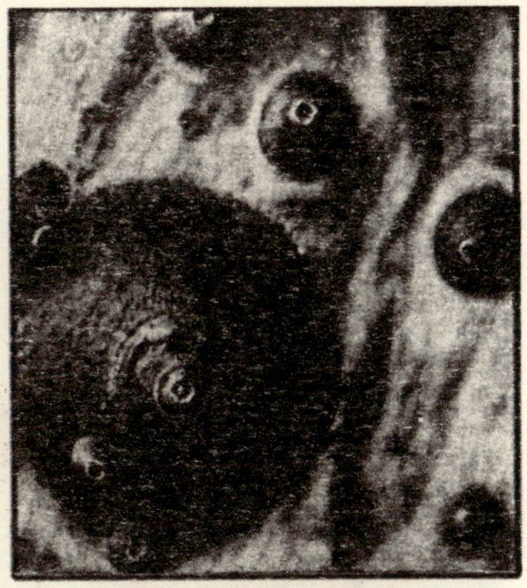

Scale insects from Jamaica

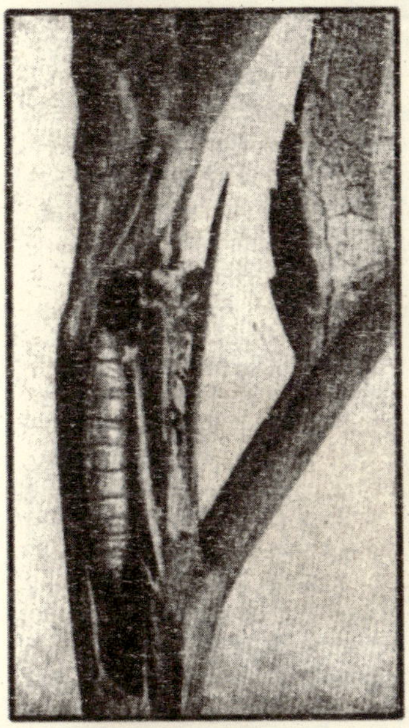

Fruit moth larva in twig

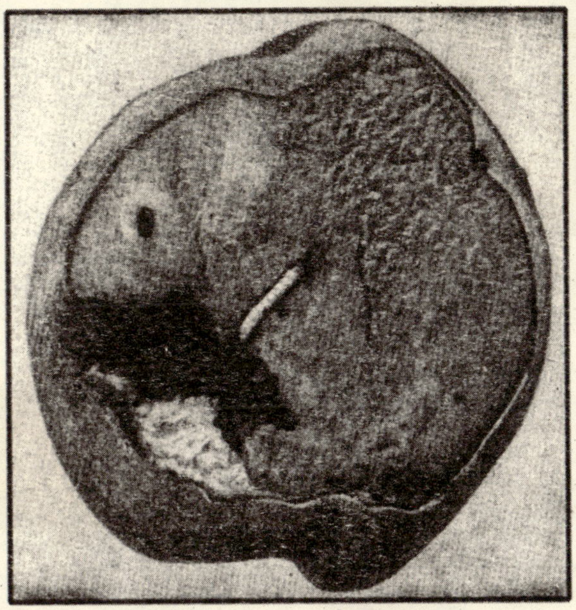

Oriental fruit moth larva at work in peach

Damage to foliage

Coffee berries damaged by coffee beetles

Cigarettes ruined by cigar beetle

RAVAGES OF COFFEE AND CIGAR BEETLES, FRUIT MOTH AND SCALE INSECTS

No matter what the cultivator wishes to grow there seems to be a pest waiting to contest the right of consumption with him. The bottom left-hand photograph shows some coffee berries ruined by the coffee beetle while the three centre photographs are of the oriental fruit moth, which is attacking a peach tree. This moth was first identified in the district of Columbia in 1913, whither it probably arrived from Japan. In America it has learned to eat plums and peaches. The upper photographs are of scale insects (magnified) in the West Indies. Photos J. J. Ward & H. Bastin

Natural History, N.Y.

insects by the damage they do to us increase our cost of living by at least this percentage, and their absence would enable man's industry to support a ten per cent. larger population than it does at present. Taking the world population at a round figure of one thousand millions, we should be able, but for our insect enemies, to feed and clothe with our present resources no less than one hundred million more than is the case at present!

It must be clear, therefore, that mankind is continuously engaged in a world-wide war on a gigantic scale; a war that puts into the shade the comparatively feeble attempts that man makes at damaging himself by fighting with his own species and a war that is all the more dangerous and insidious because its very existence is by no means obvious to the average member of the community.

J. J. Ward

FIGHTING AN IMPORTED PEST IN U.S.A.

Bands of sticky substance check the larvae of the gipsy moth. The lower photograph shows a male (top) and a female, while in the upper photographs we see (left) larvae foiled by a sticky band and (right) a wood. The leafless trees were unprotected by bands.

THE realization of this situation has been very slow, even among those concerned in ruling the peoples of the world, but a marked change has come over the situation in the last thirty years, and there are hardly any civilized governments that do not now maintain entomological experts attached to their agricultural and medical services. At the end of the last century there was not a single economic entomologist in the government employ in the British Empire. Though there are now some 150 of them, they are a mere handful of the army that is needed.

Even among the public generally the idea that an entomologist is a mildly eccentric individual with green spectacles and a long white beard, who occupies his time in running madly after butterflies, is slowly fading. The modern entomologist must in fact be a highly trained scientific man with a wide knowledge, not only of insects themselves, but of the principles of agriculture, chemistry, medicine and other subjects associated with the problems they involve.

One of the difficulties that has arisen from the relatively sudden realization of the importance of economic entomologists has been that of devising machinery for training them in sufficient numbers to meet the pressing demands for them all over the world. This demand has not yet been adequately met in this country, though some even of the older Universities have begun to realize the great economic importance of entomology.

In conclusion, it should again be emphasised that the insects are among the most formidable enemies of mankind and that an endless and tireless war must be waged against them. Already the problem of feeding our ever-increasing world population is setting the experts thinking seriously. Every year mankind has less and less food to share with the insects